Brighter Day

Brighter Day

Ken White

White & Wilkinson

Published in the United States of America
ISBN: 978-1-7340222-0-9 (Soft Cover)
ISBN: 978-1-7340222-1-6 (Case Bound)
ISBN: 978-1-7340222-2-3 (Cloth Bound)
ISBN: 978-1-7340222-4-7 (ebook)
Fiction / Coming Of Age
Fiction / General
Library of Congress Control Number: 2019914634

Summary: As the tumultuous Sixties come to a close, a California college student risks everything he cares about as he traffics with the lunatic fringe of radical politics and culture in his quest to make sense of a government he no longer trusts and a war he no longer believes in.

2430 Tully Road, Suite 20-058 | Modesto, California 95350 USA
1.209.567.0600

DEDICATION

For my hometown.

My deepest gratitude to those who inspired me to tell stories and those who helped along the way.

A special thanks to those who shared their experiences and wrote about this benchmark year.

A long goodbye to those we've lost.

I could not have told this story without a little help from my friends, family, classmates, experts, mentors, researchers, colleagues, and those who were there.

To the three amigos.

ACKNOWLEDGEMENTS

First and foremost, last and never least-most, my wife Robin, whose support allows me to tell my stories.

Carl Baggese for his perspective, experience, and guidance.

Many thanks to the following. Listed in the order, not magnitude, of their contribution, a few of whom are no longer with us.

Chuck Horne, Tim Helfer, Mike Walt, Dale Muratore, Bruce Grimes, Catherine New, Ron Adams, Lee Riggs (UC Davis Shields Library), *Davis Enterprise*, Gayle Heuer, Ron Leonardo, John Decker, Bob Buzbee, Paul Seideman, Kelly Graham, Scott de Camp, Dave Dolan, Sheila Ruiz Harrell, Mark Peterson, Roger Davis, Carol Gant, Dave Wherry, Nancy Wolff, David Bradford, Jeff Highiet, Mark Chadwick, Tom Myers, Don Bean, Robert Zeff, Hal Flesher, Andy Maurer, Mike Johnson, Alan Arnopole, Jennifer Burke (Selective Service System), Jay Barber, Hugh Rowland (California Historical Society), Daniel Goldstein, Kevin Miller (UC Davis Shields Library Special Collections), Ed Conrado, Dennis Negley, Paul Cornwell, Chris Guptill, Don MacRitchie, Jim Autry, Federal Bureau of Investigation Records Management Division, Vanston Shaw, Robert Moresi, Mike Normoyle, Sacramento Muscular Dystrophy Association, National Personal Records Center, Stella Beratlis, Modesto Junior College Library & Learning Center, Cal Aggie Alumni Association, Henry Diltz, Rich Horowitz (Morrison Hotel Gallery), Dorian Fletcher, Bob Barzan, Wenner Media, Don Setaro, ZZ Top Fan Club, Shelly Thompson, Olga Castaneda (Classic TV Database), Barney Eredia, Emily Graves (National Archives and Records Administration), Peter Koetting, Kathleen Holder (*UC Davis Magazine*), Jocelyn Anderson (*UC Davis Magazine*), Colleen Blackman, Greg Sutton, Dave Rogers, Dan Onorato, Steve Couture, Garrad Marsh, Jim Pfaff, Stephan Marlow, Arie Kligier, Ames Countryman, Jane Veneman, Will Linn, Bob Sims, Steve Ford, Gary Hyman, Linda Thurston (War Resisters League), Bruce Johnson, Patrick Walt, Katie Smith, Rob Gordon, Sharon Keasling, Jaimeson Durr (Hyde Street Studios), Robin Lee Whinery, Jeff Wexler, Jack Dertzman (Hyde Street Studios), Ted

Mattingly, Stephen Barncard, Bill Halverson, Steve Campos, Chris Murphy, Liz Robbins, Tyler Noroña, Debbie Walt, Wendy Lucas, Roberto Delgadillo (UC Davis Shields Library Research Support Services), Philip Neustrom (DavisWiki), John Arakaki, Janet Lancaster, Brian Clark (*The Modesto Bee*), Lindsey Maldonado (Continuum Estate), Sheri Darrough (CSU Stanislaus Vasche Library), Gary Nielsen, Christi Cassidy (*Publishers Weekly*), Nora Cary (The Palms Playhouse), Lauren Frausto, John McCloud (Stanislaus County Library), David Schroeder (foto Modesto), William Harris, Shannon Polugar, Alyn Brereton, Dave Garcez, Gini Krumbein Gledhill, Angela Maani (California State Library), Sara Gunasekara (UC Davis Shields Library Special Collections), Dan Wettstein, Heather Lanctot (Yolo County Library), Jon Rowland, Tim Venn, Tim Held, (CSU Stanislaus Vasche Library), Craig Brown (Selective Service System), Tom Devine (Selective Service System), Tom Cash, James Ewing, Ron Wilkinson, Cathie Peck, Barbara Owens, Bill Peck, Ron Darpinian, Philip Johnson, Dawn Collings (UC Davis Shields Library Special Collections), David Collins (Wingspan Press), Richard Slevin, Tom White, Leona White, Wendell White, Penny White, Debbie Farrell, Sammy White, and Jo White.

"Then I reflect that all things happen, happen to one, precisely now. Century follows century, and things happen only in the present. There are countless men in the air, on land and at sea, and all that really happens happens to me."
— *Jorge Luis Borges, Argentine writer, essayist, and poet*

"History may not repeat itself, but it certainly rhymes."
— *Paraphrased from a Quote Attributed to Mark Twain, American writer, humorist, and lecturer*

"The cave you fear to enter holds the treasure you seek."
— *Joseph Campbell, American writer, editor, and lecturer*

"It takes a long time to become young."
— *Pablo Picasso, Spanish painter, sculptor, poet, and playwright*

"All war is the failure of man as a thinking animal."
— *John Steinbeck, American writer*

PRELUDE

"Tyranny of the Downbeat"
Remembrances of Things Musical

It was twenty years ago today,
That Sergeant Pepper taught the band to play.
They been goin' in and out of style,
But they're guaranteed to raise a smile.
So let me introduce to you,
The band you've known for all these years,
– The Beatles, "Sergeant Pepper's Lonely Hearts Club Band"

There's a saying. Our mortality is measured by the music we grow old with; that songs are the score to our lives. I remember exactly who I was and what I was doing by certain records. Every time I hear one, I'm back to what I was at that moment. In the Sixties, music marked the time of our lives. All the events, all the experiences, all the memories from that time are linked forever to a mesmerizing melody or smashing power chord, a mobilizing lyric or communal chorus.

There's another saying. Everything is changeable. Only change is eternal. It is inevitable. It is persistent. As predictable as time. As tyrannical as the downbeat. The Sixties were a time for change and a time of change. Rock 'n' roll provided our anthems.

Because I lived in the Central Valley, I wasn't part of what was happening in San Francisco, The City. So I participated, vicariously, on my time machines – the radio and one particular pulp magazine.

"The Herald" who signaled the beginning of our trip was, appropriately enough, a music critic: Ralph J. Gleason, with back-up from Ben Fong-Torres and a handful of disc jockeys. Some on AM, but most on the first underground, free-form, FM stations, like KMPX, then KSAN in San Francisco, and for us valley kids, KZAP 98.5 in Sacramento. It was Tom "Big Daddy" Donahue, or Creedence playing the long version of "Suzy Q" at a street dance. The official journal of the journey was not Gleason's *San Francisco Chronicle*, but a "rock tabloid." A new publication that commented on the counterculture by writing about the music it made. A rag dedicated to printing "All the News That Fits." That journal was Jann Wenner's *Rolling Stone*, which he co-founded with his mentor Gleason. In 1969, it was my primary source of information.

Why fate chose The City as the location for this flowering of music and gathering of tribes will never be known. But it did. And it gave us an incredible amount of music and musicians – The Charlatans, The Grateful Dead, It's A Beautiful Day, The Beau Brummels, The Jefferson Airplane, The Steve Miller Band, Big Brother & the Holding Company, Moby Grape, The Youngbloods. I hear Quicksilver's "Pride of Man" and I think of Chet Helms and "The Family Dog."

The new children will live,
For the elders have died.
I wave goodbye to America,
And smile hello to the world.
– Tim Buckley, "Goodbye and Hello"

I remember the first "official" outdoor rock concert. "Magic Mountain" at Mt. Tamalpais in Marin. Singer-songwriter Tim Buckley backed by Carter C.C. Collins. I wondered if I should wear flowers in my thinning hair.

"Pushin' Too Hard." Sky Saxon and the Seeds. The first time I smoked dope. "The Loner." Neil Young's first solo album. My first experience with psychedelics. We were all counterculture cowboys, denim Indians like him. Fringed, buckskinned, and alone in our melancholy.

"Feel-Like-I'm-Fixin'-to-Die-Rag" will always be Vietnam and a long bus ride to Fresno for my induction physical. I was terminally healthy. There was a longer trip to the Oakland Draft Resistance Center, knowing that if I didn't do something I was going to war. After all, when the numbers were called the night of the lottery, I was number twenty-four.

"Light My Fire," The flip side of the awakening. The Doors at a roller-skating rink in my hometown of Modesto. On the inside, Jim Morrison was smoking and sultry. On the outside, two gangs were beating the hell out of each other. The old and the new: one living, one dying, in 4/4 time.

"Long Time Gone." The Polo Grounds. The Moratorium. The first taste of revolution, of defiance, of togetherness. Crosby, Stills and Nash wearing those furry coats. I remember walking by them and thinking how short they were.

There was a point when music and movies, the other cultural touchstone, came together. Films like *The Graduate* and *Easy Rider* broke new ground in many ways. But I remember them especially as the first movies to use popular music and rock 'n' roll to help tell the story. Indelible music such as "The Sound of Silence" and "Mrs. Robinson," "Born To Be Wild" and "Ballad of Easy Rider."

In a speech in Cape Town in June 1966, Robert F. Kennedy said, "There is a Chinese curse which says, 'May he live in interesting times.' Like it or not we live in interesting times. They are times of danger and uncertainty; but they are also more open to the creative energy of men than any other time in history."

The origin of the notion of "living in interesting" times has had a clouded history. Kennedy attributed it to the Chinese, likely due to a speech made by Frederic R. Coudert at the *Proceedings of the Academy of Political Science* in 1939, who said, "Some years ago, in 1936, I had to write to a very dear and honored friend of mine, who has since died, Sir Austen Chamberlain, brother of the present Prime Minister, and I concluded my letter with a rather banal remark, 'that we were living in an interesting age.' Evidently he read the whole letter, because by return mail he wrote to me and concluded as follows: 'Many years ago, I learned from one of our diplomats in China that one of the principal Chinese curses heaped upon an enemy is, 'May you live in an interesting age.' 'Surely,' he said, 'no age has been more fraught with insecurity than our own present time.'"

This phrase has been considered by some to be a blessing, by others to be a curse, often spoken ironically, implying that times of peace are less, or more, interesting than times of chaos. The Sixties in general, and 1969 specifically following the political unrest and assassinations of 1968, were interesting times to live in, regardless of how you interpreted the phrase. They were anarchic and creative, oppressive and liberating, uninspired and innovative, deadly and enlivening, predictable and startling, ordinary and outrageous, disappointing and compelling, violent and peaceful, mind-numbing and exhilarating. Whatever they were, and it was, the Sixties and 1969 shaped me and a generation of my peers.

This fictional memoir is a narrative of the year 1969. It is a remembrance of things past. My past. The way I recall it. The five senses conjuring déjà vu and the familiar as surely as Proust's tea-dipped *madeleines*. This story chronicles who I was, where I was, what I was doing, when I was doing it, and why during the decade that many people say, "If you remember it, you weren't there." I remember it and I was there. This is my older self now looking back at my younger self during that defining year. It is the best, most honest story

I could tell based on the research as I did it, the facts as I know them, and the memories as I recall them. The experience of returning and revisiting these moments can be unsettling, but not surprising. It's predictable. Like time. It's persistent. Like change. It's inevitable. Like the downbeat. This is my story and I'm sticking to it.

When I wrote *Getaway Day*, I was asked if I had considered writing a prequel, or a sequel. I hadn't thought about it. But, I had contemplated writing a "Baby Boomer" novel; a novel about my experiences and the experiences of my peers. *Getaway Day* was the first book in that journey. *Brighter Day* is the second. I hope you enjoy it.

Lately it occurs to me,
What a long, strange trip it's been.
– The Grateful Dead, "Truckin'"

CHAPTER 1

"All the News that Fits" – January Edition

The band, Traffic, breaks up. D.A. Pennebaker releases his documentary, *Monterey Pop*. Janis Joplin rehearses with a new band. The Family Dog is denied a permit, meaning it can no longer hold dances at the Avalon Ballroom. A new club, The Matrix, opens in San Francisco. President Richard Nixon appoints Henry Cabot Lodge as chief negotiator at the Paris Peace Talks, replacing Averell Harriman. San Francisco State reopens following violent, student-led protests and a campus-wide strike. Governor Ronald Reagan asks the California legislature to "drive criminal anarchists and latter-day Fascists off the state college and university campuses." The trial of accused Robert Kennedy assassin, Sirhan Sirhan, begins in Los Angeles. Senator Ted Kennedy of Massachusetts is elected Senate Majority Whip, the youngest ever to hold that position, paving the way to a projected run for the presidency. After predicting it, Joe Namath and the New York Jets beat Johnny Unitas and the Baltimore Colts in the AFL-NFL Championship game, known officially for the first time as the Super Bowl. President Lyndon Johnson delivers his last "State of the Union" address. The radical group United Slaves kills two Black Panthers on the UCLA campus. The inquest into the seizure by North Korea of the USS Pueblo begins. Wrigley Field in south Los Angeles, the home of the Pacific Coast League's Los Angeles Angels, is demolished. Torrential winter rains lead to flooding and mud slides, resulting in California being declared a national disaster area. In the National Football League draft, O.J. Simpson of USC is picked first by the Buffalo Bills. The Beatles perform in public for the last time on the roof of Apple Corps. New book releases include *The Sleep of Reason*, C.P. Snow; *Bruno's Dream*, Iris Murdoch; *Thirteen Days*, Robert Kennedy; *The 900 Days: The Siege of Leningrad*, Harrison Salisbury; and *The Age of Discontinuity*, P.F. Drucker. *Fig Leaves Are Falling*; *Celebration*; and *Red, White and Maddox* open on stage. New films include Jean-Luc Godard's *Weekend* and *Sweet Charity* directed by Bob Fosse, starring Shirley MacLaine. New music includes *Led Zeppelin*; *Yellow Submarine*; *Moby Grape '69*; Creedence Clearwater Revival's second album, *Bayou Country*; *Neil Young*; and Frank Sinatra's single, "My Way."

The moon on the brink of the New Year was luminous silver, blanketing Modesto and the Central Valley in dazzling light. A symbol of purification and renewal, it portended a brighter day.

I turned from the frosted window and looked back at the gloved hands of the Mickey Mouse wall clock, ticking off the downbeat. Almost midnight. It was time to say goodbye to 1968 and hello to 1969. The rubberized platter of the Pioneer turntable spun round and round and round. "There are places I'll remember," the first line of "In My Life" by the Beatles, rolled from the speakers. That song conjured a vivid memory, as music did, of all the things that shaped who I was and how I saw the world. They were my ever-present past.

We were celebrating New Year's Eve at the ranch, an almond orchard owned by the parents of Robert Zeff, a high school classmate. The parents lived in town, so this is where we partied. The mammoth Voice of Theater speakers connected to his custom sound system thrummed the walls. Robert was a genius with anything related to engineering, sound, or cars. He souped up sound systems the way our other buddies tricked out cars. He made some real money on the side installing car stereo systems and doing sound for concerts in Modesto and the Bay Area for bands like Boz Scaggs and Joy of Cooking. Some of us would help him out from time to time, depending on our availability and who we wanted to see and hear.

I had gotten to know "Roberto" when we were sophomores at Davis High School. We hung out with the same people and dated girls who were friends. Robert would do the sound for garage bands that played at my house. My mom and stepdad, Paul, preferred that my friends and I were safe, so they encouraged us to have parties at home. Robert and I hung out on weekends at his house, or my house. He enjoyed giving Mom a hard time. She enjoyed giving it back. One time, while he was working on the timing for his '47 Cadillac in our driveway, he got shocked, jammed three fingers into the fan blades, and nearly lost his pinky finger. Tore it up. He wore a huge soft bandage for weeks after. It didn't slow him down. Mom made him a red onion and mayo sandwich on Wonder Bread and he was fine.

The keg was flowing at the ranch. The Red Mountain was pouring. The smell of dope was filling the air. The other partiers included more high school friends, junior college classmates, and Mud Bowl buddies. Unfortunately, Kelly, my girlfriend of the last seven years, was visiting family in Palm Springs. Gary Rawlings, my best friend since elementary school was there. He was my date for the night. It wasn't the first time. It wouldn't be the last. He'd had a few beers and was singing along with The Stones' "Honky Tonk Women" and flailing away on the ottoman. My other sometimes "date," who was also a former Grace Davis Spartan and a current University of California, Davis Aggie roommate, was busy dancing with Nancy Soares, another of our high school and JC classmates. Michael Gover Johnson stood about six-two and she measured about five-seven. He was hunched over so badly in his cheek-to-cheek embrace and horniness, I guessed it was a matter of time before his back gave out.

Nancy and I first met at Roosevelt Junior High. We spent a great deal of time at her house during the year, but especially during the summer, playing ping-pong and driving around in her red Jeep. Starting in our sophomore year, we wrote lengthy yearbook inscriptions filled with sexual innuendo, hoping it would embarrass the other when the parents read it. I'm not sure they ever did. Get it, that is. She and her friend, Cindy Ruhman, sat with us boys at lunch during our junior and senior years. Adults that we were, we wadded up tiny bits of paper and tossed them at Nancy, hoping they would drop in her cleavage. Her mother always asked why there were so many pieces of paper on the floor after she'd changed clothes following school. Confetti, she answered. We were such idiots.

Nancy was part of a group of girls we had met in class, or through Hi-Y and Tri-Y, which were boys and girls clubs organized by the YMCA. Eventually, some of us dated. There was Julia Bloomer, who we nicknamed "Simon;" Cathy New; Linda Bacciarini, or "Bacc;" Sherry Blackledge, also known as *Negraborde* thanks to those of us who had taken Spanish; Anita Battle; Janis Maxfield, or "Max;" and Nancy Ogden. At various times in high school and JC, I dated Julia and Nancy, Gary dated Linda, and Robert dated Sherry. The girls also went out with a few of the other guys in our group. It was an adolescent version of musical chairs. These young women were bright, fascinating, and talented. Some were academics, others were artists, who sang or painted, and some were activists. We were fortunate they allowed us to be around them.

I kept to myself that New Year's eve because I was never much of a drinker and drugs scared me. So I stood watching the tiny color TV tucked in the corner of the living room of the main house. KCRA's late news broadcast was flashing images of 'Nam. The body count was climbing. As of January 1, 1969, almost 40,000 soldiers had died since we became involved in 1956, as we tried to keep the dominoes from falling and hoped to save the world for democracy. There had been 16, 899 casualties in 1968 alone, which was the largest to date. I was sure our government would come to its senses before too many more died. They had to.

"Thanks for the reminder," a voice behind me said. It was Daniel Biggs, another classmate and, for a period of time, part of the Hi-Y Vikings, which was the name of our YMCA club.

"Sorry. It was on. I wasn't really watching," I apologized.

"I'll be one of those grunts before long."

"When do you leave?"

"Bus to Pendleton departs at 5 a.m. sharp."

"You won't be getting much sleep."

"None at all. I'll crash on the bus."

"How long is basic?"

"Four weeks."

"You sure it's Vietnam after that?"

"Almost guaranteed."

"Maybe they'll keep you stateside?"

"Naw, I wanna go. Got some gooks to shoot."

"You ever shot anybody?"

"Ducks."

"Not the same," I said.

"Doesn't matter. It's what I signed up for."

"I don't know how you can do it."

"Your time will come."

"Not if I can help it."

"It's your country, dude."

"Right or wrong."

"Damn straight."

"I love my country, but if it's wrong. I'm going to tell it like it is," I replied.

"We'll see."

"Yes, we will."

"They'll be watching you. All of you."

"Who?"

"The government. The feds."

"I've got nothing to hide."

"Yet." He lifted his glass of what smelled like bourbon. "*Semper fi.*"

"Safe journey," I said, and walked toward what was left of the food.

I grazed until I heard people say, "It's almost time." We gathered in the living room. When both of Mickey's hands were pointed straight up, we watched as the ball dropped in Times Square. Kisses, hugs, handshakes, and toasts were exchanged. And the party resumed.

With the New Year official, I checked to see how Gary was doing. He tried to focus on my Yankees baseball hat. Mickey Mantle was still my guy, even though injuries and age had reduced his playing time. I knew what was coming. Gary flipped my Yankees hat off my head, like he usually did. He was so predictable. This time, he almost took my glasses with it. I had started wearing glasses to correct nearsightedness my senior year of high school. My first pair, and the pair that nearly went flying, were wire-rim glasses. Not Granny glasses, which were all the rage, but Woodrow Wilson-style, gold-rim glasses. The first time I had returned to Davis High as a college guy for a dance with Kelly and her friend, Sally Shea, who was a senior, I had been given a hard time about my "hippie glasses" by a senior wrestler and football player. He was drunk, so I ignored him, like I ignored what Gary had done. I retrieved my hat.

"I'm rolling," I told Gary. "You need a ride?"

"I'm good," he said. He didn't look good. He was wasted.

"You sure?"

"I am."

"I don't think you should drive."

"I'm gonna crash here," he slurred.

"Cool. Come by tomorrow and watch the bowl games. Mom and Paul would like to see you."

"10-4."

I took one more look at his blood-shot eyes, his goofy grin, and punched him lightly on the shoulder.

"Later."

"Later."

I hit the head before heading out. Washing my hands, I noticed a beautiful red orchid. I was envious. I loved orchids and tried to grow them. My black thumb sometimes killed them. It was funny how the mind worked. I conjured up a song from the Disney version of *Alice in Wonderland*. In the song, "All in the Golden Afternoon," Alice sang: "You can learn a lot of things from the flowers." My mind jumped to another thought. Flowers have no memory. Memory dwelled in the past. Memory produced nostalgia, occasionally regrets, even fear. It was time to go home.

CHAPTER 2

Long after midnight, I said my goodbyes and drove along Paradise Road toward home. I was driving "Ugly Orange," my 1947 Ford pickup. I could see the first streaks of daylight mottling the sky. It was January 1st, 1969. A new day. A new year. It would get better. I truly believed that. It had to.

Following Paradise, I pulled over and walked out to the edge of the Tuolumne River. It was flowing fast with heavy winter rain. There was this thing about flowing water. People loved it. Maybe it was because we were 75 percent water ourselves. Maybe it stemmed from a heritage of gills and webbed feet. Naturalist Loren Eiseley once said, "If there is magic on this planet, it is contained in water." That thought reminded me of something I'd read. Standing in a river, you could look upriver at your past. Your present was where you stood. Your future was downriver. I looked back upriver and thought of the red orchid. I looked at the river in front of me and contemplated the moment. I looked downriver and wondered what the future held. My brain was skipping around like a flat rock across calm water, as it typically did.

I turned to face east. I raised my arms. A few birds took flight. Windows in the houses overlooking the river blinked on. An alarm clock buzzed faintly. A train whistle moaned. I clapped my hands. The sun broke the hazy horizon. I smiled. 1969 officially began.

As I drove north on Carpenter, I glanced at the row of backyard fences lining the shoulder of the road. I noticed a solitary man walking ahead on the right side of the road. He wore a dark overcoat, a newsboy tweed cap, and carried an umbrella. I thought to myself, *That hat looks a lot like one we gave Dad the last Christmas he was alive.* As the distance between us shrank and I got a closer look at the face, the salt-and-pepper moustache and longish sideburns reminded me of what my father would have looked like if he had lived. As I passed him, he tipped his cap. I blinked and tried to catch another glimpse of him in the passenger side-view mirror.

I was interrupted by the throaty rumble of a Harley roaring up behind me. I checked the rear-view. A Hells Angel in full colors astride a chopper loomed. His stringy long hair and scraggly beard flowed. Wraparound sunglasses hid his eyes. He flashed his Cyclops headlight and passed, doing about eighty. I caught a glimpse of heavy, black work boots, greasy Levi's, a leather jacket over a denim vest with nothing underneath, and a cigar clamped between his teeth. *He must be freezing his ass off,* I thought. When I saw the leering skull and "Hells Angels Oakland, California" on the back of his vest, I realized it likely wasn't a problem. The Angels got their name from a line in John Milton's *Paradise Lost.* Satan, formerly called Lucifer, was the most beautiful of all angels in Heaven before he fell. In the poem, he addressed the Legion of Angels residing in Hell, and proclaimed: "Better to reign in Hell than serve in Heav'n." I figured this Angel would be fine.

Until he wasn't.

I saw the headlight jerk right then left and go down flat. It spun like a pinwheel. I pulled over and was out of the truck before the bike spun to a stop. The guy lay on top. He'd ridden it down. When he laid it out, he didn't get caught underneath, but stayed on top. He lay face down. I smelled gasoline. The sun glinted off a puddle pooling beneath the teardrop gas tank, slowly inching toward the smoldering cigar butt. I grabbed him by his thick black belt and tried to yank him off the cycle. He weighed a ton. I wasn't that big or strong, but the adrenalin had kicked in and was making up for it. I pulled him closer to my truck. I propped him up against the front wheel. His hands and the tips of his boots were shredded from trying to stay on the bike as it whirled.

The bike blew, showering metal bits across the road. That opened his eyes.

"Fuck, dude, my bike."

Lights popped on in nearby houses. A few people opened their back gates. I could hear a distant siren.

"Hey, man, you okay?" I asked.

"Fuck," he said again. "That's a lot of bread burnin'."

"What's your name?" I asked, trying to make sure he wasn't in shock.

After another glance at the burning cycle, he said, "Merle. Friends call me 'Motown.'"

I looked confused.

"As in Modesto town. Not Detroit."

I nodded in understanding. "You live around here, Merle?"

"Yep."

"Where?"

"Over on Victoria."

"Cool. We'll wait till somebody gets here, then we'll get you fixed up and back to your house."

"Fuckin' frog," he mumbled.

Now I was thinking he was finally in shock. "Frog?" I asked. "What about a frog?"

"I swerved to miss the little fucker."

Now I was in shock. This big-ass biker had flopped his cycle to avoid killing a frog.

"Dude, that's crazy."

"No shit."

A Modesto Fire Department truck pulled up, followed by a Modesto Police Department cruiser and an ambulance. The paramedics checked Motown, while the firemen doused the flames. The police asked me a few questions. As the paramedics struggled to load Motown onto a gurney and into the ambulance, he looked at me and nodded.

"I owe you, brother," he said. He extended a closed right hand toward me. I could see the head of a fire-breathing dragon snaking out from under his leather jacket. He turned his hand over, opened it, and tossed me a chromed head bolt. "Got to take care of each other," he said.

The ambulance doors slammed shut, the siren whined, and the ambulance pulled onto Carpenter. I climbed into my truck and followed. I took one last look in my rear-view at the smoldering wreckage and flashing lights, as a tow truck arrived.

CHAPTER 3

I parked Ugly Orange along the curb in front of 1532 Del Vista.

Home.

We had moved down the street from the corner house at 1500 not long after Mom and Paul got married. There were too many memories and they wanted a fresh start – a place of their own. We stayed in the neighborhood so all the kids would be close to their friends and attend the same schools. We'd had enough disruption after Dad had died to last us a lifetime.

I entered through the back door off the garage into the kitchen, the way everyone came into our house. Nobody ever used the front door, unless you were the Jehovah's Witnesses or Mormons or hobos. The Del Vista house was comfortably small. Fourteen hundred square feet. Three bedrooms, one bath, like the rest of the houses on the block, including our old house down the street. The layout was flipped one-eighty from 1500. Facing the house, the living room and two bedrooms were on the right, while the master bedroom, bathroom, dining room, and kitchen were all on the left. In place of the large outdoor patio we had at 1500, a previous owner had added on a family room with a fireplace. An area rug and checkered brown and white linoleum covered the floor, water-stained composite fiber tiles lined the ceiling, windows above wood paneling ran along one wall, wood storage cabinets filled the other, a fireplace butted up against the garage, and a bank of latticed windows faced the backyard.

Paul and I had cut holes for speakers in the ceiling and ran wires to a stereo system in the top of the first storage closet on the right as you entered. It was the perfect party room. We'd hosted many kid and adult parties in that room. Almost every garage band in town had played that room during high school. We'd roll up the carpet, move the furniture, shut the french doors leading into the dining room, and start "cuttin' a rug." Mom and Paul would sit in the living room watching TV while Diane and Cheryl, my two little sisters, would peer through the panes of the french doors to get a peek at the big kids, one or two of whom were clutched in what looked like death grips, but were making out.

As I came in, I saw in the small dining room off the even smaller kitchen, my mom at the table drinking coffee, smoking a cigarette, and counting Raleigh coupons. Paul sipped his coffee, puffed on his pipe, and read the

Wednesday edition of *The Modesto Bee*. My stepdad's full name was Paul Kenneth Thompson. He was phone company, like Dad had been, except he was a third-line supervisor. My mom and us kids had known him for years thanks to Pac Bell Christmas parties, summer picnics, retirement parties, Pioneer award ceremonies, and other company gatherings. Paul's wife had died of brain cancer not long after Dad passed away. We all liked Paul. Apparently my mom really, really liked him. They dated briefly and married the summer between my high school graduation and my freshman year at Modesto Junior College. He'd now been a permanent part of our lives for two-and-a-half years. He was a good man. Steady, reliable, kind, and easy-going with a sick sense of humor. He wasn't my dad, but he was very much like him, which was good for all of us. The one who seemed to have an issue was Willy, but that's because he was a hormonal teenager who only cared about rock 'n' roll. My phantom brother, Tim, Jr., wasn't around enough to have an opinion one way or the other.

"You look like something the cat drug in," Mom said. "You hung over?"

"No, just tired," I said. "I didn't drink."

"It's okay not to drink," Paul said.

"I feel like I'm coming down with a cold."

"You say that every year," Mom said.

"That's because it happens every year," I replied.

"Drink some orange juice," Mom added.

"How was the Bauman's party?" I asked.

"We danced a lot," my stepdad said.

"Was all the Garrison crew there?" I asked.

"Pretty much," Mom said. "The Normoyles, Wilkinsons, Carrascos, Gardners, Baldwins, the Rawlings."

I looked through the closed doors into the family room. Diane and Cheryl were watching cartoons. Two of the family cats were cuddled around them.

"Timmy and Willy sacked out?" I asked.

"Yep," Paul replied.

"Willy won't be up until at least noon," Mom said.

"I'll wake them up for the football games."

"Who you picking in the Rose Bowl?" Paul asked.

"I hate USC, but I hate Woody Hayes more, so I'm going with the Trojans."

"You going to see Kelly before you go back to Davis?" Mom asked.

"I've got John's funeral to go to tomorrow, then Gover and I are driving back after that."

"What's the hurry?"

"School starts Monday and there's no telling what shape Rick left the apartment in."

"He still have that filthy hawk and those slimy snakes?" Mom asked, cringing as she did.

"Unfortunately, he does."

"Well, you need to make time for Kelly. I know it's been tough with you both away at school, but she worries about you."

"Don't worry, Mom. I'll take care of it. I'll see if she can come over."

"That would be nice." I leaned down and kissed her cheek. I pushed open the french doors, stepped down into the family room, and closed the doors behind me. I chose not to share what happened with Merle and his Harley. I didn't feel like getting into a long conversation.

As for the Rose Bowl, unfortunately, Ohio State shellacked Southern Cal 27-16. Not even O.J. could save the Trojans.

CHAPTER 4

Kelly stopped by after the game. We walked through Pike Park under an overcast sky. We sat on the bleachers of the baseball diamond. Familiar and friendly grounds.

"You okay?" she asked.

"I'm fine."

"You don't look fine."

"I didn't get much sleep."

"I know the feeling."

"How's everybody?" I asked.

"They're all good."

"And yours?"

"Good."

"Are you mad at me?" she asked.

"Just the opposite."

"Then what's bugging you?" she asked, as she took my hand.

"I miss you. I hate having to leave."

"You'll be back for spring break."

"That's in April."

"You can always come to Berkeley," she suggested.

"I hate Berkeley."

"I know you do, but that's where I am."

"You can always come see me."

"I don't have a car and your roommates are sweaty boys."

"Your roommate isn't much better."

"But, there's only one of her."

"College was supposed to be so cool because you could do anything you wanted. With anybody."

"Within reason."

"I'd rather be doing it with you." She kissed me.

"That makes it worse." I explained.

"I'll call you."

"Not the same."

"It will have to do."

"What if they don't extend my 2-S? What if I get drafted?"

26

"I don't know. You tell me."

"I wish I knew."

"You might want to start thinking about it."

"It's all I've been thinking about," I said. "Other than you."

"Aren't there people on campus you can talk to?"

"Yeah, after classes start."

"You know how I feel about it."

"The same way I do."

"Then let's see what we can do to make it work. For everyone."

"That's my plan," I said. I looked up at the hazy sun and added, "Kelly, I'm really worried."

"I know."

"How can you possibly know? You're a girl. You don't have to serve."

"I have a brother. And good guy friends. And you. I don't want any of you to die over there."

"Small comfort."

"You don't mean that."

"No, I don't. I'm pissed. And scared. It's a bullshit war. It's not doing anybody any good. I've got friends I've known all my life who are dying."

"Like John?"

"Like John."

"When's the service?"

"Tomorrow."

"Where?"

"First Methodist."

"You want me to go?"

"No. I don't even want to go."

"It's the right thing to do."

"I hate funerals. Almost as much as I hate Beserkeley."

"Okay, you've made it clear how much you 'love' Berkeley."

"But, I . . . love you. I think." That caught her off-guard. She paused, then pushed on.

"Going to the funeral is inconvenient for you, but it means the world to his family."

"It's uncomfortable."

"Be the better man, Mikey," she said. "Always be the better man."

"What if it's an open casket. I hate open caskets. I want to remember them the way they were. When they were alive."

"I get that. I know you're not a big church person." I chuckled. She glared. "Just remember, to everything there is a reason."

"To believe," I said.

"What? That's not a part of *Ecclesiastes*."

"No, Tim Hardin."

"You and music."

"Relates to everything."

CHAPTER 5

The First Methodist Church was located in downtown Modesto near the old McHenry house. The church had been built in 1932, having survived the wave of building condemnations and demolitions prompted by the City of Modesto's building code changes. Old churches were especially hard hit. A few of my friends and classmates were members. We had gone to DeMolay and Job's Daughters dances in the social hall. DeMolay was a Methodist social group for boys, while Job's Daughters was for the girls. It was nice. For a church. Open and airy with a tall bell tower. Much more inviting than the College Avenue Congregational Church, which was the only church our family had ever attended.

As I trudged up the front entrance steps, lost in my thoughts, my way was blocked by The Hustler. He wore a black bandanna around his neck, a faded denim jacket, patched Levi's, and sandals. We never knew his real name. He was always The Hustler. A pool shark. Like the movie. He was two years ahead of us in high school. I'd known him from Little League and Babe Ruth. He was a very good athlete. Once upon a time. He liked to party hardy. He gave up baseball for pool. The focus that made him such a good athlete made him an even better pool player. He plied his trade at Family Billiards on Yosemite Boulevard. He never lost.

We quietly entered the foyer. I signed the guest book.

"Anything down there about his soul?" The Hustler asked.

"About what?"

"Maybe he lost it in the jungle. *"Shit-head*," I thought, and left him to sign.

I entered the sanctuary and sat in the last pew. Like I always did. I never sat in the front. Anywhere. Ever. School. Movies. Especially not in church. I kept a low profile. I was a behind-the-scenes guy.

The Hustler walked down the center aisle, like he was the groom at a wedding. He sat right in front. Brass balls. No fear.

I stared at the open casket. I could see the tip of John's porcelain pale nose. I had known him from seventh grade on. We were in different sponsor rooms, so we never had any classes together. But, we played "C" league sports at Roosevelt Junior High. The intramural sports program there was divided by size, in order to make the competition fair. "A, B, C." We were both on the small side, so we were "Cs." We lost touch in high school, especially after we both stopped playing sports. We'd see each other on campus or at football games or Hob Nob Pizza. We were never close, but we had some history.

He'd joined the Army after a semester at MJC. He had told me school wasn't his thing and thought he might make a career out of the military. He'd come back from 'Nam badly messed up. He hung himself in the bedroom he grew up in, surrounded by trophies, posters, albums, photographs, keepsakes. All the things you collected that made you happy and held memories you hoped would remind you of your youth and the good times you had, comforting you as you grew older. They never had the chance.

I was lost in thought when someone stopped beside the pew. It was Mr. Leach, my fifth-grade teacher and Little League coach. He had coached John in Babe Ruth.

"Mind if I join you?" he asked. I slid over to make room. "Sad story," he said.

"It is."

"He was way too young."

"They all are."

"It's not worth it."

"What's that?" I asked.

"Sending our children off to die."

"Government seems to have their reasons."

"Not very good ones," he said.

"Not a lot we can do about it."

"That's not true. People are writing letters, signing petitions, marching."

"Doesn't seem to be doing much good."

"They're hearing us."

"Not loud enough."

"It will get there," he said. "So long as we work together. A community, not as individuals. If we go our own way, they can more easily separate us."

"I'm not that optimistic."

"Hope is a powerful thing, Michael. Very powerful."

"How's Mrs. Leach?" I asked, not wanting to get into a political discussion with my elementary school teacher.

"Her eyes are bothering her, but it's nothing serious."

"Whose eyes?" a voice asked. It was Gary. Another of Coach Leach's students and Little League players.

"Corny's," Coach replied.

"You mean Mrs. Leach?" he said, smiling.

"Yes, Mrs. Leach."

"She okay?" Gary asked.

"She's fine."

Gary squeezed in front of us, plopped between us, and immediately popped me on the shoulder.

"Hey, buddy," he said.

"Hey," I replied.

As he was about to continue giving me a hard time, the church organ played "I-Feel-Like-I'm-Fixin'-to-Die Rag" by Country Joe and the Fish. John had a warped sense of humor.

CHAPTER 6

The wake was held at John's house near Fremont Elementary School. It was a modest three-bedroom, one-bath bungalow on a tree-lined street. It looked like most of the other homes built during the post-World War II growth and occupied by returning servicemen, their wives, and their children – us Baby Boomers.

Gary and I sat on the back patio beneath the bare Modesto ash tree.

"Only 22 more days and I'll be official," he said. "We can drink now."

"I'm happy for you," I said

"Just because you don't like to drink doesn't mean you have to spoil it for me."

"I don't mind drinking. I just don't like how people act when they're drunk."

"How do they act?"

"They're assholes. I've seen you drunk. You're an asshole," I chuckled.

"That mean you're not going to join me on the momentous occasion?"

"I'll be there."

"I knew you would."

Through the glass of the sliding patio doors, we heard "No Expectations" by the Stones. It was on *Beggar's Banquet*, their latest album that had released in December.

"I love the lyrics of that song," I said.

"Not very optimistic," Gary replied.

"But real," I said. "Expectations are unreal, so it's better not to have any."

"Our own Central Valley Socrates. What else you got?"

Taking my cue, I went on, "Change is inevitable. Loneliness is absolute. Laughter is essential."

Gary thought about it, "With that view of the world, laughter is critical."

"So is music."

"And beer," he added. "Stones are supposed to tour this year."

"You interested?" I asked.

"Naw, I'm a Beatles guy."

"Me, too."

"I know people who think the Beatles are too clean-cut. They like the Stones' bad boy image."

"All the girls seem to."

"Guess that's why I'm single."

"No, you're an asshole," I reminded him.

"Beatles are better singers and musicians."

"I agree."

"Stones can rock, though. Harder than the Beatles."

"Now that the Beatles are into drugs and meditation, they've changed." I said. "I'm not sure I like the new them."

"Me, either."

"Still write bitchin' songs."

"So do the Stones. Just different."

"Day and night, night and day."

"Cole Porter," a deep, gravelly voice said from behind us. It was Mr. Gordon.

Mr. Robert "Bob" Gordon was my neighbor, my teacher, my mentor. The Gordons had lived across the street from us when we lived at 1500 Del Vista. Before we moved down the street to 1532, they had moved to a larger house on Enslen. I had taken California history and current affairs from him at MJC. When I decided I wanted to be a history major and teach history, he was the one who advised and guided me. He was stocky, but sturdy. His athlete's body had rounded, but he was solid. He was bald with a fringe of gray hair, wore dark horn-rimmed glasses, and smoked a pipe. Next to my dad and Coach Leach, he was the other most influential male figure in my life. His area of interest and expertise was America's Civil War, although he was well-versed in all of mankind's past. He had served as an aid to General Patton in World War II. He had that ramrod military bearing and gruff officer voice. There were times I wanted to be him. Other times, he scared me.

Gary and I jumped to our feet, like nervous recruits.

"At ease, gentlemen, at ease." We both sat. How's school?" he asked.

"It was a good quarter," I answered right away, aiming to please. "Got 'As' in Russian history and English history."

"That's my boy."

"All three classes next quarter will be history classes."

"When do you go back?"

"Tomorrow."

"Make us proud," he added.

"Thanks, I'll try."

As an afterthought, Mr. Gordon looked over at Gary.

"Doing good," Gary immediately said. "Stan State is easy. So far."

"How do you know John?" I asked.

"He was enrolled in one of my history classes. He was bright, but I could tell that school wasn't a priority."

"He lost his student deferment when he dropped out," Gary said.

"Joined up and got sent overseas," I added.

"It's a shame seeing all these young men coming home in caskets."

"It is," I said.

"It's not the same," Professor Gordon went on.

"The same?" I asked.

"Our war was fought for a good cause. Do you know what that cause was, Mr. Rawlings?" he asked, ever the teacher.

"A fight against fascism. Dictators like Hitler and Mussolini and Tojo."

"Plus the fact that they attacked us."

"You've become a 'peacenik?'" I asked.

"I have. I'm not the only veteran who has."

"I'm against the war, too," I said. "But what I really hate is seeing what it's doing to people my age. Even if they believe in the war, it's tough."

"War must be the last resort. When there is no option. It should never be the offspring of expediency or greed or pride or laziness."

"Most of the country seems to support it," Gary added.

"That will change. It has to."

"There are voices here and there, but no critical mass," I said.

"A phalanx of spears is more effective than a single spear," he observed, "folks will come around. It will take time, and likely some pain, but people will come around."

"I hope you're right," I said. "I don't think I'd do well in the army."

"What's your status?" he asked.

"I've got my student deferment," I answered.

"Good for you," Mr. Gordon said.

"Me, too," Gary answered. "But, my doctor said I might get out. My eyes are sort of messed up."

"He sees double," I said, smiling. "And that's when he's sober."

"Another good reason to stay in school and get good grades."

"We'll lose the deferment when we graduate," I added. "They aren't giving any to graduate students. Looking into options, in case they cancel all deferments."

"What kind?" he asked.

"Conscientious objector, reserves, National Guard – "

"My dad said he would drive me to Canada," Gary interrupted.

"I'd hate to see that happen," Professor Gordon replied. "That would be a terrible loss. A waste of our young men."

"We may not have a choice," I said. "I won't kill somebody I don't know who's defending their country. That's crazy."

"Killing for peace is like fucking for chastity," Gary blurted out, immediately regretting it.

"Killing somebody is not a pleasant experience," Mr. Gordon said, ignoring Gary's outburst.

"It's incredible to me that a few men in power can determine the fate of an entire generation," I said.

"It wouldn't be the first time. But, I'm confident you learned that in your history classes."

"I did," I continued. "But, I also learned that organized resistance works. 'Human energy can overcome the burdens of history.' John Reed wrote that."

"*Ten Days That Shook the World*," Mr. Gordon said.

"Something I would never have read if I hadn't taken Russian history."

"There are two sides to that coin, as you've undoubtedly also learned, especially in Russian history. Violent and non-violent."

"The Black Hand killed Tsar Alexander to stop the oppression."

"In that case, things didn't change. They got worse."

"'Those who cannot remember the past are condemned to repeat it.'" I said. "I think I first heard that in your class."

"Another philosopher wrote, 'We learn from history that we do not learn from history,'" he added.

"Hegel."

"Good memory."

"Good teacher."

"Good words to live by," he said. The opening chords of "Born to Be Wild" brought us back to our current reality.

Gary's saying "fuck" was uncharacteristic. He didn't swear. Neither did I. Some of the people I knew enjoyed it. Whether it was for shock value, or trying to be cool. None of my family did. When Mom or Dad or Paul swore, we knew we were in deep trouble. I didn't use jargon, either. I cringed when I heard it. It sounded so phony. So calculated. So hip. But, I slipped from time to time. I swore when it was bad. And used jargon when I needed to fit in.

CHAPTER 7

I had a different song playing on the radio of Ugly Orange. I had bought the truck from an old farmer in Patterson on the west side of the Central Valley. I paid around two hundred bucks for the rusted out junker. It was so homely it was beautiful. It was a rough ride, but a reliable one – a half-ton with a flathead V-8. It had a three-speed manual transmission with the stick shift on the floor, plus a compound low. Zeff had installed a combination Pioneer 8-track player and AM/FM radio with decent speakers, which made it a target for thieves. I didn't care. I liked having the sounds. I had tossed a bale of hay in the back to give it some stability and to cement my image as a UC Davis Aggie.

Playing music while driving Ugly Orange back to Davis made the time and miles go by faster. We were listening to the long version of "Suzy Q" by Creedence Clearwater Revival. Creedence had once played in Davis when they were the Golliwogs. They originally hailed from El Cerrito, a small town near Oakland and Berkeley. "Suzy Q" was from their first album, which had been released at the end of May in 1968, peaking at #11 on the Top 40 charts. It clocked in at 8:37. I first heard it on KMPX, a funky progressive-rock radio station in San Francisco.

Today, we were listening to it on KSAN, 107.7, an FM station that featured albums instead of singles. When Tom "Big Daddy" Donahue, the program manager at KMPX, got into a dispute with management, he and the staff who were loyal to him went on strike. Metromedia, the owners of KSAN, seized the opportunity. They switched from classical to freeform rock, then hired Donahue and most of the people who supported him. KSAN became the hip station. As we rolled along Jack Tone Road, which was one of the many back roads we took to avoid running "Ugly" on the freeway, I was thinking that at this moment, everyone who was listening to this station was united by this one song, in this one moment. We were one tribe. To my college-inspired brain, that was a powerful concept. We listened in silence.

When I said "we," I meant my roommate, Michael Gover Johnson, and me.

Gover had moved to Modesto from Buffalo, New York, in our sophomore year of high school. He came to the parties I had at my house and we got to

36

be good enough friends to become roommates in college. He was tall and thin with dirty blonde hair that hung low over his forehead and ears. He wore thick black glasses and was often dragging on a cigarette. He had a sister, Jan, who was one year older and a younger sister, Robin, who was four years behind us. He lived on Bowen near Beard Elementary School with his parents, Cal and Mary. When he first arrived in town, we had made fun of his accent. "Wagon" sounded like "waygun" and "pillow" resembled "pallow." Mom teased him about his flat butt and skinny legs. She called them "polio legs" and told him more than once, "I've seen better bones in soup." It was our way of welcoming him to his new hometown.

"I don't think your little sister likes us," I said.

"Why's that?"

"I overheard her say something to your mom about 'those stinky boys.'"

"We do stink. Especially today."

"I don't. I took a shower."

"So did I, but I've got vodka oozing out of my pores."

"How late did you stay?"

"Not long after you split."

"I'm ready to get back to the apartment."

"Me, too."

"How's your quarter look?" I asked.

"I'll see when I get there. Mind if I close my eyes? I didn't get much sleep."

"Sure."

He scrunched down and was out like a light. We followed Jack Tone to Highway 12 and on to 160, which ran north, winding alongside the Sacramento River. We continued on 160 until we hit Highway 80 in West Sacramento and chugged along it, west into Davis. I knew I was back each time I took the Olive Drive off-ramp. My roomie didn't wake up until we pulled into the parking lot of the Vanguard Apartments off Sycamore Lane.

Vanguard sat among a cluster of apartment complexes catering to students. There was Sycamore Lane across the street and Wake Forest next door to Vanguard to the west. At the end of our cul-de-sac was Webster-Emerson, which were upscale, off-campus dorms. That's where we had our meal ticket, which saved us from having to cook. South on Sycamore Lane was a small shopping center with a grocery store, a House of Sound record store, and a Nation's Giant burger place, which served killer hangover breakfasts.

There were four of us in the second-floor apartment facing east onto Sycamore. All Modesto boys. I shared a room with Dave Threlfall, AKA "Tree-Fall," who was never there. The only way you knew I had a roommate was that his blue, down sleeping bag was on his unmade bed. Describing him as disheveled would be a compliment. His hiking boots were never tied, he generally wore hiking shorts, a well-worn work shirt, and unruly hair. Johnson shared a room with Rick Slevin, AKA "Sleveen," who was never not there. He was a year ahead of us and a vet in training. He had rescued a red-tailed hawk, which now lived on our balcony. There was a stream of bird excrement running down the apartment wall that grew as the year progressed. Slevin also kept baby rattle snakes in a small glass terrarium. He lost them from time to time, which made for tense moments. Johnson had his own menagerie after he saved a gopher from an anatomy class. We named it "Gover." Of course, once you named something, you were responsible for it. Unfortunately, the tiny guy didn't last long. I wasn't sure if he died of natural causes, or lack of attention. Following a short ceremony and a few toasts, we buried him. Gover had been doing a few odd jobs for the apartment managers, one of which was cementing in the concrete holes that held the below-ground garbage cans. The manager wanted the cans moved out by the parking lot, so the holes needed to be filled. That was one of Gover's tasks and it became the rodent's final resting place. As the concrete set, Gover inscribed: "Here lies Gover Gopher, January 1969, RIP."

We didn't use the kitchen much because none of us were cooks and, luckily for us, we had the meal ticket. We had to get our money's worth, so we never missed a meal at Web-Em. Once in a while, when the dining commons were closed for a holiday or a ptomaine scare, we were forced to cook. We were in that situation now because we'd returned before the campus had re-opened. A buddy of Slevin's had given him some venison, which we had popped in the freezer. Gover decided he would make venison stew. It was a tasty idea, until he took a break to call Nancy, forgot to turn down the heat, and scorched the bottom. We ate it anyway.

CHAPTER 8

KDVS 91.5 FM was our campus radio station. Its studio was located in the basement of Freeborn Hall. The DJs were students who had done radio, or wanted to. The models for the station were the free-form FM stations like KSAN and KZAP. Like all such stations, they combined music, talk, and public service programming. I would sometimes listen while doing my homework because they often broke the latest news on bands, albums, and concerts.

One of the hipper DJs was a jock named Tyree. He came on at midnight. I tried to catch his show when I could because he generally had something to say.

"My fellow Aggies," he said one night. "It's time for a short history lesson. World War II was over. The world had recovered. Europe and Japan had been rebuilt. All the things that hadn't been available during the war and shortly after the war in the Forties and Fifties, things like food, money, cars, and luxury items, were now abundantly available. It was a time of tranquility. The time was ripe for new conflicts, new revelations, and new revolutions."

He paused. I could imagine him leaning into the microphone for dramatic effect and urgently whispering said, "Life is not a spectator sport, my friends. You've got to get down out of the stands and onto the field. Talk changes nothing. Action does."

Of course, he followed those pearls with "For What It's Worth," by Buffalo Springfield. My all-time favorite band.

There's something happening here,
What it is ain't exactly clear,
There's a man with a gun over there
Telling me I got to beware . . .

I fell asleep and dreamt of marching, charging people.

I was more a believer in fate than serendipity. Things happened for a reason.

I didn't know how or why and I didn't know who was pulling the strings, but things definitely happened for a reason. During our first week at Vanguard in the fall of 1968, there was a kegger by the pool to greet the new residents. It was an excellent way to meet the people you would be seeing on an almost daily basis for the rest of the year. On the second floor, directly across from us, lived another four dudes, two of which we would get to know well. Mike Walt was from Davis, Doug Uhland from Arbuckle. They had been dormies, with several others I would soon meet, at Ryerson Hall as freshmen. Walt, who came to be known as Wally or Wally Gator, was younger than us Modesto guys. He played softball, loved beer, and liked his country music, which gave us a couple connections.

I had been fortunate to have people in my life who I could always talk with about sports, beer, and music. Gary, Willy, and now Gator. Any time I wanted to catch a game, sip a cold one, or listen to a song, I could count on at least one, and sometimes all three, to be right there with me. Over the years, we would create a trunkload of memories together.

One of the first weekends we were in Davis the previous October, Wally's apartment had hosted a poker game. Merle Haggard, Patsy Cline, and Johnny Cash were on the stereo. Gover told Wally a sob story about not having wheels so he could visit his high school sweetheart Nancy, who was attending San Jose State. Without batting an eye, Wally put down his cigarette, pulled the keys to his Opal Cadet out of his Levi's pocket, and tossed them to Gover. That was who he was.

Wally was another native Californian. He had grown up in Berkeley. His dad's family had owned a drugstore near the campus. His dad had been deputy director of finance under California Governor Edmund G. "Pat" Brown. The family had moved to Davis in the fall of 1965, but spent their summers on a ranch in Fort Bragg on the Mendocino coast. He had two younger brothers, Tim and Pat, and three younger sisters, Kim, Jennifer, and Carol. His dad had also been a Marine, having fought in Saipan, where my father had also fought. His dad's first cousin once removed, General Lewis M. Walt, had been the commanding general of the Marines in Vietnam from 1965 to 1967. An uncle on his mother's side was an FBI agent. Gator was a cowboy, so his world view skewed to the right. Oh, and he had a temper. Hair-trigger. Particularly after a few drinks. Wally wanted to be a veterinarian. His family had other plans.

While at Ryerson, this group had played every intramural (I.M.) sport. The name of their team was FYNC, or Farming Youth of Northern California. In the fall of '68, they had needed a wide receiver and safety for their football team, which was playing in the off-campus league because they were no longer living in the dorms. I applied and got the job. We were competitive, finishing in the top ten in our league. That January, we weren't thinking football. We were thinking softball.

So, how did he become Wally and Gator? We couldn't have two Mikes – Walt and Johnson – so we had to create nicknames. "Wally" was obvious. Gator came about after a night of heavy drinking at a frat party. Surprise, surprise. Delta Sig, maybe. One of the rites of passage at those frat parties was something called "Doing the gator." Basically, if you were drunk enough, or not, when the frat boys chanted "Gator," you dropped down to your belly, writhing and flopping around on the floor. The whole exercise reminded me of Gary's high school "froth and foam" routine where he imitated an epileptic fit to entertain our high school friends. We were easily amused. Gator could writhe and wriggle with the best of them. The name stuck.

CHAPTER 9

I had another full load of classes this quarter. "Proseminar in History," "Russian History 1856 – 1914," and "History of England." I loved history. I preferred non-fiction over fiction; the real versus the imaginary. I truly believed that those who did not study history were doomed to repeat it. Of course, making history wasn't totally in my hands and wasn't something I felt I was destined to do. I planned to teach, like Mr. Leach and Mr. Gordon. My mentors had groomed me to join their ranks. To broaden my horizons, I added a somewhat related course, "The Golden Age of Russian Poetry."

The poetry class was held in Olsen Hall, while the rest of my classes were located in the History Department, which was housed in Voorhies Hall. It was an ugly building and depressing in the wintertime. All concrete, glass, and hard surfaces. Tough rooms to stay awake in when your profs were droning on about Plantagenets and Romanovs. But, I knew how the game was played, so I paid attention. There was one important lesson I learned early in my career as a student, especially in college. Get to know your profs and let them get to know you. I regularly stopped in during office hours, even if there was no reason. It usually paid off.

Davis, California, was a city of bikes. It had the most bikes per capita of any city in the world, or so the Chamber of Commerce claimed. That's how you got around. Class change near the quad made Rome and Paris look like child's play when it came to traffic congestion. Another Modesto boy ended up dropping out of Davis after he got involved in a horrible bike crash coming out from under the Olsen-Shields Library pedestrian bridge and onto the roundabout at the southeast corner of the quad. It was a crazy domino crash. He recovered physically, but never quite got over it emotionally.

I owned a gold Schwinn ten-speed racing bike. It was a beauty. A tad heavy, but solid, it had no fenders. When it rained, I'd generally have a wet streak up my back from the water spinning off my wheels.

My school uniform of choice during the dreary winter was a light blue Bracero work shirt worn over printed T-shirt, Levi's, tennies or waffle stompers AKA hiking boots, a dark blue trench coat, blue and gold muffler, and a funky old brown Fedora hat I'd found in a thrift shop. Gover said I looked like a stalker, adding it was no wonder girls cast worried glances over their shoulders any time I suddenly appeared on the bike path behind them.

The first week of winter classes, there was a concert at Freeborn Hall to welcome us back. Delta Sigma Phi hosted a show that featured Spirit, Womb, The Kak, and Oxford Circle. Spirit was an LA band with a few hits, like "I Got a Line on You." The Kak was a group of locals who were getting some attention. So was Oxford Circle, who named themselves after the street near our apartment where the Webster-Emerson dorms were located.

It didn't take long for the rough beast – politics and protests – to return to life, slouching towards Bethlehem. The Davis campus held a sympathy strike on the concrete quad in front of Freeborn for the students and faculty currently striking at San Francisco State. It was a rally "for the purpose of creating an awareness." Speakers from the American Federation of Teachers, the Black Students Union, the Students for a Democratic Society (SDS), and the Third World Liberation Front discussed plans for a strike of our own.

SF State had been in turmoil beginning on November 6th of last year. The student strike began when George Murray, an English instructor and minister of education for the Black Panther Party, was fired for openly advocating the arming of black people and the unification of minorities against racism. The BSU was supported by other student groups, collectively known as the Third World Liberation Front (TWLF). During the second week of the strike, police were called in and violence erupted a number of times.

SF State President Robert Smith closed the campus to prevent more violence. When Smith reopened the campus, a small group of students interrupted classes and battled with police. When it didn't look like things would cool down, or that Smith could control the campus, the trustees replaced Smith with acting President S.I. Hayakawa, a professor of English. When classes resumed after the Thanksgiving holiday, there were several clashes. On December 2nd, this led to a standoff with the campus administration that worsened when Hayakawa climbed onto a truck and ripped the wires from a loudspeaker during a student rally. Shortly after that, the American Federation of Teachers expressed their support for the strikers. President Hayakawa responded by saying the campus would close a week early for the Christmas holiday, hoping things would cool down. When school re-opened on January 6th, nothing had changed. The AFT voted to officially strike.

The speakers at our rally gave an update on the strike and spoke about institutional racism. The co-chairman of SF State's SDS spoke, saying the problem with education was that it was designed to serve corporate interests. He went on to state that racism was a tool used by government and corporations to divide white and black workers and students so they couldn't effectively fight the forces controlling their lives. He closed by saying it wasn't enough to support the strike at State. We needed to attack racism in Davis.

I understood why they were striking and why we were planning our own in support. I understood the reference to the relationship between business and education and Eisenhower's military-industrial complex. Eisenhower had coined the phrase in his farewell address to the nation in January 1961. He was referring to an informal alliance between the U.S. military and the defense industry and their influence on public policy. It was eventually extended to include Congress, a relationship journalists termed the "iron triangle." The three entities worked together to influence funding through political contributions, military spending, lobbying, and government oversight.

Eisenhower warned, "We must never let the weight of this combination endanger our liberties or democratic processes. We should take nothing for granted. Only an alert and knowledgeable citizenry can compel the proper meshing of the huge industrial and military machinery of defense with our peaceful methods and goals so that security and liberty may prosper together."

I got it, but I had never been much of an activist, or a joiner. I took action in my own way.

The following Tuesday we witnessed President Lyndon Johnson's sixth and last "State of the Union" address. The country was in turmoil. A "law and order" president had been elected.

Johnson closed his speech with these words, "I hope it may be said, a hundred years from now, that by working together we helped to make our country more just, more just for all of its people, as well as to insure and guarantee the blessings of liberty for all of our posterity. That is what I hope. But I believe that at least it will be said that we tried."

Johnson was sixty years old and bone tired. He had had his fill of Washington, the presidency, the war, and the press. He was ready to go home to Texas.

When he left, he told friends, "I'm going to enjoy the time I've got left."

Johnson's retirement was bittersweet. He could have beat Nixon if he had run, but he didn't. Now we had Nixon. With Johnson leaving, it was possible we might see a change in Vietnam. He inherited a mess in Southeast Asia. Johnson didn't tolerate weakness. He wasn't going to be the first president to lose a war, especially to the Reds. He escalated the war. When he left, we were losing. It had been Kennedy's war when it started. Then it was Johnson's. Now it was Nixon's. Kennedy and Camelot, we might have forgiven because we loved him and he tragically died young at the hands of an assassin. Johnson and the Lone Star State we might have given the benefit of the doubt, since Johnson's Great Society and Civil Rights support had tried to help domestically. In fact, had it not been for Vietnam and his "win at all costs" mentality, Johnson might have ranked with FDR due to his social programs. But, Nixon and his California cronies? Not a chance.

The next day was Tim's birthday. I called him. Tone-deaf Gover and I sang a ragged rendition of "Happy Birthday," a tradition I had begun when I moved away. It was never pretty, but it was sincere.

CHAPTER 10

Richard Milhous Nixon's bloody, Macbethian ascension to the throne became complete the following Monday when he was officially inaugurated as our 37th President. His wife, Pat, stood by his side holding two family Bibles. Each was open to the same passage in Isaiah 2:4: "They shall beat their swords into plowshares, and their spears into pruning hooks; nation shall not lift up sword against nation, neither shall they learn war anymore." In his inaugural speech, we were treated to Tricky Dick's view of the world. It was gut-wrenching.

We watched it at Gator's apartment. Someone had come up with an appropriate drinking game. Every time Nixon lied or sweated, we drank. We were messed up almost before he finished thanking his family.

One of the more memorable lines from his speech was, "The greatest honor history can bestow is the title of peacemaker. The honor now beckons America." He was promising the American people he would find peace with honor. I was skeptical. We'd see.

There were plenty of distractions on campus for those who didn't want to study, or were tripping on something, whether it was acid, dope, alcohol, or caffeine. At least once a month, the "Flick-It-In Theatre" would present films at 194 Chem, which was the largest lecture hall on campus. "Flick-It-In" said it all. I wasn't tempted, but my roomies were. I'd be hiding out in the basement of Olsen Hall drinking vending machine coffee and cranking out my latest term paper. I liked getting things done ahead of time.

Music continued its influence on my life, when, a few days later, Reprise Records released Neil Young's first album. The album cover had no artwork, simply a painting of him with a cityscape floating below and a wild landscape on fire behind him. I would later learn that the wildness was Topanga Canyon in Los Angeles, where Young was living. I went to the House of Sound and bought the record immediately. I was a fan of Buffalo Springfield and of Neil Young and Stephen Stills in particular. I was blown away by the opening instrumental, "Emperor of Wyoming." "The Loner" felt familiar. I thought he was way too young to have written something so powerfully nostalgic as "Here We Are In the Years." But, what did I know? I was younger than he was. The lone photograph was inside the fold and showed Young opening a Lipton tea bag, a kettle on the stove, and cooking utensils hanging on the wall behind. The lyrics for all the songs were hand-written on the opposite side of the inside cover. The songs were published by Cotillion Music, Inc., Broken Arrow Music Publishing Co., and Marcus Music. Cotillion had published some of Buffalo Springfield's songs and Broken Arrow was Young's company. I noticed that the recording had used something called the Haeco-CSG system. I had never heard of it. Turns out it made stereo records playable on mono equipment.

Gary's birthday was January 24th. I always circled the date so I wouldn't forget to call him. But, it became a red-letter day that year for another reason. A UCD student named Pete Schurman had moments earlier finished a speech in his rhetoric class on the unconstitutionality of the Selective Service System. He pulled his draft card from his wallet and burned it. The professor of the class, Dr. Harry Sharp, had all the speeches videotaped that day so students could see themselves. Now Schurman's act was forever etched in acetate.

Once every American male turned 18, they had to sign up for the draft and were required by law to carry their draft cards with them at all times. If you destroyed it, you could face up to five years in prison and a $10,000 fine. It was not something you did lightly. It was a line in the sand and Schurman wasn't the only one drawing it.

Ironically, that same day the Draft Counseling Center opened on the second floor of South Hall after a long delay, likely due to the college's concerns about providing such a service. The counselors were ministers and priests from the Davis area. The center would not encourage resistance, but the counselors would work with students to make sure they had all the information they needed to make the best decision for them. As with my profs, it wasn't going to take me long to get to know the counselors.

Later in January, Nixon would direct the Department of Defense to develop a plan to end the draft and create a volunteer army. We were all up for that, but we didn't think the Hawks in the federal government would let him get away with it. They needed bodies for Southeast Asia. The prez had given us a faint glimmer of hope that we wouldn't have to go. Of course, that meant most of the men serving in the military were ones who were unemployed, or couldn't afford to go to college. The concept smacked of the Civil War when rich families paid poor tenement dwellers to take their son's place in the army, including Teddy Roosevelt's father.

Ralph Gleason's January editorial in *Rolling Stone* had me thinking. It felt like our elders didn't want us around. Or, at least, wanted us to pipe down.

He had written, "This society fears its young people deeply and desperately and does all that it can to train those it can control in its own image."

I thought he was on to something. Little wonder most of us didn't trust anyone over 30. The government, corporations, the military, Nixon and Reagan, the alphabet soup agencies all seemed to be gunning for the hippies, the longhairs, the students – anyone who didn't fit the Fifties stereotype. It was scary. But, we weren't about to roll over.

College gave people of a certain age the freedom to educate themselves and get involved with important issues. In 1969, there was a raft-load of critical issues. On January 29th, another major concern pushed the others off the front page when 200,000 gallons of oil leaked off the coast of Santa Barbara. I was a part-time environmentalist. I got pissed when things like this happened, but I didn't do much to change it. I loved nature, but wasn't a "tree hugger." Basically, I didn't litter.

On the next to the last day of January, KDVS got my attention when they announced that the Beatles had played a concert on the roof of the Apple Corps building at 3 Savile Road in London. It was stopped by police after neighbors complained about the noise and the traffic as people congregated below, many of whom were on their lunch break. Rumors were flying that the band was thinking about retiring from performing live. The show had been filmed for a proposed documentary.

The Beatles had been together starting in 1962. There was never a day when they weren't. They now had lives outside their music, with wives and children. They were tired of touring. They wanted to concentrate on the music, not performing in front of fans who couldn't hear them. They weren't going away. They would continue to record. They weren't playing live anymore.

On January 2nd, they had found themselves rehearsing in front of cameras at Twickenham Film Studios for their next album, which was tentatively entitled *Get Back*, after a new song Paul had written. It had been twelve weeks since they'd finished the *White Album*. It may have been too soon.

The plan was to spend a few weeks rehearsing, then record the new album with everything being documented by director Michael Lindsay-Hogg, so fans could see how much fun they had working together. The problem was, they weren't having fun and the cameras didn't lie. Making the album took a little over a week. The film would no longer be called *Get Back*. It would now be *Let It Be*. Not long after that, Lindsay-Hogg came up with the idea of a live, rooftop concert.

Shortly after midday on January 30th, reports came into London's *Evening Standard* of a "tremendous racket" coming from the roof of a building in

Savile Row. It was soon realized by curious shoppers and office workers that it was the Beatles. Lindsay-Hogg had convinced them to be and play like the Beatles of old one last time, the way they used to, as an appropriate way to complete the film and end the unpleasant experience of making it.

When they finished, John said, "Thank you very much. We hope we passed the audition." It would be their last public performance.

It was going to be an interesting year.

CHAPTER 11

"All the News that Fits" – February Edition

The Red Cross resumes relief efforts in Biafra. Actor Boris Karloff dies. Eric Burden and the Animals disband. At the Palestine National Congress, Al-Fatah leader Yasser Arafat is elected chairman of the Palestine Liberation Organization. John Madden is named head coach of the Oakland Raiders. John Lennon, George Harrison, and Ringo Starr hire Allen Klein as the Beatles' new business manager, against the wishes of Paul McCartney. McCartney hires the law firm of Eastman & Eastman, Linda Eastman's father's law firm, as general legal counsel for Apple Records. Bowie Kuhn becomes Major League Baseball's fifth commissioner. The U.S. population reaches 200 million. In a six to one vote, the Federal Communications Commission moves to bar cigarette advertising from television and radio. *The Saturday Evening Post*, which was started in 1869, publishes its last issue. Johnny Cash and Bob Dylan record together in Nashville with one song, "Girl from the North Country," released from these sessions. The leaking oil well is capped in Santa Barbara. Golda Meir is elected the first female prime minister of Israel. Gabby Hayes, the cantankerous pre-hippie sidekick of Roy Rogers, dies at 83. The PLO attacks an Israeli El-Al airline plane in Zurich. At Hollywood's 26th Golden Globe Awards, Peter O'Toole wins best actor for *The Lion in Winter*; Joanne Woodward wins for *Rachel, Rachel*; while *The Lion in Winter* wins for drama and *Oliver!* wins for musical or comedy. The Beatles begin recording "Abbey Road." Mariner 6 completes a fly-by of the planet Mars. General Hafez al-Assad stages a military coup in Syria. A Los Angeles court refuses Sirhan Sirhan's request to be executed. Dan Hicks and His Hot Licks sign with Epic Records. New book releases include *Providence Island* by Calder Willingham; *The Tragedy of Lyndon Johnson*, Eric F. Goldman; *The Peter Principle: Why Things Go Wrong*, Laurence J. Peter and Raymond Hull; *Portnoy's Complaint*, Philip Roth; and *Forfeit* by Dick Francis. *Play It Again, Sam; Canterbury Tales; Ceremonies in Dark Old Men*; and *Dear World* open on stage. New films include *The Prime of Miss Jean Brodie* starring Maggie Smith, Costa-Gavras' Political thriller *Z*, and *Change of Habit* with Elvis Presley and Mary Tyler Moore. New music includes

Gram Parsons and the Flying Burrito Brothers' *Gilded Palace of Sin*, Jethro Tull's *This Was*, and the Jefferson Airplane's live album, *Bless Its Pointed Little Head*.

Founded in Philadelphia in 1821, *The Saturday Evening Post* was published weekly and had become an American institution. It espoused conservative, front-porch American values and entertained its readers with stories about celebrities; short fiction by London, Fitzgerald, and Faulkner; and homey, nostalgic illustrations by Andrew Wyeth and Norman Rockwell. After its February 8th issue, it was gone, likely because there was no common ground anymore; the nation was fractured. Or, to the fact it lost a massive defamation suit surrounding its allegations that two coaches had conspired to fix a college football game.

Another American institution had returned to the recording studio. Following the success of his comeback television special in December 1968 simply entitled *Elvis*, his manager, "Colonel" Tom Parker, wanted Elvis Presley to release a record as soon as possible. Memphis had replaced Nashville as the place to record. Dusty Springfield had released *Dusty in Memphis* to rave reviews in January. That same month, Elvis went to work at Chips Moman's American Sound Studios with a legendary group of sidemen. In ten days, he would record "Long Black Limousine," "In the Ghetto," and "Suspicious Minds." He returned in February to record more tracks, including "Kentucky Rain." The result was *From Elvis in Memphis*. Elvis was back and never sounding better.

That same month, Dylan was laying down tracks at the Columbia Music Row Studios in Nashville. He was tired of being labeled "the voice of his generation." He wanted to try something new. That something new was country. The result was "Lay, Lady, Lay" and *Nashville Skyline*.

Two signature voices of different generations were traveling down new roads.

It was no big deal to me when the FCC barred cigarette companies from advertising on television and radio. I tried smoking once, got sick, and gave it up. But, Gary and Gover were committed smokers, not that they cared about advertising. My parents had smoked my entire life. Raleigh's unfiltered. Mom collected the coupons. She would wrap them in rubber bands and stash them in an empty Folger's coffee can until she had enough to buy something she wanted. Paul smoked his pipe. The house smelled like stale tobacco absorbed into every fabric in the house. I got used to it because I stopped noticing.

One of the purposes of a college education was not only to learn, and perhaps become proficient at something you could make a living doing, but it was also meant to broaden your horizons. It was designed to break kids out of their provincial, hometown perspective and open them up to new experiences and new people. I was something of a loner and shy, likely thanks to my mother being such an extrovert. I was something of a chameleon, preferring to blend in. I wasn't aggressive about asking girls out. I was too afraid of being turned down, or looking stupid. Calling a girl to go on a date was torture. I was clueless when it came to any hint a girl was flirting, or might be interested. In class, I sat at the back and didn't volunteer unless called upon, particularly since this was only my second quarter at the Big U. That meant I didn't meet many new people in class. I was in and out and never the twain shall meet. Most of the people I did get to know, I encountered at parties, or bars, or playing intramural sports. That applied to guys mostly. When it came to the ladies on campus, I was out of it. Plus, even though Kelly and I were beginning to show signs of problems sustaining a long-term relationship, I still had her as a girlfriend. For now. So I wasn't looking.

That didn't mean I wasn't looking looking. I was always checking out the female students. Thus, the Stalker nickname. If it was easy, I would get to know my classmates and fellow Aggies. If it wasn't, no big deal. I wasn't obsessed by it. I was there to learn, not socialize. That *modus operandi* changed with my Russian poetry class. I met three people – a girl, a boy, and a prof – that I got to know well. That changed my perspective.

The girl was named Lucius Dolgushkin. She was a third-generation White Russian immigrant from San Francisco, thus the interest in the class. Her grandparents had eluded the Soviet purge by escaping to Japan through Siberia, as part of the wave of aristocrats, intellectuals, and officers of the Imperial Russian Army fleeing the Bolsheviks. It was straight out of Boris Pasternak's *Doctor Zhivago*, as directed by David Lean and portrayed by Omar Sharif and Julie Christie. *Zhivago* was an epic novel and movie that fascinated the romantic in me because it was a love story and the historian because it was Russian history.

Luci's parents had met and married in San Francisco. She was an only child. Her family was part of an extensive community of Russians who lived in the Richmond District, a community that spoke Russian and frequented shops and restaurants catering to pre-revolutionary émigrés.

She was smart, cynical, funny, and athletic. With long, straight red hair, patched Levi's, fringed buckskin over a denim work shirt, macrobiotic diet, a monarch butterfly tattoo on the back of her neck, and patchouli oil, she was an Earth Mother. She preferred being called Luci. She hated the name her father had cruelly given her. He was an ancient civilizations professor, with a concentration in the Roman empire. Lucius Versus was heir to emperor

Hadrian and became the co-emperor with Marcus Aurelius in 161 AD. Her father had written his dissertation on the relatively unknown emperor. Obviously, he had wanted a son, but Luci was what he got. She reminded me of a quote I'd read in a poem by Sylvia Plath.

Out of the ash
I rise with my red hair
And I eat men like air.

The guy was named Stephan Marlow. He was an Air Force brat from Colorado, who had followed his older sister to Davis. He was scary bright, sarcastic, with a dark sense of humor. He was a poet and an admirer of the Russian decadent poets, thus his reason for being in the class. Sporting long hair, moustache, French cigarettes, Italian espresso, and Bohemian clothes, he carefully affected the garret scribe look. He reminded me of Eric Clapton in his Cream days. When it came to his world view, he was as radical as he looked. The prof was named Rodney L. Patterson. He was a native of the California foothills near Chico. Wild-eyed, blonde-haired and moustached, devilishly eyebrowed and chiseled handsome, he was an ex-military man. He had studied Russian literature, language, and history while attending UCLA, with the idea of eventually working for the foreign service. He bailed on the government but stuck with Russian studies. He was somewhat of a rake and raconteur, who tooled around town in his Jaguar XKE. The co-eds loved him. Alas for them, he was married to a stunning blonde named Marilyn. They had met while he was studying. She had done some acting. Rod had become a liberal-leaning pacifist thanks to his time in the service and his dealings with certain shadowy elements of the government.

Our paths crossed and our lives converged that January in a dreary classroom in Olson Hall.

The class was a survey course: "Study of Russian Versification – Readings from Pushkin, Lermontov, and Other Poets of the First Half of the Nineteenth Century." It was a rich time in that country's history. It was also a time of social upheaval.

CHAPTER 12

Each time I began a new class, I scoped out the seat arrangement and picked a spot in the back. I sat in the same seat for the rest of the quarter. Most students did the same. To my pleasant surprise, Luci sat next to me. Steph next to her. I was a copious note-taker. They weren't. Professor Patterson was a dynamic lecturer. Nobody slept in his class. His savage eyes and eyebrows kept us engaged. He also used photographs and film clips to better illustrate the content, which was also riveting. It was a class I truly looked forward to. For obvious reasons.

Luci wasn't a good student. Not because she wasn't smart enough. She was. But, she was lazy. I helped her by loaning her notes and explaining the things she missed, or didn't get. It gave me a chance to see her. Most of the time, we talked school, art, music, movies, Russian poetry and history. It was her heritage, but she knew little about it.

I became a confidante of sorts; her sounding board. There was one area of my studies that deeply interested her and that was the underground revolutionary movement of the late 1800s. I told her about Dostoevsky's book, *The Possessed*, which was based on the life of Russian terrorist, Sergey Nechayev. He was part of the Nihilist movement, which rejected the power of all authorities. The name came from the Latin word for *nihil*, which meant "nothing." Nechayev believed that revolution was necessary and should be achieved by any means required, including violence. He didn't feel it was crucial for revolutionaries to gain the support of the people to succeed. Instead, he was convinced that by victimizing and terrorizing the common folk, they would be incited to rebellion, primarily because they were propagandized to conclude it was the government that was responsible. Luci was transformed by this revelation and by all the repression that was happening around the world. The nurturing Earth Mother was becoming the radical Che. I still wanted to be near her. Moth to the flame.

Several times during the early weeks of school, I ran into Luci. She would stop. We'd chat. She'd flirt some. I couldn't tell if the encounter was by accident or design. It seemed too frequent to be a coincidence. On those occasions when I saw her and she didn't see me, she was often spending time with the more radical students on campus. It was said that people could tell the quality of your character by the quality of the people you walked with. I was beginning to wonder who she really was.

I was hanging more with Steph, as well. He lived at the La Casa de Flores apartments off Russell, not far from my Vanguard apartment. His lady friend was named Jo, a petite, dark-haired beauty. He had a skittish Irish setter named Samba. I'd visit after class. We'd listen to music, classical or jazz. He'd smoke and drink espresso. I'd have a beer. If he wasn't working on a story, or playing acoustic guitar, he was doing pen-and-ink drawings of exotic places, people, or things. One in particular was the image of a Bedouin man sitting near a campfire, holding a hooded, hunting hawk.

He had once said to me, after a day when nothing went right, "People with great imagination have a hard time living in the real world."

Steph worked part-time at the Browsing Room in the library. It was an area where students could go to find quiet, listen to music, and read the daily paper, or latest magazines. Each seat had its own turntable. Steph checked out headphones and albums. You could sit for hours listening to the new albums he had ordered and carefully catalogued. Each weekday at noon, Steph would play a new album for whoever was in the room. It could be classical, jazz, rock, or world music. It was there I was first exposed to electronic music, such as the work of Walter Carlos and Morton Subotnick, whose albums *Silver Apples of the Moon* and *The Wild Bull* were mesmerizing, as was the cover artwork. Released by Nonesuch Records, the title for *Silver Apples* was inspired by the poem, "The Song of Wandering Aengus," by W.B. Yeats. The same poem had been responsible for the title of Ray Bradbury's collection of short stories, *The Golden Apples of the Sun*.

Steph had become friends with Rod. It was no surprise. They were similar. Inquisitive, bright, free thinkers. Men who could blend in with the Russian expatriates who lived in Paris during the time of Hemingway, Joyce, and Fitzgerald. Rod's home was in the country off Mace Boulevard. It was an older home with a concrete fence, both painted green, camouflaged by bushes and trees. It was open and airy. They had a menagerie of animals. Steph and I would join them in the evenings and on weekends for coffee and conversation. We discussed Nixon, the war, the draft, Reagan, the university, People's Park, and their efforts to free Russian Jews from the Soviet Union. Rod was an innovator. He was continually looking for ways to improve and enhance learning and teaching.

"You ever heard of reader's theater?" I asked him one night, as we polished off a bottle of red wine.

"I've not," he answered.

"We've done traditional theater," Marilyn added.

"It has elements of that," I said. "Basically, it combines the spoken word with music and imagery to tell a story. It's presented on a stage with lighting. It can be poetry, fiction, or non-fiction, visualized using slides, film, video, or animation."

"I read in one of the art magazines we get in the Browsing Room about something that sounds similar. Called 'multimedia,'" Steph said. "A singer and artist named Bob Goldstein used different types of media to promote a show of his."

"I believe McLuhan wrote about that," Rod added.

"You're right, he did," I said.

"I keep trying to figure out ways to enliven and enrich our classes," Rod continued. "The language classes can be deadly dull. This might be a way to do that."

"It's fun to produce," I said. "The last one I did was for a class at Modesto Junior College. It was a montage of images and stories about 1968."

"*Montage* is a French word. It means editing," Marilyn clarified.

"Soviet filmmakers like Sergei Eisenstein introduced the concept to film editing," Rod added. "Have you seen any of his films?" he asked.

"I haven't," I answered.

"You should. *Strike, Battleship Potemkin, October,* and *Alexander Nevsky* are all wonderful."

"Dear, you should talk with the department about doing a film series," Marilyn said.

"A wonderful idea," Rod answered. I was beginning to realize that Rod became genuinely excited about new things. It was a sincere enthusiasm that was infectious.

"I also want to figure out how we can do something with what you described," Rod said to me.

"Maybe for one of your classes," Steph said.

"I'm teaching 19th Century Russian literature in the fall. Maybe then?" Rod suggested.

"That could work," I said. "I was planning to take the class."

"There's a department on campus that uses television to teach courses. It's called Instructional Television, or ITV. They're located upstairs in Olsen Hall. I know they've done work with Kathy Fisher and the genetics department. We might be able to talk them into doing something with us," Rod said. We toasted our new idea with the last of the wine.

As I sat amongst this group of Bohemians and looked into Rod's animated face, he reminded me of Merlin and the other mentors who guided Arthur and the heroes of myth and literature on their quests of individual identity and communal salvation. I was intrigued by the prospect of embarking on a journey with him and the others.

CHAPTER 13

I called Kelly on Valentine's Day. She thanked me for the cute collection of children's Valentine's cards; the ones I gave out to my crushes in elementary school. I told her I'd kept them all these years for just such an occasion.

"And thanks for the little Valentine heart candies," she continued.

"You're welcome."

"Brought back some memories."

"For me, too."

"I always wondered who would give me one of those hearts and what it would say on the inscription."

"I'm glad you liked them. I wasn't sure."

A moment's silence, then she asked, "How's school?"

"Good. And you?"

"Some tough classes, but I'm slowly figuring out this whole away-from-home-college thing."

"I'm not worried," I said.

"You had time to talk with anybody about the draft?"

"A few."

"Any news?"

"Nothing concrete. I'll keep you posted."

"Please do. It will all work out."

"You're such an optimist," I said.

"That's why you love me."

"It certainly is," I answered. It was a better conversation than I had anticipated, but I mostly expected the worst.

I was not an "Everything is great" optimist. I was a "glass half-empty" pessimist. For some reason, I believed that expecting the best in every situation seemed to lead to failed expectations. This view of the world was known as "defensive pessimism" – hope for the best, prepare for the worst. This philosophy was based on the idea that if you set your expectations low and prepared for everything that could go wrong, it could lead to something going right. It worked because I worried less about the outcome. I was less anxious about what might happen. If it didn't turn out, if I didn't get what I wanted, or thought I needed, it was no big deal because I hadn't counted on it in the first place. It was easy to just let it go.

Luci and I sat across from each other in the Coffee House in East Hall, which had re-opened for the new quarter in January. It was a funky place where students could get serious java and get serious. It was the hip place to hang that year. We hung there regularly.

"This is such bullshit, man," Luci hissed. "How can Hayakawa get away with this crap?"

"He's the president of the university," I replied.

"That's 'cause none of the regents have balls enough to kick him out."

"Ronnie Ray-Gun's backing him."

"Our governor's a dick."

"He's in good company then, I guess."

"We need to go," she said.

"And do what?"

"Show our solidarity. Support the strikers."

"What about midterms?"

"What about freedom? What about justice? Get your priorities straight, man." I was stunned by her anger. She obviously trusted me with it.

"You ever been to the Primate Center?" she asked, suddenly dropping the subject of the strike as quickly as she brought it up.

"I don't even know what that is."

"It's our own tiny zoo. They've got a bunch of different types of monkeys and apes and things."

"Never heard of it."

"They do tours and stuff. I've got an anthro assignment and I need to go. I thought you might want to tag along."

"When?"

"This Friday at four."

"I've got intramural basketball practice."

She gave me that "get your priorities straight" look again and said, "Next time."

"Sure, next time," I answered.

UC Berkeley had begun picketing in support of the November strike at San Francisco State. Picketing moved into boycotting and into striking. On a Wednesday near the end of February, what began as a peaceful day of picketing at Cal erupted into a rock throwing, club swinging, head cracking riot, as police and strikers clashed at various sites around campus. It was a day of arrests and broken windows and ended with the closing of Telegraph from Bancroft to Haste. A rain of rocks, bottles, fruit, and cans greeted police, as they tried to clear Sproul Plaza. Students resumed picketing at Sather Gate. Everything was quiet until a member of the Alameda County Sheriff's Department attempted to arrest a black man. When they couldn't make the collar, they charged the crowd.

The police cleared Sproul Plaza and cordoned it off. A group of strikers broke inside the ring. Students shouted, "Pigs off campus!" as more strikers joined the fray and police arrested them. When a CHP captain was asked why members of *The Daily Californian* newspaper were attacked, he replied, "If you had to see through a fogged-up face shield maybe you wouldn't be able to see a press pass either." Around 3:30 that afternoon, demonstration leaders urged the crowd "to get your things together and come back tomorrow."

On the last Saturday of February back in Davis, folk singer Judy Collins performed at Freeborn Hall. She was on tour promoting her latest album, *Who Knows Where the Time Goes?*, which had been released in November. I talked Luci into going with me. It was crowded. Too crowded. There was a rumor going around that the Memorial Union Student Council (MUSC) had lost money on a few previous concerts and were selling as many tickets as they could print to make up the deficit. The crowd kept being asked to move forward to make room for the concert goers crowding in from the lobby. Finally, we all said "no," a few other choice words, and stopped moving. Our discomfort melted away as soon as Judy Blue Eyes stepped out. She sang "My Father" and "Pretty Polly" from her new album. From *Wildflowers*, she did "Both Sides Now" and "Michael from Mountains." From *In My Life*, she sang "Just Like Tom Thumb's Blues." She had piano, bass, and drums backing her when she wasn't playing solo guitar, or piano. Dressed in green and white, she entertained us for two and a half hours with a short intermission. For her encore, she did a mesmerizing rendition of Leonard Cohen's "Suzanne," accompanying herself on guitar. I was hoping Stephen Stills would show up, considering they were dating and he had played on the album. She did. He didn't.

CHAPTER 14

San Francisco State College was located in the south of San Francisco, sandwiched between the Outer Richmond and Outer Mission districts. It was founded in 1899 as a state-run school to train teachers. It became a state college in 1921 and part of the California State College system in 1935. It had historically had a progressive reputation. The rolling, hilly campus was located a few miles from the Pacific Ocean. I had considered it when applying to colleges, but decided it was too cold and foggy. As Mark Twain once said, "The coldest winter I ever saw was the summer I spent in San Francisco." That type of weather wasn't meant for me.

From the beginning of the strike on November 6th, there had been clashes nearly every day between students and San Francisco Police tactical squads: burley pigs with clubs and face-masked helmets. Students, faculty, and community activists were demanding more equal access to education, more minority faculty, and more classes that reflected the ethnic diversity of the community. There had also been issues with the ROTC recruiting on campus, the college's practice of providing the selective service with a student's academic standing, and ongoing opposition to the war in Vietnam. There'd also been confrontations between Black Student Union students and conservative white students, including the editor of *The Daily Gater*, the campus newspaper.

When the campus reopened in January, the faculty went on strike and set up a picket line around the campus. They wanted educational reform, the removal of the police from campus, agreement to student demands, and a collective bargaining agreement for all California State College teachers. Acting President Hayakawa didn't agree with the students, or the faculty who were on strike. The campus was tense.

We arrived on the last Sunday of the month.

Because I was taking this much less seriously than Luci, I invited Gary and my brother, Tim, to meet us in the City. Kelly couldn't join us because she had gone home to celebrate her father's birthday. I was cool with that since it would have been awkward with her and Luci.

Gary and I had a history of doing day trips like this, mostly to visit a friend who had been hospitalized at the Oak Knoll Naval Hospital in Oakland. Chuck Horne was a year older than us. He grew up in the same neighborhood as some of our high school classmates, including my college roommate Dave Threlfall, our buddy Steve Gant, and Andy Maurer, a classmate and neighbor of Threlfall's and Gant's, who we had nicknamed "Ace." His younger sister, Katie, was a freshman at Davis. Chuck spent time with us because he wasn't all that close with the people in his class. He came to the parties at our house and often said Mom and Dad were like his second parents. My friends had said the same thing through the years. Chuck told me once that nobody called or wrote after he joined up. He had also gone to Davis, but had had some issues. He was the one who had caused the massive bike pile-up at the roundabout between the Quad and Olsen Hall.

Shortly after, he dropped out and lost his 2-S. He went to our draft board and asked if there was any way he could avoid serving. They laughed at him. He tried to join the Coast Guard, but the wait list was too long, so he enlisted in the Navy. He had some problems there, too. He was sent home to Oak Knoll for psych evaluations. There was nothing wrong with him. He wasn't meant to be in the military. Gover once said, after taking a psych class at Davis, that a man's mental health was based on his ability to adapt to changing situations. Unfortunately, Chuck wasn't particularly adaptable. From time to time during the summer, we'd pick him up and go to San Francisco for the day. We'd catch a movie at one of the downtown theaters, like *2001: A Space Odyssey* at the Golden Gate Theater, and wander over to Hippo Hamburgers for a killer burger. Then it was back across the Bay, drop Chuck in Oakland, up and over the Altamont to home. I had thought about inviting him to join us at State, but decided it might be too much. For him and us.

Inevitably, I caved to Luci, who insisted this wasn't a pleasure trip. We skipped the burgers and met Gary and Tim around 10 a.m. at the corner of Holloway and Monticello. This was the first time they, or anyone from the valley, had met Luci. The introductions were short and business-like. We had things to take care of.

With our cars parked in a packed neighborhood east of campus, we walked down Holloway toward the school. As we approached 19th Avenue, we could see the outer edges of a large crowd. Closer, we saw a group of students holding signs and shouting. Beyond them was the teacher's picket line. Beyond that was the line of billy club wielding Tac Squaders. Behind them were cops on horses.

We turned right on 19th, walking north to reach the outer edge of the student mass. Farther north and toward the ocean, I heard, rather than saw, what sounded like revving motorcycles. It was hard to distinguish. There were so many sounds and they were all blending into one muddled roar. As we walked, other students handed out flyers. Another handed out business cards that read, "War is good business. Invest your son."

A student clambered to the top of the bus stop shelter at 19th and Holloway. Someone handed up a bullhorn.

"What do we want?" he shouted.

"Equal access!" the crowd responded.

"When do we want it?"

"Now!"

"What do we want?" he continued.

"Pigs off campus!" they responded.

"When do we want it?"

"Now!"

The first chunk of brick bounced off the plex face-shield of a cop in the center of the line. He went down. Hard. It was followed by a hail of refuse. The phalanx of cops closed ranks. Except for one, who darted to his left and used his baton to crack open the head of a black student who had gotten too close. Then the shit hit the fan.

The students surged forward, pushing the teachers into the cops, who lashed out with their batons. People in the front went down and were trampled by those rushing from behind. The outnumbered cops dropped back and let the mounted cops form a barricade with their horses.

That's when the Angels weighed in. It had been their bikes I had heard. Even though they'd been hanging with the hippies at be-ins and concerts, they were still "my country right or wrong," "law and order" believers. They hated protestors. They shored up the left flank of the police, which was exactly where we stood. We felt, before we saw, the rush of bodies fly past us and hit that flank. It was a gang of black students, many of whom looked like football players. They were big and fast and hit hard. As they tackled the bikers, more people poured into the area from the north along 19th and behind us.

We were swept up in the wave flying toward the cops and bikers battling the black students. The roiling tide of bodies rolled back toward the quad. Once it hit the open area, it fanned out to fill the open space. I was able to keep us together by grabbing Gary and Tim's hands and corralling Luci in the middle.

We tried to break free of the crowd once we reached the quad. Gary turned to lead us away when he was confronted by a Tac Squad cop who didn't look that much older than us. He raised his baton. Before he could crush Gary's skull, a dragon-tattooed hand grabbed the baton, yanked it loose, and tossed it into the crowd. It was Motown, the Modesto biker I had pulled from his burning Harley. He jack-hammered the cop to the ground.

"Get the fuck out of here," he yelled, glaring at me as recognition flashed through his eyes.

I nodded. And we did.

We crossed 19th without getting hit, moved up Wyton to Junipero Serra, back to Holloway and our car. It was a quick, silent trip back to Davis and Modesto.

CHAPTER 15

I celebrated our survival the following Tuesday when we gathered at Larry Blake's Rathskeller in downtown Davis to celebrate Gover's 21st birthday. I still wasn't old enough yet, so I used a fake ID I'd had made in Modesto. Wally wasn't, either. He wouldn't turn until January 1st. He was a New Year's baby. His fake ID was way better than mine. Although he looked younger than me, most people decided not to card him once he'd shot them one of his black glares.

"The Skeller" was a basement bar that was part of Larry Blake's restaurant. There were shelled peanuts covering the floor, graffiti covering the sheet-rocked walls, and cheap pitchers of beer. Like Gary, Gover was one of the first of our Davis High graduating class to turn old enough to drink, although we'd all done our fair share before we were legal.

Wally was there, along with his roommates and some of our teammates from the intramural team. Threlfall and Slevin made it for a while. Because it was a weekday night, Nancy couldn't join us from San Jose. Gant drove down from Arcata. He had been studying at the University of the Pacific in Stockton when something happened and he dropped out of school.

We had known "Stevie" since junior high. He wasn't sure what he planned to be when he grew up, but it would take some time and money because UOP was an expensive, private university. He thought he might be a teacher, but his parents had grander visions for him. His older brother was a dentist, so the parents were hoping for another professional in the family. Whenever he was at loose ends or doubting himself, he'd show up on our doorstep. Steve was a quiet guy. Until he drank.

Steve was on his "break" from UOP when he arrived. He had grown his hair, was experimenting with drugs, was drinking more, and had been bouncing between friends at various colleges up and down the state. Maurer was attending Humboldt State, so that's where Steve was calling home this quarter. He and Gover had gotten into trouble together in high school, driving around in Steve's black Volkswagen bug. Now the bug was parked out front of Blake's.

Inside, Steve and Wally were locked in a mortal wrist-wrestling contest. We didn't know why, but they had taken an instant dislike to each other. They were going to settle it like men. Steve was the bigger of the two and had played football in high school. Wally was wiry, but strong. They were both drunk. It was dead-even until an old football injury flared up and Steve's shoulder popped out of its socket. He went down on the peanut-shell-encrusted concrete floor. Wally helped him into his chair, while the rest of us cheered the gladiators.

"I was pulling away," Gant said.

"Maybe," Wally replied. "Guess we'll never know."

"Guess not."

If Steve hadn't popped his shoulder, the next step would have been to pull on the boxing gloves. Wally kept a set in his apartment for just such occasions. He and Gover had mixed it up more than once, one or both ending the battle with bloody noses and/or battered eyes.

I bailed early and dropped Threlfall outside the house of a girl he'd met in one of his psych classes. Her name was Nancy, too. They were inseparable, which meant I didn't see much of him or his sleeping bag.

I was deep into a dream when the front door slammed open. Gover and Gant stumbled into the apartment as I came out of my room. Gover went to the refrigerator in search of more beer and munchies. Gant sat on the couch and immediately lit his farts. I flipped them both off.

"Keep it down, or they'll toss us."

"We've got a signed lease," Gover said. "A year."

"Doesn't matter."

"Gargle my balls," Gover shot back.

"Another time," I replied. We all chuckled at the familiar back-and-forth.

"You got any fruit juice?" Gant asked.

"There's nothing in the fridge," Gover replied.

"I'll take a look," Gant said and got up.

"You been at Blake's this whole time?" I asked Gover.

"Not exactly."

"Something happen?"

"We closed the Antique," Gover answered. "Dropped Walt. Thought we'd take a drive in the country."

"I wanted to see the stars," Gant said, as he returned with a large jar of dill pickles that was empty except for the brine.

"You've got juice," Steve said, as he plopped.

"You don't want to drink that," I cautioned.

"Why not?"

"It's dill pickle, numb nuts," Gover said.

"It's been in there a while," I added. Steve looked at both of us, smiled, and drank it down. I nearly gagged and I loved vinegar.

"What happened?" I asked.

"We had a few beers," Steve answered.

"So, we tossed our dead soldiers out the window and cracked two more," Gover went on. "That's when the red light popped on behind us."

"And the siren."

"He tells me to empty my beer on the floor," Gover adds. "'They can't bust you for an empty container,' he says."

"We both turn our beers upside down and I pull over."

"The Davis cop comes up, taps the passenger window, and motions to roll it down. I do. Man, it smells like a brewery. There's gotta be an inch of beer on the floor."

"But, our cans are empty."

"'Gentlemen,' he says. 'I believe I saw you throw what looked like beer cans out your window.' 'No, sir,' we reply. He stares at both of us, looks down at the floorboards, sniffs, looks back at us, and says, 'Gentlemen, I want you to go back to town. On your way, I want you to pick up every empty beer can you see. You got that?' And we say, 'Yes, sir, we will.' He smiles and says, 'Be careful,' and goes back to his cruiser."

"It took us a while to pick up all those cans," Steve said.

"And that's where we've been."

"You guys were lucky," I said.

"Darn right," Steve said.

"I'm glad I didn't have to bail you out."

"You and me both," Gover answered.

"Good night," I said.

I closed my door. I could hear John Wayne in *The Green Berets* on the TV. Every time the Duke drank a shot of Jim Beam, they drank. I heard another crash. I reluctantly and slowly opened the door in time to see the two of them throw punches at the sliding wooden door of the hall closet. Gover's hand went through the thin laminate. Gant's hand didn't. It hit a support and he dropped to his knees. He had popped the knuckle on his index finger. When we looked closely, the knuckle was almost down to his wrist. I tried to talk him into going to the health center, but he refused.

"It'll be fine in the morning," he mumbled, collapsing on the couch.

"It'll be fine in the morning," Gover echoed and staggered off to his room.

"Sure it will," I said.

It wasn't.

Sober in the early morning light, Gover took him to the health center and got him patched up. Gant went home to Modesto, a haircut, and some explaining.

We had another birthday to celebrate at the end of February, but we wouldn't be celebrating in person with the birthday boy. Mark "Billy" Peterson was a Beard Elementary kid. He was the one who had the delicious roast beef sandwich I traded my Twinkies for when we attended Roosevelt Junior High. I didn't spend much time with Mark at Davis High. What I remember of him from those days was he was usually smiling, was a sharp dresser, and drove a nice car. He was a successful wrestler, having gone to the state championships a few times. I got to know him better when he played in the Mud Bowl, our annual Thanksgiving football game. He had been invited to join us by Terry Shaw, another high school classmate. I'd see them both in November.

Mark couldn't join us in a birthday toast because on January 1st, following a New Year's Eve Concert at Winterland in the City, he had joined the Holy Order of MANS. HOOM was a prominent New Age spiritual community founded in San Francisco. Billy was searching for something and we all hoped he would find it.

CHAPTER 16

"All the News that Fits" – March Edition

After 88 weeks, *Sgt. Pepper's Lonely Hearts Club Band* drops off the *Billboard* charts. Singer Jim Morrison of The Doors is arrested for exposing himself during a show in Miami. Pirate Radio 259 begins operation off the coast of France. China and Russia clash over borders. Apollo 9 makes 151 earth orbits over ten days. During Spring Training, four American League teams experiment with the designated pinch-hitter. Levi Strauss of San Francisco begins selling "bell-bottom" jeans. At the 11th Annual Grammy Awards, "Mrs. Robinson" by Simon & Garfunkel wins record of the year, while Glen Campbell's *By the Time I Get to Phoenix* wins album of the year. U.S. Supreme Court Justice Abe Fortas resigns over alleged ethics violations. The members of the Beatles continue to record with mixed results and reception. John Lennon marries Yoko Ono in Amsterdam and, during their honeymoon, they hold their first "Bed-In for Peace." George Harrison releases *Wonderwall* and gets busted for pot possession. Paul McCartney marries Linda Eastman. James Earl Ray is sentenced to 99 years for the assassination of Martin Luther King, Jr. UCLA beats Purdue in the 31st NCAA Men's Basketball Championship, winning for the fifth time in six years. Dwight David Eisenhower, the 34th President of the United States, dies. New book releases include *Grant Takes Command* by Bruce Catton; *In Review: Pictures I've Kept*, Dwight D. Eisenhower; *The Godfather*, Mario Puzo; *Slaughterhouse-Five, or The Children's Crusade: A Duty-Dance with Death*, Kurt Vonnegut, Jr.; *Except for Me and Thee*, Jessamyn West; and *Twelve Cities* by John Gunther. *1776*, *Winnie the Pooh*, *Of Thee I Sing*, *Come Summer*, and *Billy* open on stage. New films include *Support Your Local Sheriff* with James Garner; *Mackenna's Gold* featuring Gregory Peck and Omar Sharif; *The Illustrated Man*, based on the Ray Bradbury book; *Where Eagles Dare*; *The Love Bug*; and Michelangelo Antonioni's *Zabriskie Point*. New music includes *Delaney and Bonnie and Friends*; Bob Dylan's *John Wesley Harding*; Blood, Sweat & Tears' *Blood, Sweat & Tears*; Linda Ronstadt's *Hand Sown. . .Home Grown*; Simon & Garfunkel's single, "The Boxer;" and new albums by Donovan, the Incredible String Band, Pentangle, Van Morrison, and Merle Haggard.

The old saying that "March comes in like a lion and goes out like a lamb" traditionally applied to the weather. I wondered if it would apply to politics. We would soon see, particularly if our experience at State was any indication.

Things were getting ugly in America. Something had to change. The status quo couldn't hold anymore. I wasn't sure how and what role I could, or should, play, but it felt like I needed to do something. School was important, but there were bigger things happening all around me and I needed to be a part of it. Somehow. Nearly having Gary badly hurt had shaken my perspective.

March 1st was a red-letter day for me. That was the day my hero and namesake, and the man my father worshipped until the day he died, finally hung up the spikes. At the Yankee Clipper Motel in Fort Lauderdale, Mickey Mantle announced his retirement from the New York Yankees, the one team he had played for his entire career. "I'm not going to play baseball anymore," Mantle said during a press conference. "That's all I know. I can't play anymore. I don't hit the ball when I need to, I can't steal when I need to. I can't score from second when I need to." He obviously had debated the issue for a long time. He made his announcement as spring training was starting. "I will never want to embarrass myself on the field or hurt the club in any way or give the fans anything less than they are entitled to expect from me," Mantle added. "Anyhow, there are a lot of young fellows coming into their own. It's a young ball club with a lot of promise and I wish I were 20 years old again and part of them." Between 1951 and 1968, while "The Mick" patrolled center field and batted clean-up, the Yankees won 12 American League pennants and seven World Series. He won three American League MVP awards, was a 16-time All-Star, won the Triple Crown in 1956, and ranked third in career home runs with 536 behind Ruth and Mays. He set World Series' records for home runs (18), runs (42), RBIs (40), total bases (125), and bases on balls (43). For baseball and for me, it was the end of an era.

According to the class syllabus, one of the subjects we would be studying in my Russian history class was terrorism, which was defined as "the unlawful use of violence and intimidation, especially against civilians, in the pursuit of political aims." Terrorism had a long history in Russia starting from the time of the Russian Empire. Revolutionaries had used terrorism to disrupt the social, political, and economic systems and enabled rebels to bring down the Tsarist government. It was estimated that in the last twenty years of the Tsarist regime (1897-1917), more than 17,000 people had been killed or wounded in terror attacks.

We would be examining the role of Russian revolutionary movements during the nineteenth century, including *Narodnaya Volya* ("People's Will"); the Nihilist movement; as well as Mikhail Bakunin and Sergey Nechayev, both idealists of these movements; the Socialist-Revolutionary Party, and similar organizations, whose tactics influenced Joseph Stalin and other Russian revolutionaries. I had learned some of this material in my previous Russian and world history classes. We would be going into much greater detail in this course.

When listening to the radio or reading *Rolling Stone*, I had been tracking the news about a new "supergroup," a term coined to describe the coming together of well-known musicians from several famous groups into one *uber* collaboration. One in particular had caught my attention because it involved Stephen Stills of Buffalo Springfield. He had been a somewhat unwitting party to precipitating the notion of a supergroup when Al Kooper of Blood, Sweat & Tears recorded and released *Super Session* in May 1968. It featured Mike Bloomfield of the Paul Butterfield Band and Electric Flag on side one and Stills on side two. It was an inconsistent record, except for their rendition of Donovan's "Season of the Witch," with Stills wailing on the wah-wah pedal.

Rumor had it that Stills, David Crosby of the Byrds, and Graham Nash of the Hollies were forming the "sweetest sounding legal firm in the music biz." They supposedly had started recording in LA on February 9th and had signed with Atlantic Records.

The Springfield had imploded in May 1968, primarily due to differences between Stills and Neil Young. They had released *Retrospective: The Best of Buffalo Springfield* in February. I, of course, bought it immediately. I was curious what was next.

Following class on Wednesday, Luci asked me to walk with her. She was shaking and she hadn't had any caffeine. As we crossed the quad, she stopped. She asked me to stand in front of her. Confused, I complied.

"You see anybody behind me?"

"Students on bikes. Students walking. Students talking."

"Anybody in a dark suit and shades? Looks out of place?"

I looked over her shoulder, squinting to see better. Finally, I saw a young guy in dark suit, white shirt, black tie, sunglasses, and shiny black shoes. He turned around and moved toward the Memorial Union.

"Now I see him. Why?"

"He's been following me."

"You sure?"

"A couple weeks now. Not always the same guy, but there's usually someone around, whether it's at the apartment, in town, or on campus."

"Why?"

"They like to keep an eye on things."

"Who?"

"The feds."

"Paranoid."

"That's what I thought. Until they were everywhere all the time."

"I'll start keeping an eye out."

"Thanks."

We continued our conversation as we walked through the Arboretum along Putah Creek.

The Arboretum was founded in 1936 as part of campus teaching and research. It stretched more than 100 acres along Putah Creek, or Poontang Creek as my fellow Aggies liked to call it. A series of gardens had been created to emulate different climatic, geographic, and horticultural settings. The Patwin people once lived in the area. An ancient oak marked the boundary of an early Mexican land grant. There were remnants of the wagon trail that had run between the east coast and San Francisco. The Pony Express once stopped here. It was also home to the oldest reservoir in the Central Valley, built by Chinese workers in the 1860s.

Luci was preoccupied. I watched the ducks tending their young.

"I'd like you to meet some people," Luci said.

"They students?"

"Yes."

"You have classes together?"

"Yes and no," she replied.

"Beers or coffee?"

"Depends on the time of day. Why so many damned questions?"

"Curious."

"Trust me. These are people you should know. People who can help you sort some things out."

"Now I'm really curious."

"Good."

"Who is it?" I asked.

"SDS."

"Really?"

"Really."

I had always been a middle-of-the-road guy. I avoided extremes. Of any kind. Food, friends, drugs, girlfriends, politics, clothes, entertainment, the company I kept. I was neither square nor hip; sane nor insane; conservative nor radical; sober nor addicted; repressed nor liberated; timid nor adventurous; Bircher nor hippie; follower nor leader. That's why my "friendship" with Motown seemed so unusual; why being involved with Luci was so surprising; why following her lead was so crazy. But, it reflected how far I had been pushed by what was happening in my world. Radical actions required opposite and equally radical reactions.

CHAPTER 17

Students for a Democratic Society (SDS) was a student activist organization. Founded in 1960, the organization had over 300 chapters nationwide by 1969. The SDS was originally involved in the civil rights movement. The "Port Huron Statement," a manifesto written by Tom Hayden and Robert Alan Haber, clearly stated their objectives. The opening sentence read, "We are people of this generation, bred in at least modest comfort, housed now in universities, looking uncomfortably to the world we inherit." In one of the closing paragraphs, it stated, "To turn these mythic possibilities into realities will involve national efforts at university reform by an alliance of students and faculty. They must wrest control of the educational process from the administrative bureaucracy. They must make fraternal and functional contact with allies in labor, civil rights, and other liberal forces outside the campus. They must import major public issues into the curriculum – research and teaching on problems of war and peace is an outstanding example. They must make debate and controversy, not dull pedantic cant, the common style for educational life. They must consciously build a base for their assault upon the loci of power."

Following its publication, the SDS focused on protesting the U.S. involvement in Vietnam. The SDS promoted participatory democracy – citizens dedicated to being involved in the decisions that affected their lives. They believed that Americans had no influence over the nuclear arms race, or authoritarian university administrations. They proposed direct action to oppose "white supremacy" and "imperial war," and to achieve civil rights and fight racism. The organization didn't trust the government, or corporations. The group organized a national march on Washington, D.C., in April 1965. After that, the SDS became more militant, especially about the war and the draft. Their protest tactics included occupying university and college administration buildings.

We met at a coffee shop downtown. Luci wanted clear heads and no distractions from alcohol, or dope.

"This is Jesse," Luci said. "He's with SDS."

"Mikey Wright," I said extending my hand.

Jesse shook it and said, "No last names here."

"Okay," I said.

"Luci says you're worried about the draft."

"I am."

"What have you looked into?"

"My dad will take me to Canada. I've researched the reserves. Haven't spoken to them. Some friends have gone the CO route. Peace Corps. Try to add some classes and keep my 2-S. Maybe go to Europe and not come back."

"You talked to the draft center?"

"Yep."

"And the resistance?"

"Not yet."

"Do it, sooner rather than later."

"I plan to," I answered, not happy with being told what to do.

"You go to Canada, you can't come back. Reserves can be called up if it gets bad enough. You better be very religious and believe in God with a capital 'G' if you want to be a CO. When was the last time you went to church?"

"Christmas."

"Peace Corps you still have to serve. It's just delayed. Eventually you're going to run out of classes. You can't stay an undergrad forever."

"So, what have you got?" I asked. "Your organization has been busy."

"I've got some suggestions," he said.

"Like what?"

"I'll get back to you on that. We need to check you out first."

"Afraid I'll go to the cops," I said with a smile. He didn't return the gesture.

"Let me tell you a story before I leave. This white chick asked Malcolm X what she could do to help. 'Nothing,' he said. It wasn't what she wanted to hear. She had some guilt she needed to deal with. She wanted to feel good about herself. He knew she would get in the way of the real battle because she wasn't committed. We're not looking for weekend activists, you dig. It's what you do, not what you say. If you're not part of the future then get out of our way. End of story."

Jesse was gone. I was staring at the constellations in my coffee cup. Luci was staring at me.

"What do you think?" she asked.

"I'm not sure I'm ready."

"I think you are," she answered. "Let's go to my place." I didn't resist. I thought she wanted to continue the discussion.

Luci shared a duplex on F Street with a poly sci student named Travis. Her room was in the back with her own small bathroom and a door that opened onto a tiny yard, a fence, and a Taco Bell beyond that. The room was cluttered, but clean. Mostly books, records, projects, and artwork. There were posters on the wall of the Stones, Che, Huey, and other counter culturists. It smelled of patchouli. She sat cross-legged on her waterbed, which was covered with a green, Cost Plus Indian-print blanket. I sat in a blue Naugahyde bean-bag chair.

I thought about how we had gotten here. It started with a class, some coffee and conversations, common interests, a curiosity about who she was, where she came from, where she and we were going. A familiar mating dance. This ancient ritual began when you acted like you were interested in her; what she had to say, thought, liked, and what mattered to her. You were and you weren't. All you really wanted to do, you thought, was get her in bed. The intriguing thing was, she was thinking the same thing. That was totally new and mind-blowing. And cool.

Luci stretched her hand out to me. I hesitated, leaned forward and took it. She stood, pulled me to my feet, spun me around, and pushed me onto the bed. I sat up. She removed her blue work shirt and Levi's. I had a hard time looking elsewhere, so I knew she never wore a bra. Now I knew she never wore anything. She let me look at her. All of her. She closed her eyes and touched her breasts. She heard me reach for her, opened her eyes, caught my hands, and pushed me back onto the bed.

She straddled me, unsnapping my Wrangler shirt, pulling it off, and tossing it onto the floor. I kicked my tennis shoes off. She rolled off me, unbuckled my belt, unbuttoned my pants, and yanked them to the floor. Slid my boxers off. She left my socks on. She touched me. I tried to kiss her, but she held me down with her empty hand. There was no doubt who was in charge. She opened a bedside table drawer, removed a rubber, and delicately rolled it on. She kissed it. I was dying.

She motioned for me to move further onto the bed, which I did. She smiled, but said nothing. She placed my hand on her breast, then moved it and my other arm above my head. She moved over me and eased herself down on me, guiding expertly. The blood throbbed in my veins. I wanted to close my eyes, but didn't want to miss watching her. She smiled and closed her eyes. She placed her hands on my chest and moved ever so slowly. I reached out, touching her swaying breasts and her butt. I was sure I came before she was ready. She squeezed, then lay down on top of me, kissed me, and laid her head on my shoulder.

We lay there, connected, listening to the silence of the house. I touched her back and butt. She shivered. She rolled off me, stepped onto the floor, pulled on a red kimono, and disappeared in the bathroom. I laid there as the cool air hit my uncovered body. I waited, hoping she was coming back. I thought how easy it would be to become addicted to this, if this was all one lived for.

She came out of the bathroom. She was dressed. Business as usual. I was embarrassed about being naked.

"Sorry to spoil your post-coital euphoria, but I have someplace to be."

"Not a problem," I said, as I scrambled to find and put on my clothes.

"See you in class."

"Sure."

"Let yourself out," and she was through the door.

I finished dressing and lingered, gazing around her room. I looked at the books on the shelves and the floor. I glanced at photos on a bulletin board of her and her friends and maybe an old boyfriend. I picked up some sketches. I wondered if she had a diary, not that I would violate her privacy. I didn't find one, on the floor or in any of the drawers. Nothing unusual. I was somewhat disappointed. As I stood there surveying the room, I heard Leonard Cohen's "Suzanne" playing in my head. Luci reminded me of Cohen's women. Exotic, half-crazy, living by a river in France, feeding me tea and oranges. Our lady of the harbor. Or Dylan's Sweet Melinda. The one who leaves you howling at the moon. The Goddess of Gloom. She was also so much like one of our female cats at home. If you didn't pet her the right way, she bit you. I let myself out. The long walk across campus to the apartment gave me time to weigh things.

CHAPTER 18

The winter quarter classes ended on Saturday, March 15th. Final exams started the following Monday and ran until the Saturday after. Spring break began on Saturday and ended on Sunday, March 30th. If you scheduled it right, you had over two weeks for spring break. Like porridge, my schedule was just right.

Gover was sitting on the couch watching TV and drinking a beer. I was in the kitchen making a tuna sandwich. Slevin was in his room. Threlfall was asleep in ours.

"When's your first final?" Gover asked.

"I've got two on Monday and one on Tuesday."

"Getting 'em done early."

"Home to Modesto Tuesday afternoon. Gary and I are driving down to LA on Wednesday. Spring Break at Disneyland and Knotts Berry Farm."

"Haven't been to Disneyland since we moved out from New York."

"How about you?" I asked

"Finals on Friday and Saturday, then off to San Jose to see Nance. Home for a few days. Then back to the grind."

"Why don't you come with us?"

"Sit in a little VW with two smelly butts when I could stretch out in a bed with my date. Hell no."

"We'll send a postcard."

"Save the stamp."

"Sure."

"I've been thinking more about your coffee with the lunatic fringe," he said.

"They're not crazy."

"From where I sit they are."

"They've got some good ideas."

"Like what?"

"Stopping the war. Ending racism. Getting people involved. Keeping corporations and the government accountable."

"Not going to change anything. The government will kick their ass."

"They've won some battles."

"I'd keep my nose clean."

"I'm keeping my eyes open."

My finals routine didn't include our apartment. There were too many distractions. I alternated between time in the study lounge at the Sycamore Lane Apartments, at the library, or Olsen Hall. Sycamore was across the street. They had a better class of student, so the lounge was clean and silent. The library was also quiet. I could find a carrel in a recessed area that gave me solitude. I could concentrate on the task at hand. If I fell asleep, nobody was the wiser. Plus, I loved the smell of books enveloping me. My other study destination was one of the empty classrooms in the bowels of Olsen Hall. Olsen smelled of cold concrete, body odor, and stale vending machine coffee. I loved it. It was quiet and nobody bothered me. Once I found an unoccupied, corner room, I'd settle in for the day drinking cheap coffee, studying, falling asleep, drinking more coffee. I always selected coffee with cream, hoping it would soften the bitter taste. Unfortunately, the vending machine never mixed it thoroughly. It was often watery. From time to time, the machine was empty and I went without.

It was an anachronism; a contradiction in terms. I was a creature of habit. I took comfort in routine. But, I disliked having to do something on a regular basis. Anything. The same thing over and over again. Like chores, or exercise, or eat right, or be considerate. I especially avoided having to be someplace at the same time on the same day routinely. I liked keeping my options open; my schedule clear. Perhaps it had something to do with expectations.

The vernal equinox happened on March 20th in 1969. On this day, daytime and nighttime were approximately the same duration all over the planet. It was an amazing concept. Day and night exactly the same down to the nano-second. The equinox signaled the end of winter and the beginning of spring; of brighter, more beautiful days. I was counting on it.

Toward the end of the month, Tricky Dick made noise about ending the war in 1970. Nobody believed him, but everybody hoped he would.

UC Davis would have a new chancellor. James Meyer had been unanimously voted by the California Board of Regents to replace the retiring Chancellor Emil Mrak. We weren't sure what this meant, but Meyer seemed like a good guy; a father figure, which we could use. The second chancellor of the campus, Mrak was an American food scientist and microbiologist, having moved the food technology department from UC Berkeley to the "University Farm" at Davis. He was known for his authoritative work in food preservation and the biology of yeasts. Mrak was also instrumental in making Davis a bike-friendly community, when he instructed his planners to build a "bicycle-riding, tree-lined campus."

Chancellor-designate Meyer taught animal husbandry. He seemed to be a quiet, modest man. Raised in Idaho, Meyer got his undergraduate degree at the University of Idaho before serving in the Marines during World War II. After the war, he got his master's and doctorate at the University of Wisconsin. He came to Davis in 1951, serving as an instructor, professor, department chair of the Animal Science Department, and dean of the College of Agriculture. I was curious how he would handle everything that was happening on campus in the coming months.

My finals went well. I was a decent writer and could put together a convincing essay under pressure, which is what most of my finals were – regurgitating in some coherent form, or connecting what had been presented in the lectures. If we wanted to know our grade before the official transcript was mailed, we were asked to leave a self-addressed postcard with our name and the name of the class. The teacher would write down our test score and final grade, as well as a few comments if they felt like it. I did that for each class. Some people never wanted to know. I did.

I wrapped up Tuesday morning, said goodbye to Luci, cleaned up my room, packed Ugly Orange, and went home.

CHAPTER 19

I met Kelly late Tuesday afternoon at MOAB's, a local hamburger joint, on Tully Road. We sipped Cokes and shared a basket of fries. She had taken her finals at Cal early and caught a ride home with a girlfriend.

"He had some good ideas, but he was scary," I said.

"How'd you meet him?" Kelly asked.

"A classmate." The way I answered got Kelly's attention. She was perceptive.

"Information is good," she said. "Just be careful."

"It'll all work out."

"Don't be naïve."

"I'll be careful."

"You aren't the problem."

"I can take care of myself."

"Really? How exactly?" she asked.

"I can outrun them."

"Not bullets."

"Please, it'll never get that serious."

"People are getting shot over less."

"The government won't do this to us. They won't kill their own kids."

"That's what I love about you," she said.

"What's that?"

"Your blind optimism." I smiled, recalling our Valentine's day conversation.

The entire family was home for spaghetti dinner that night. It was nice catching up on the home front. My stepdad had a second job at the Barbour Station on Ninth Street. Money was tight. Mom was spending too much on things we didn't need. Tim and Laura were together and both attending MJC. Their childhood teasing and taunting had moved into a serious relationship. They were talking marriage. Willy, who was a freshman already, was in a band with a neighbor kid named Bob Sims and a few high school friends. They called themselves "Pax," which was an appropriate name for the times. They'd had a few gigs, playing mostly covers of Beatles songs. I promised I'd catch his act the next time I was in town. Diane was getting used to being a seventh grader at Roosevelt. She was enjoying her home economics and sewing classes. Cheryl was a fifth grader at Garrison. She was growing up. Being with the family allowed me to forget for a moment all the things crowding in on me. I could simply be the son and big brother. I could hang with my friends and talk old times, music, and sports. The important things. It was safe harbor and I didn't want to leave.

Bright and early Wednesday morning, armed with coffee and donuts from Dee's Bakery, Gary and I pointed his VW bug south on Highway 99. We'd stay at the same modest hotel near the park I'd checked into in 1962. Our plan was to visit Disneyland, Knott's Berry Farm, and some other sights. Before leaving, I had done some research about all the musicians who were living and making music in the canyons above Sunset Boulevard, including Stephen Stills and Neil Young; Stills in Laurel Canyon and Young in Topanga. I was determined to track one down, or maybe both. I wasn't interested in an autograph, although I did have signed photos of both thanks to letters I'd written to their record companies and promoter Bill Graham. I wanted to see them up close and visit where they spent time. Breathe the same air for a few moments. Nothing too weird.

Highway 99 cut like a knife through the Central Valley, sometimes freeway, sometimes stop and go through rural towns. In a landscape as flat as a billiard table, only the dust moved. And the ants. Heat shimmered above the four-lane blacktop. The freeway passed towns, fields, orchards, vineyards, and farms, large and small. When it wasn't foggy, it was hazy from all the field work. Not everything on either side was agrarian. As often, there was the debris and offspring of civilization, whether it was a junkyard, a gas station, a drive-in, or an oil rig, breaking the hypnotic monotony.

The Central Valley Heartland. There was no other place like it on earth. The lush garden first seen by mountain men like Jedediah Smith, explorers like John Fremont, and naturalists like John Muir. It was flat. It was dry. It was desolate. Once it was a sea, filled by rivers of the Sierra Nevada. What was then a sea of water was now a sea of grass. It was the world's most fertile, most productive farmland. Crops could be grown here around the clock, around the year. It was put here for farming.

Gary's bug didn't set any land speed records. He'd been given it new when he turned sixteen. It was comfortable and got good gas mileage, but it was a snail. Between stops to pee and eat, it took us about seven hours to get to Anaheim, which gave us time to talk. And change the world.

"Those people are creepy," Gary said, after I'd told him about my meeting with Luci and the SDS guy. "Don't they riot a bunch?"

"Gets people's attention."

"For all the wrong reasons."

"I'm running out of possibilities. I can't wait around and count on things somehow magically working out."

"I'm not waiting around."

"You know what I mean."

"What about Canada?" Gary asked. "Remember, my dad's ready to drive me there."

"My stepdad offered the same. It's tough. I keep thinking about me looking in the rearview mirror and seeing my country disappear. For good."

"I guess there's no coming back once you're there."

"Think anyone would visit us?"

"No problem."

"Easy to say now."

"You mentioned the reserves and National Guard when we spoke with Mr. Gordon," he said.

"It's still the military. If things got bad enough, I might have no choice."

"Didn't Mr. Leach help some guys get out on religious grounds?"

"Yeah, but like I told Mr. Gordon, I don't have any religious, or moral ground, to stand on."

"You could cut off a finger, or shoot off a toe."

"I hate guns and the sight of other people's blood, let alone mine."

"What about the Peace Corps? 'The philanthropic extension of American imperialism,'" he said, grinning.

"It's merely a deferment. Delays the inevitable. I wouldn't mind the experience, but I'd have to serve eventually."

"What about our 2-S? That's still good for something, right?"

"Depends on what the government decides. It's also up to our draft board. Modesto is conservative. The local members don't look favorably on anyone who doesn't want to serve their country."

"They are conservative, although Susie's dad, Mr. Bienvenu, isn't as conservative as the others."

"He's one vote."

"That sucks."

"I've been thinking about a trip to Europe."

"I'll go."

"You might come back alone."

Gary was silent. What all this meant had hit him. His best friend in the world, the guy who probably knew him better than anyone, might not be around much longer. We were all facing the same problem. Gary, Gover, me, and everyone our age. We were in it together, but what we would decide to do would be purely individual. Together, but alone. I hoped Gary would get out because of his eyes. I hoped Gover would get out because of a football injury to his knee. A couple less friends to lose. I hoped I'd get out for something. It was a long, painful conversation, but it made the time fly. Before long, we were dropping down into the Los Angeles basin and pulling into Anaheim.

We crashed at the Jolly Roger, which was the same place I'd stayed at when I came searching for Mickey Mantle, chauffeured by Mr. George Lucas. We checked in, ate our Taco Bell Bellburgers, tacos, and burritos, chased with Burgermeisters, AKA Burgies, purchased by Gary now that he was legal. We called our parents from the pay phone in the lobby to let them know we'd arrived safely. We watched TV then nodded out.

CHAPTER 20

Croz, Captain Manyhands, and Willy, as they would become known, had started recording in early February, so we knew we needed to hustle if we had any chance of catching a glimpse before they finished and went on tour to support the album. We got an early start Thursday morning, knowing the rush hour traffic would be ridiculous. Ridiculous was a favorite descriptive word of ours, always pronounced with the emphasis on the "dic" drawn out. We hit the road around 6 a.m., stopping on the way for coffee at a Denny's. Graham Nash mentioned in an interview that they usually arrived at the studio around 2 p.m. and worked through the night, finishing in the early morning hours. Sometimes they'd frequent Norms Restaurant, which was open 24 hours, for breakfast, then go back to the studio for a few hours. My game plan was to swing by the studio first, a short stop at Norms, and on to the neighborhoods where they were living.

The March issue of *Rolling Stone* reported that CSN was recording at Wally Heider Studios, located at North Cahuenga and Selma. We jumped off the freeway when we reached downtown LA and followed surface streets until we reached Cahuenga, simply enjoying the scene. We found the intersection and parked on the west side of Cahuenga. Because it was a little after the time when the band called it a day, we didn't have high hopes they would be there, or we would spot them, but we were optimistic. Eternally.

Wally Heider was born in Portland, Oregon, in 1922. He attended the University of Oregon and Hastings Law School. He practiced law briefly, but music was his passion. Heider began his career as a recording engineer during the Big Band era of the 1940s, producing records for Woody Herman and Alvino Rey. He worked as an assistant for Bill Putnam, an engineer many considered the father of modern studio recording, at United Western Recorders in Los Angeles. In addition to his studio work with bands in Los Angeles and San Francisco in the Sixties, Heider became known for his remote recording of events like the Monterey Jazz Festival and the Monterey International Pop Festival. He opened the Wally Heider Recording Studio in Los Angeles in 1967 in the building at the corner of Cahuenga and Selma. Earlier this year, he had opened Wally Heider Studios on Hyde Street in San Francisco in a building that once housed offices, screening rooms, and storage for 20th Century Fox. He made the decision to open the studio after recording

San Francisco bands at Monterey Pop, sensing the need for these artists to have a studio in their backyard. When space became available next door to the LA studio, Heider bought it. He built a facility to the same specifications as Putnam's well-reputed Studio 3, even calling it Studio 3.

That's the building we were now staring at.

Gary, who was gutsier than me, most of the time, said, "Let's go."

"Go where?" I asked.

"Inside."

"They're not going to let us inside."

"Won't know unless we ask."

"You're embarrassing."

"You're embarrassing."

"I said it first," I said. We did this back and forth all the time, especially when we were kids.

"I didn't drive all this way to stare at the outside of a building," he said.

He got out of the car, fed the meter, crossed the street, and walked toward an ornate doorway at 1604 North Cahuenga. I followed him, looking around as we went. I hated looking stupid. I wasn't even sure about what. Mom did it to us all the time. She didn't care. She'd approach some celebrity, or someone she thought was a celebrity, and start talking to them, while we kids shrunk in mortification.

I wished I had her guts, especially now as we stood staring at an ornate wrought iron and glass door. There was no sign. We could see a hallway and an elevator at the back of the lobby. Gary tried the door. It was locked. He knocked. We waited. No answer. We walked next door to 1602. Also locked. No response. We went around the corner onto Selma. There was an entrance at 6371. Locked. No answer to our knocks. 6373 was locked and quiet, too. Next up was a weathered wooden door. Locked. We knocked. Nothing. We looked back toward Cahuenga and then down Selma. We saw a puff of smoke float out of an alley a few feet away. Gary motioned for me to follow. I threw up my arms in a "This is stupid and we're going to get into trouble" gesture.

"I'm just going to bum a cig," he said, smiled, and walked toward the smoke. I followed.

A girl about our age leaned against the building wall. She had the requisite surfer girl blonde hair, white lipstick, and Twiggy eyelashes, even though they were now out of style. She was dressed in what could best be described as thrift store LA hip. She took a final drag, dropped the butt onto the alley asphalt, and crushed it out as we turned the corner. She smiled.

"Can I help you?"

"Got a smoke?" Gary asked.

"I do, but I'm sure it's not your brand," she replied, grinning. She was stoned.

"Never mind," I said. "Thanks for the time," I added, grabbing Gary's arm.

"Could you tell us who's recording today?" Gary continued, pulling his arm loose.

"I'm awfully sorry, but I can't tell you that," she replied sweetly. "Bill would fire me."

"Bill Halverson?" I asked. "The engineer?"

"How'd you know that?" she asked, her blood-shot eyes narrowing.

"I read it in *Rolling Stone*."

"All the News That Fits," she recited.

"Why can't you tell us?" Gary persisted.

"To protect the artist's privacy. They rely on us to do that, you see."

"But we drove all the way from Modesto," I added.

"That's a long way."

"It is," I said, trying to elicit sympathy for our cause.

"I have cousins who live there," she went on. "They grow almonds in Ripon."

"That's just down the road," Gary said.

"Seems like everybody knows somebody from Modesto," I said.

"Who exactly are you looking for?" she asked.

"Crosby, Stills, and Nash. *Rolling Stone* said they were recording here," I replied.

"You seem to get a lot of your news from them."

"I do," I answered.

"They usually get it right," she replied. "But, I really can't say."

"We're not going to do anything," I said. "We only want to see them."

"People say that and then they do weird things."

"We're not weird," Gary replied.

"I can see that," she said and smiled. She looked like she might be softening.

"You know people who live in the valley," I said. "It's still a very small town. After all, you have family there. So you know."

She stepped out of the alley onto Selma and looked up the street toward the doors we'd passed. She turned to face us, glanced up the street again, and said, "Okay, here's what's happening. They are recording here, but not until later today. They're out with Henry Diltz taking photographs for the album cover. I overheard something about an abandoned house on Palm Avenue in West Hollywood near an Orange Julius. They left moments ago."

I smiled and gave Gary a punch in the shoulder.

"If anyone finds out, I'll lose my job," she said. "You wouldn't want that to happen now would you?" she asked, batting her long-lashed eyes and melting our country mouse hearts.

"No," we both stammered.

"Thanks!" I said.

We backed out of the alley, waved goodbye to our angel, hustled back up Selma, crossed Cahuenga, and piled into the car.

"Good job," I said.

"I can't believe we did that," Gary replied.

"One stop first," I said. "Norms Restaurant. They eat there. Maybe they stopped to get a bite before heading out."

"Where is it?"

"Not far. Sunset and Vine."

"Ah, Los Angeles."

We drove south on Cahuenga to Sunset, turned left and continued east until we hit Vine. We spotted the Norms mid-century modern orange sign and façade from a mile away. We turned right, parked on Vine, put a few coins in the meter, and crossed over to the restaurant. We entered and told the waitress we were looking for someone when she asked if we wanted to sit. We scanned the booths lining the window and the chairs along the counter. We walked between the booths and the counter to the back. We didn't recognize anyone. We retraced our steps, out the front, and back to the car.

"That was brief," Gary said.

"Worth a try."

"Always."

We piled into the VW, which was probably getting tired of us jumping in and out, followed Vine south to Santa Monica Boulevard and turned right. When we got to West Hollywood, we turned right on Palm. As soon as we turned, we saw a dilapidated, small white house with palm trees and weeds. On the front porch was a broken down, purple couch. We didn't see anybody. We parked in a lot to the right of the house, got out, and walked around.

"Looks empty," Gary said.

"This can't be the place she was talking about," I said.

We continued around the house again, peeking into the windows. As we finished our circuit, we stopped in front of the couch. We searched for any signs of recent visitors. On the concrete porch, I noticed some cigarette butts. I leaned down to check them out. There was also the tiniest roach. I tore off a corner of a newspaper sitting on a dirty old ottoman next to the couch. I scooped up the butts and roach.

"Exhibit A," I said. "They're smokers and tokers."

"Could have been any bum or hippie," Gary answered.

"Maybe. Maybe not."

"Considering nobody's here, I guess we'll never know."

"Guess not."

"What now?"

"Let's drive up the street. Sunset is up ahead. That'll take us to Laurel Canyon. Stills is renting a place up there. Maybe we'll get lucky and find another funky house on the way with a photographer taking pictures of some rock stars."

"We going to just drive by, or you going to speak to the guy if you see him?"

"Don't know unless we try," I said, echoing his words.

I tossed the paper and butts aside, we returned to the bug, and drove along Palm. It was a short street, so it didn't take long. We didn't see another house or a photographer or rock stars.

CHAPTER 21

We turned right on Sunset, driving northeast, and followed that until we found the road to Laurel Canyon. Haight-Ashbury South. Our next stop in the hunt. We turned left and drove north into the canyon.

The canyon was what you think of when you think of Southern California. Chaparral, sycamore, yucca, and the smell of eucalyptus. A wispy golden brown in the Southern California light. Quiet except for the dogs and birds. Snaking single lane roads. Crumbling bungalows and decaying mansions. The Los Angeles basin spread out below. A tranquility that I sensed immediately. It felt like I belonged here. It felt like home. It was the same feeling I had any time I visited San Juan Bautista, Santa Barbara, or Palm Springs – any classic California place.

Laurel Canyon had been inhabited for thousands of years by the Tongva tribe, likely due to a reliable water supply provided by a spring-fed stream. Spanish ranchers grazed sheep on the hillsides in the late eighteenth and early nineteenth centuries. More Americans, also attracted by the year-round water supply, settled in the canyon following the Mexican–American War and statehood in 1850. Access to the canyon was mostly by foot, or mule. An 82-mile dirt road was built in 1907. The following year, the Lookout Mountain Park and Water Co. was formed to purchase, subdivide, and market mountain vacation properties. The company also built the Lookout Mountain Inn at the summit, which was destroyed by fire in 1918. A few years later, Charles Mann, a real estate developer and Richard Shoemaker, an engineer, built a trackless electric trolley bus line to increase accessibility. It was discontinued when ridership dwindled, as more automobiles were able to make the drive

From what we'd read and heard, the movie stars and rock musicians had migrated here because of the isolation and solitude. They were close, but far away. Apparently, they loitered around. You could run into them anywhere. So, we worked our way up the canyon, keeping an eye out. Everybody must have partied late last night because the streets were empty. On my lap, I cradled the map of the rock 'n' roll stars residing here I had culled from a variety of sources, including *Rolling Stone*.

I was thinking the band might have gone back to Stills' house until their session started, which wouldn't fire up again until the afternoon. Stills was renting a house on Shady Oak Road, which was on the valley side of

Laurel Canyon. Peter Tork of the Monkees had lived in the house before Stills, comedian Wally Cox before that. Stills had met Tork while they were both performing in the New York folk scene in the early Sixties. Stills had auditioned for TV producers Bob Rafelson and Bert Schneider, who were putting together a new television series about four pop-rock musicians, to capitalize on the popularity of the Beatles and other rock quartets. Stills was turned down because they felt his hair and teeth wouldn't photograph well on camera. They asked Stills if he knew someone who looked like him, only better, and he suggested Tork. Imagine what the music world would have been like if Stephen Stills had been a Monkee?

Shady Oak was tucked far behind a labyrinth of streets in Studio City. I didn't realize how long a road Laurel Canyon was. We drove and drove until we found the right street. Shady Oak dead-ended in a "No Trespassing" sign and a gate with brick pillars on each side. We backed up and parked below the driveway near a trail leading into the brown hills. We got out, stretched, and looked around.

"Pretty quiet," I said.

"They probably crashed if they've got a late session. Rockers don't like the daylight any more than vampires."

"I saw somewhere that Stills never leaves the studio. He could be at Heider's right now."

"We've come this far, let's at least knock on the door," Gary said.

"It says 'No Trespassing.'"

"So?"

"You know I hate doing that."

"Worked the last time."

"I guess."

As we walked up the paved driveway that twisted up and to the right, I glanced behind to make sure nobody was watching. It was a hike. But, it was beautiful. Coastal sage scrub in bloom dotted with oak trees. It smelled dry, dusty, and woody. It smelled like California. Jasmine and honeysuckle. The driveway ended in a large asphalt parking area. It was a good-sized house with several connected buildings. It appeared as if it had been added to over the years, like a Winchester Mystery House.

Gary went to the front door and knocked. I stayed by the car. Nobody answered. He knocked again. Some neighbor dogs barked. Nothing. He shrugged his shoulders. He looked around and motioned to follow him. I didn't want to get busted, so I stood my ground. He waved again and moved toward the right side of the house. Since it had been my idea to make this journey, the least I could do was see where it would lead. I caught up with him and we walked along the side of the house toward the pool and some attached buildings. He snuck up onto a wooden porch and stared in the window. I waited. He shook his head and came back to stand beside me.

"I read somewhere that rooms in one of those buildings had been converted to a studio and rehearsal space," I said, pointing to a structure at the edge of the complex.

"Why didn't you say that before?"

"I didn't think we'd get this far."

We walked toward the pool and along a bower bridge cascading with bougainvillea that connected the house to the two-story pool house. We continued to the last building. He tried the door. It was unlocked.

"Trusting souls," he said.

"It's the canyon," I answered.

We stepped inside. It smelled musty. Cigarette smoke, patchouli, grass, alcohol, sweat. The room was filled with gear, including acoustic and electric guitars, amps, a piano and Hammond B3 organ, a drum set, microphones and stands. There were bottles of wine, whiskey, and tequila, and ashtrays overflowing with butts.

"Damn," I said.

"Looks like they've been rehearsing," Gary replied.

"Let's split before the cops come. I'd rather not have to call the parents to bail me out." We took one last look, exited the room and closed the door quietly, retracing our steps alongside the pool and main house, down the drive, and to the car.

"How about Joni Mitchell's house?" I said. "I know Nash is living with her and they sometimes rehearse there."

"Wasn't that where the three of them first sang together?"

"Some say it was there. Some say it was Mama Cass' house."

"She's like the Gertrude Stein of LA rock."

"Folks seem to end up there when they're in town," I said. "Let's take a look."

"Got nothing else to do," Gary replied.

We retraced our long, winding road back south on Laurel Canyon until we found Lookout Mountain. We turned right. Lookout was another crazy, twisty road. Not only did Joni Mitchell live here, but nearby, at the corner of Lookout Mountain Avenue and Laurel Canyon Boulevard, resided Mr. Frank Zappa of the Mothers of Invention. He lived in the Tavern, a famous 1915 "log cabin mansion," owned years ago by cowboy movie star, Tom Mix. It had an 80-foot living room, floor-to-ceiling fireplace, bowling alley, and indoor sunken swimming pool. Also residing in the neighborhood was Elliot Roberts who, along with partner David Geffen, managed Joni Mitchell, CSN, Neil Young, and a host of other LA singer-songwriters. They named their company Lookout Management.

I had first heard about Joni Mitchell when a folk singer named Tom Rush covered her song, "The Circle Game." It was on the 1968 album of the same name he had done for Elektra Records, the company that had put out all The Doors' albums. Judy Collins covered Joni's "Both Sides Now" on her album released the same year, *Who Knows Where the Time Goes?*. I liked what they did with the songs, but nobody could sing her songs like she could. She also had the look. Long blonde hair, willow thin, no makeup. A natural beauty. It was a look chicks everywhere were imitating.

Born Roberta Joan Mitchell in Saskatoon, Saskatchewan, Mitchell began singing in small nightclubs in her hometown and western Canada. She moved to Toronto and sang in the streets and nightclubs. In 1965, she moved to the U.S and performed in coffeehouses and folk clubs. Word got around about her songs and other folk singers recorded them. Reprise Records noticed, signed her, recorded, and released her debut album, *Song to a Seagull*, in 1968, with the help of David Crosby. Mitchell recorded the album in Los Angeles and soon moved there. Crosby introduced her to Elliot Roberts and David Geffen, who became her managers.

I was thinking about serendipity like that, as Gary and I drove past a green wooden fence set back from the road. We pulled into the driveway because there was no room to park on the street. I was flipping out.

"I feel like those rabid teeny-boppers that stalk the Beatles."

"We're not doing anything illegal," Gary replied.

"Just weird."

"It was your idea."

"Which I regret."

We left the car and peered through the open gate. The coast was clear. We walked through. Ahead we could see a small bungalow with a sloping wood shingle roof and rough wooden siding painted light green. It looked like photos I'd seen. We climbed a stone stairway and moved along a stone pathway to the stone porch, which seemed to be covered with a light soot, and on to face a massive, ornately carved front door. A cat jumped out from behind a little tree near the porch and rubbed itself against Gary's leg. Inside the house, another cat eyed us suspiciously from behind a smallish, lead-bordered, stained-glass pane hanging in the middle of the multi-paned front window. The cat jumped out of sight, as we stepped onto the porch.

The house was tiny. It looked like one bedroom with many windows, terrific light, and pleasant views. Gary knocked lightly. Quiet. He knocked again, louder. Only the birds and bushes were making noise. He shrugged and we took a peek through the front window. It was all wood inside. Tongue-in-groove knotty-pine floor and walls. A large fireplace with a beautiful wood mantel. There was a piano, a dulcimer, and some guitars. A Tiffany lamp on a table and artwork leaning against walls and furniture. A massive and truly ugly wooden pig stood near a couch. More ashtrays and cigarette butts and roaches. Man these people liked their tobacco and weed. It looked vacant. No luck again.

"Let's try the Country Store," I suggested. "That's where they hang out."
"You gonna talk to any of them, or gawk."
"Gawk."
"What's the point?"
"No point. I only want to see them in the flesh."
"They're not Gods."
"I know. I'm curious. Like, how tall are they? Do they look the same in person? That kind of thing."
"We drove all this way to see how tall somebody is?"
"And Disneyland."
"Fine," Gary said, firing up the engine.

The Canyon Country Store was down the road a piece. We parked in the lot next door where mangy dogs were prowling and drug deals were going down. We walked toward the front door, above which was an old, metal Coca-Cola sign with the store name printed on it. People were sipping coffee, reading papers, and visiting at a few tables out front. I didn't recognize anybody. We went inside. The ceiling fans moved the air and the flies. Memorabilia of the movie and music business and its stars dotted the walls, dusty and faded. Trying to be inconspicuous, like the rest of the tourists hunting for somebody famous, I bought a Royal Crown Cola and bag of Fritos. Gary got a Nehi orange and a bag of peanuts. Again, no rockers or celebs.

We walked outside to the far left edge of the terra-cotta tile patio and stood next to the wrought iron railing leading down to the street. We drank our soft drinks and ate our snacks, waiting for a sighting. Nothing. We noticed a couple scrawny girls scrounging for food in the rubbish bins scattered below the patio and along the street. They scored some goodies and hustled away to a stand of trees across the street. Curious, we went down the stairs to the side of the store.

Waiting in the trees was a dude holding an acoustic guitar. No case, only the guitar. He didn't look familiar, but he did look eerie. And not unlike Jesus Christ except with wild hair and wild eyes. We inched closer to the edge of the street, thinking he might be somebody. We pretended to be looking at the house behind and above the store where Jim Morrison lived. The guy in the trees had an "X" on his forehead. It could have been a tattoo, or something he inked or carved himself. He looked crazy enough to have done it himself. I hadn't noticed before, likely because they were grimy, but the girls had "Xs" on their foreheads, too. He kissed the girls and stuffed the food in a knapsack lying at his feet. He looked up and saw us. We froze. He smiled and we turned tail, hustling for the car.

"Not our lucky day," I said.

"Or everyone's recording or on tour."

"Or hangin' out at Cass' place."

"What now?" he asked.

"Let's see if we can find Neil Young's place. He's a canyon, or two, over. Somewhere on Fernwood Pacific Drive in Topanga Canyon."

"Let's roll," Gary replied and we pulled onto Sunset.

CHAPTER 22

It was a long and serpentine route. We passed Coldwater Canyon and Benedict Canyon. And some of the most beautiful and expensive real estate in the country. We drove past UCLA and the Bel Air Country Club, Will Rogers State Park and the Riviera Country Club, ending up at Sunset Beach on Highway 1. We grabbed a bite at a cheap seafood stand and continued north on Highway 1 until we reached Topanga Beach. We turned north on Topanga Canyon and wormed our way around until we found Fernwood Pacific. We twisted and turned on a number of small streets until we reached Skyline Trail. We stopped in front of 611, the address I'd researched as Neil Young's house. The house was a rectangle of redwood on a precipitous hillside. The three connected wings looked like wooden milk cartons. We parked out front on the narrow street. A black 1953 Pontiac hearse with Ontario license plates sat in the driveway. I wondered if it was the same one he was driving on Sunset Boulevard when he ran into Stephen Stills and Richie Furay, which led to the forming of Buffalo Springfield in 1966.

We climbed the incredibly steep stairs. Walking up and down these puppies each day would keep you in shape. As we went up, we heard a small dog barking above us. We reached the porch deck that led to the front door. We could see a small, whiteish dog. I assumed it was Winnipeg, Neil's pooch. We knocked. Quietly. Winnipeg barked. No answer. Then louder. Winnipeg howled. Still nothing. We could hear a low thumping sound from what appeared to be a basement area. We knew someone was there. We knocked again, louder. The thumping stopped. Winnipeg whimpered. We smiled. And waited. Nothing. Winnipeg ran toward the back of the house, which looked out over the canyon. Whoever was in there didn't want to see us. We gave up.

"Struck out again," I said.

"Like the Detroit Tigers did seventeen times against Bob Gibson in game one of last year's World Series," Gary, the baseball stat machine, commented.

"They choked."

"Like you and Kelly."

"Thanks for reminding me."

"That's what I'm here for."

"We're fine."

"You hope."

We hopped into the bug and continued down Topanga Canyon until we reached Sunset Beach. We wanted to catch the sunset at the beach named for it. We had called a couple high school buddies who were at UCLA and agreed to meet them at the beach. We bought some beers and snacks, parked the car, and found a spot on the beach. We gathered some driftwood to start a fire once the sun went down and it cooled off. We pulled up some driftwood logs, planted our butts, popped our beers, and toasted the sunset. The gold and red of the sun splashed gilted crimson colors on the blue Pacific.

"This is why we live in California," I said.

"It is incredible," Gary said.

"You can have the snow."

"I like the change in seasons."

"Not me. I'll take this any day."

"I guess I will, too."

As the sun dipped into the water and the last rays of day died, Jerry Wilson and Rick Daniels walked up with blankets, jugs of Red Mountain, and fresh fish tacos. The classic California meal. We sat and rapped, catching up on old and new times and friends and the latest gossip from Modesto. The fire was toasty on my feet. The wine was warm in my belly. I was feeling mellow. The full moon cast a silver aura on the deserted landscape.

Staring at the silvery tips of the waves advancing and retreating, I caught movement off to my right. I turned. A dark shadow was plodding down from the parking lot toward the ocean. It turned and moved toward us. As it got closer, it looked like a ghostly, skeletal scarecrow. Hunched over, longish hair, a battered hat, and what looked like the neck of an acoustic guitar jutting over the right shoulder. He kept moving forward, inexorably. As he passed behind us, I turned and saw a floppy white felt hat, flannel shirt, Levi's, and bare feet. He stopped, drawn, I think, by the fire and maybe the wine being passed from hand to hand. He stepped closer and entered our small circle. He squatted down next to me.

"Mind?" he said, in a high, thin voice, I looked closer at the downcast, stubbled face. Damn. It was Neil Young.

"Not at all," I stammered.

He swung the guitar around off his shoulder and I poked Gary in the ribs with my elbow. He was already staring in stunned silence, as were Jerry and Rick. We all knew who it was. "I dig it down here. I should write a song, or do an album about the ocean," he mused.

"I'm Mikey. This is Gary. Over there are Jerry and Rick."

"Shakey," he replied. Rick passed the bottle around and I offered it to Neil. "A sip, maybe. My throat is raw. Used it too much today."

"We heard you. At least we heard the bass, or drums," I blurted out.

"I'm surprised. It's lead-lined."

"It was muffled."

"You were the knockers at my house today."

"You saw us."

"Yeah."

"You didn't answer."

"I was recording, man."

"When it stopped, we thought you might come to the door."

He glared at us a moment, with that Neil Young the Indian glare. He smiled. "I was into it."

"Your dog was protecting the place," Gary said.

"Winnipeg's a good watchdog."

"I'm a big fan," I said. "We all are."

"Cool."

"I've got everything," I continued. "All of Springfield. Your solo album."

"Not everything."

"Really?"

"Yeah, I've got a new one coming out in May."

"What's it called?"

"'Everybody Knows This is Nowhere.'"

"Great title," Jerry said.

"It just you?" I asked.

"No, I got a band. They're called Crazy Horse."

"Great name," Jerry said. He looked embarrassed for allowing such a limited vocabulary to come out of the mouth of a college student.

"Well, if it's as good as your first one, it's going to be a big hit," I said. "I really like 'The Loner' and 'Emperor of Wyoming.' The guitar on 'Emperor' sounds almost like a pedal steel."

"I had some good help. Someone who got it. A cat named Jack Nitzsche. He was Phil Specter's right-hand man, then went out on his own. Did some instrumental stuff. He's working on a film soundtrack with Jagger of the Stones."

"Bitchin'," Rick said.

"He did the production on 'Expecting to Fly' with the Springfield."

"That album has to be one of the best ever," I said. "Buffalo Springfield is my number one band. Still is."

"You liked us more than the Beatles?" he asked.

"Hands down. You kicked some serious ass."

"We thought we were going to be around for about 15 years. That's how good I knew we were."

"What happened?" Gary asked.

"Too many microphones, too many guitars, too many songs. Too many egos."

"Two lead guitarists. Three lead singers. Two sides of one album. That's not much territory to share," I said.

"Stephen and Richie were the singers."

"I liked your voice," Jerry said.

"Me, too," Rick chimed in.

"Too much pressure. Everything started to go too fast. I needed more space. I wanted to be more independent. Sing my own songs."

"I can dig it," Jerry said.

"I expect a lot of people. And myself. If they can't step up, or don't want to, I move on."

"That's cold," Rick said.

"It's real," I said.

"It is real. I don't have time to wait," he said.

"World keeps spinning," Gary said.

"Also, I've got a tiny health problem. Flares up when I get stressed."

"Bummer," Rick said.

"I didn't want to do drugs. That's the scene, you know. I don't like not being in control."

"I totally get that," I interrupted. I did. That's why I came late to the party when it came to alcohol, grass, and psychedelics.

"So I had to do something else. That's when I bought the place up in Topanga," he said, thrusting his thumb toward the hills behind us. "Gave me something solid. Something stable. After a while I gotta get back in my hole and have that long tunnel so I can see people comin'."

"Cool," said Jerry.

"You made that clear on the cover of 'Last Time Around,'" I said. "You looking the other way from the rest of the band."

"It was way past over by then. I wasn't even there when they shot that photo. They pasted me in later."

"Your songs were the best parts of the album," I added.

"It was a joke. We were never in the studio together. We were all doing our own thing. We owed Atlantic an album and they were going to get it one way, or the other. Jimmie Messina and Richie pulled it together. The mix was horrible. It sounded half-assed, which it was."

"What do you think of 'Retrospective?'" Jerry asked.

"I don't like greatest hits. I'd rather spend the time on new stuff."

"No reason to waste time," Rick said.

"Lookin' backward is not a good idea," he added.

"Damn straight," Rick continued.

"It wasn't me scheming on a solo career," he explained.

"Whatever it was, it led to some good music," I said.

"I was trying to keep it real."

"Must be nice to do it the way you want," I said. "To have control. To do it your way."

"The first pressing was a mess. I asked Jack to mix my voice back."

"Why?"

"I don't like it. It's weak," he replied. "I found out Warners used some new technology to make stereo records play on mono record players."

"I read that on the album cover," I said. "I'd never heard of it."

"Made the whole thing sound 'tinny.' Didn't sound anything like the mixes. I was totally freaked. We've been re-mixing and re-editing. It'll be reissued in November."

"Guess I'll have to replace my copy with the new one," I said.

"Hang onto it. Might be a collector's item someday," he said, smiling.

"What'd you think of the album cover?" I asked.

"It's okay. The cat who did it is a local artist. Lives in Laurel Canyon. He's a friend of my girlfriend. 'Course, the re-issue is going to have my name in big letters at the top so people know who it is. The original had my big painted face."

"You happy with the new mix?" Gary asked.

"It was over-produced. Too much over-dubbing. I don't know what I was thinking. I guess 'cause everybody else was doin' it, I thought I had to. The Crazy Horse stuff isn't like that."

"What are you working on now?"

"Some new material for the next album after 'Everybody.' I put a studio in my basement with a little help from Wally Heider."

"He's recorded a bunch of the San Francisco bands in his studio in the City," Jerry said. "The Airplane, the Dead, Creedence, Quicksilver."

"We did a some of the tracks for my solo album at his LA studio," he replied.

"We were there this morning," I said.

"Why?" he asked.

"Looking for your old buddy Stephen."

"That's right. They're recording there, aren't they. You see him?"

"Naw," Gary said. "Went by his place, but nobody was home."

"You two are real Philip Marlowes. Or stalkers."

"We're done," Gary said. "Headed home."

"Where's home?"

"Modesto," Gary answered.

"I played there once. At a high school maybe, or some type of hall or ballroom."

"The California Ballroom," I prompted.

"Yeah, that's it."

"The new album got a name?" Gary asked.

"'After the Gold Rush.'"

"The name got a story?" Rick asked.

"They all do."

"What's this one's?" I asked.

"I've got a neighbor up here. Name's Dean Stockwell."

"He's an actor, right?" I said.

"He knows masses of trivia," Gary said, pointing at me.

"Child actor. Did some TV. Kind of a new James Dean," I added.

"I suppose," he responded. "Anyway, he was making a movie with Dennis Hopper – " I was about to jump in with more trivia about Dennis Hopper when Gary put his hand on my arm. I didn't.

" – so Hopper encourages Dean to write a screenplay. Which he did. It was this far out disaster movie. End-of-the-world deal. Involved a folk singer, an earthquake, and a flood."

"Tailor-made," I said.

"I wanted to be in it. Maybe even direct it. At least do the soundtrack."

"If you're serious, I've got a friend from Modesto named Lucas who might be able to help out. Went to USC."

He shot me that glare again that said, "Cool your jets and let me finish the story." I did.

"We went around to the studios with the script. A few came up here to talk with us. It was too far out. Too arty for the suits."

"They don't do many small films these days," Rick said. He knew what he was talking about because he was interning at William Morris.

"Especially ones with hippies, or musicians," Jerry added.

"I'd dig making a film, or two. Not a studio film. More like a documentary. I've been shooting some 8mm around here. I got into it."

"Why film? Doesn't your music keep you busy enough?" asked Rick.

"It's a different way of expressing myself, you know. Sound and sight."

"Doesn't it take time away from your music?" I asked.

"Yeah, but that's good. It's a distraction. It allows me to come back to the music with fresh ears and eyes."

"Whatever happened with the Stockwell movie?" Gary asked.

"I was writing some songs around the time I read the script. One or two of them seemed to work with the film. When it all fell apart, I believed the songs were good enough for an album. Care to hear one?"

"For sure!" we all said.

"This is the title song."

He strummed a few chords and sang about knights and peasants, spaceships, time-traveling, and Mother Nature. The imagery was fascinating. He sang it as only he could sing it. A mesmerizing wail. He finished and we sat there stunned.

"It's an environmental song. About what was and is now. I love nature, man. To me, nature is church. What makes me angry is people doin' things that pollute the planet. Wishing it doesn't make it so."

"Crazy Horse going to be on the album?"

"Depends. Maybe one or two of them. And a new kid named Nils Lofgren."

"Never heard of him," I said.

"You will."

"Who else?" Jerry asked.

"Some of my old bandmates."

"Like who?" Rick asked.

"Stephen."

"For real?" I said.

"For real," he said and smiled. "We're like brothers. We fight and make up. We're a great team. We push each other. Hard. Sometimes we crash."

"Loyalty is an underappreciated trait," I said.

"I agree," he replied.

"CSN is getting some ink," Rick pointed out.

"They've got a tremendous sound. Too slick for me, but people seem to like it."

"You seen them yet?" Jerry asked.

"Just rehearsals at Stephen's house."

"We noticed some gear inside the house when we were up there poking around."

"You dudes are way too sleuthy."

"Glad the cops didn't bust us," Gary said.

"They never come up this way. It's too hard. Narrow, winding roads and no doughnuts," he smiled.

"How'd they sound?" Rick asked.

"Tight. Scary good harmonies. Like angels."

"They gonna tour?" Jerry asked.

"Their first gig is in August in Chicago. Joni Mitchell is the opening act."

"Love her," Gary said.

"She lives around here, too," I added.

"Now don't go bothering her." Gary and I looked at each other.

"Too late," I said.

"Be cool," he added.

"Promise," I said.

"So, couple days after Chicago, they're supposed to play at some music festival in upstate New York. On a farm near Woodstock."

"I've been reading about that in *Rolling Stone*," I said. "Supposed to be huge. Even bigger than Magic Mountain. They're talking about the Beatles, the Stones, Dylan, the Who."

"That's some big egos," he said.

"You going to join them?" Gary asked.

"Haven't been asked. 'Sides, I'm playing with Crazy Horse and got an album to tour come May and another one to finish. My summer could be booked up already."

"When you going to play Northern California?" Gary asked.

"Don't know. CSN is booked at Winterland in October and Sacramento in November."

"You playing around here?" Jerry asked.

"You might catch me solo, or with the Horse at The Corral."

"Small place," Rick said.

"I don't play it often."

"It must be scary with people roaming the streets searching for people like you," I said.

"Even though you're one of them?"

"Sure, but we're fine. We were only looking," Gary said.

"So are all the others."

"Any of them freak you out?" I asked.

"Some. You never know anymore. There is this one guy. Charlie. I met him through Dennis Wilson."

"The Beach Boys," I clarified.

"Yeah, I met Dennis when Springfield opened for them. This cat Charlie is a frustrated songwriter, singer. Makes up songs as he goes along. No two ever the same."

"You ever play with him?" Jerry wondered.

"We jammed at Dennis' house. Brought along these chicks he was hanging with. He's not bad. Out there, but good. Strange. Very special, but wild. Intense. Smart, but tricky. We have the same birthday. We're both Scorpios. Dig it."

"What's he look like?" I asked.

"Like Jesus, I guess," he answered.

"He have an 'X' on his forehead?" Gary asked.

"Come to think of it, yeah, he does."

"The girls, too?" I asked.

"Them, too. They said they had them because they had been 'X-ed' out of society, or some shit like that."

"I think we saw him and two young girls at the Laurel Canyon store."

"Could be. They roam through all the canyons. I gave him a motorcycle to get around."

"He got a last name?" Gary asked.

"Manson."

"He was a weird looking little man," I said.

"I put some space between us when he started talking about a race war and the Apocalypse."

"Strange days," I added.

"Could be," he replied. "On that note," he strummed a coda on his guitar, stood, and walked into the serious moonlight.

CHAPTER 23

The next morning, Gary and I rose with the roosters. We had a full day ahead. We did Disneyland first. We retraced most of the places I'd visited when I'd been here in 1962. It hadn't changed much. By Walt's design, I was sure. One of the most popular new attractions was *Great Moments with Mr. Lincoln* that utilized a new technology known as audio-animatronics, which was basically an animated robot. It was similar to an exhibit that had debuted at the 1964 New York World's Fair. Abe looked darned realistic. The park had added *Flight to the Moon*, which was a refurbished version of the original *Rocket to the Moon* exhibit. I was confident many of the NASA scientists, who were about to send men to the moon, were inspired by this attraction when they had visited Disneyland as children. The *Tomorrowland Stage* was also new. Built on the site of the *Flying Saucers* ride, it was another venue for concerts and stage shows.

The building housing the *General Electric Carousel of Progress* rotated the seated audience through a series of stages, while telling a story of the future. Audio-animatronic humans demonstrated advances in household appliances and electronics from the turn of the century until today. At each stage, the animated humans would tell jokes, describe their life, and demonstrate the marvels of their kitchen. It reminded me of Ray Bradbury's book, *Fahrenheit 451*. This exhibit also originated at the 1964 New York World's Fair. The *PeopleMover* was a scenic, leisurely ride above Tomorrowland, designed to show how people could be easily moved around a city. The small, open-air cars ran on a track through the Tomorrowland attractions. *Adventure Thru Inner Space* was a ride that simulated shrinking the rider down to the size of a single oxygen atom.

The next day, it was on to Knott's Berry Farm, which was one of the first theme parks in California. It started in 1920 as a roadside stand selling berries and berry products. In the 1940s, it added a restaurant, some shops, and a ghost town. It cost twenty-five cents to get in. I hadn't visited since our whole family came here in 1965.

The annual trip to Disneyland was our big family vacation. We would pile into the car and drive south. Dad would place pillows and blankets on the floorboards behind the front seat so one or two of us kids could sleep there. A couple more would sleep on the back seat. And the smallest, either

Diane or Cheryl, could sleep in the small flat spot above the back seat and below the rear window. It felt like we were camping. Occasionally, the older kids were allowed to bring along a friend. I brought Gary once, while we were in junior high. Starting a few years back, after I had stopped making the trip, Willy invited his best friend, Don MacRitchie, AKA "The Nipper." Don was an only child and Mom loved giving him a hard time. I remember the time Don had forgotten to brush his teeth and Mom compared his teeth to the yellow shirt he was wearing. Don took it all in stride, and gave some in return, which is likely why they kept asking him back.

Knotts Berry Farm was fun, but I preferred Disneyland. It was another exhausting, but beautiful, Southern California day.

On Sunday, we agreed to do the movie tourist thing. We visited MacArthur Park because I wanted to see the inspiration for the song Jim Webb wrote and Richard Harris sang. It was weird because we saw some of the things described in the song. Next up was Griffith Park and the observatory where they filmed *Rebel Without a Cause*. We wrapped up the day with a tour of Warner Brothers Studios. Next, we purchased a map of the star's homes from a street vendor. That was a waste of money.

One of the things my family used to do when we went to Southern California was visit my dad's relatives on his father's side. Dad was born in Los Angeles. He had aunts, uncles, and cousins that lived in Downey and Pico Rivera. My Aunt Catherine, who had taken me to Chicago to find Mickey Mantle in 1962, still lived in Poway near San Diego. Unfortunately, we didn't have enough time to visit the relatives on this trip.

On our last day, we toured Catalina Island. I wanted to see where Charlie Wrigley's Chicago Cubs had held spring training.

Catalina Island had been inhabited by the Gabrielino/Tongva tribe as far back as 7000 BC. In 1542, explorer Juan Rodríguez Cabrillo claimed the island for Spain and named it San Salvador, which was the name of his ship. In 1602, another Spanish explorer, Sebastián Vizcaíno, rediscovered the island on the eve of Saint Catherine's day and renamed the island Santa Catalina in the saint's honor. Spanish colonization led to the decimation of the native population, who either died or were forced to work on the mainland in the missions, or on the ranchos. Spain tried to maintain control of the island, but didn't have enough ships to patrol the surrounding seas. Although the Spanish prohibited foreigners from trading with their mainland colonies, Russian hunters and Americans harvested otter and seal pelts on the island.

Pirates found the island's coves suitable for smuggling. The island was overrun with gold fever in the 1850s and 1860s, although no gold was ever found.

In 1846, Governor Pío Pico made a Mexican land grant of the island to Thomas M. Robbins as Rancho Santa Catalina. Robbins carved out a small rancho before selling it in 1850 to José María Covarrubias, who sold it to Albert Packard of Santa Barbara in 1853. In 1864, ownership of the entire island was in the hands of James Lick. The island remained virtually uninhabited, except for a few cattle herders. George Shatto, a real estate speculator from Grand Rapids, Michigan, bought the island from the Lick estate. Shatto founded the settlement of Avalon and built the first pier and hotel, known as the Hotel Metropole. Shatto eventually defaulted on the loan and the island returned to the Lick estate. In 1891, the two Banning brothers bought the island and remade Avalon into a resort community. In 1915, a fire burned half of Avalon's buildings. Saddled with debt from the fire and a decline in tourism during World War I, the Banning brothers sold their shares in 1919.

After purchasing some shares from the Bannings, chewing-gum magnate William Wrigley, Jr. bought more shares, until he owned a controlling interest in what was now known as the Santa Catalina Island Company. Wrigley invested millions in improvements and attractions, including the construction of the Catalina Casino, which opened in 1929 as an entertainment center, housing a ballroom, movie theatre, and gathering place – but no gambling. Wrigley also built a mansion for his family above Avalon. The "summer cottage" was called Mount Ada. To increase tourism, Wrigley brought the Chicago Cubs baseball team, which he owned, to the island for spring training in 1921. The Cubs trained in Catalina each year until 1951, except during the war years. Philip K. Wrigley assumed control after his father's death in 1932. The island was used for military training during World War II. Following the war, Catalina became popular again as a tourist destination.

I had wanted to visit the island from the first time I had heard the song "26 Miles" by the Four Preps in 1958. After all, Santa Catalina was "the island of romance." I thought of Kelly, the lyrics bouncing around in my head, as we rode the ferry to Avalon. Thoughts of Luci intruded.

We tried to do as many touristy things as we could. We did the art deco casino, which was magnificent; the museum, which was housed within the casino; rented bikes and rode out a short distance from Avalon. We saw bison grazing, which had supposedly been brought in during 1924 for the filming of a movie entitled, "The Vanishing Breed." We feasted on fried clams and beer for lunch; explored Catalina Bay in a glass bottomed boat, which was a first for me; listened to a live steel drum band; checked out the arcade;

browsed through a few galleries and the Catalina tile company; re-boarded the ferry near the end of the day; and returned exhausted to the mainland.

It was time for the long ride home. We pulled into Modesto late Monday night. Gary dropped me off for some much-needed rest.

My postcards had arrived. Straight "As."

CHAPTER 24

"All the News that Fits" – April Edition

The Band from Big Pink announces it will tour. The Milwaukee Bucks sign UCLA star Lew Alcindor. The Monkees return to the studio minus Peter Tork. At the 41ˢᵗ Academy Awards, *Oliver!* wins Best Picture, Katharine Hepburn in *The Lion in Winter* and Barbra Streisand in *Funny Girl* share Best Actress, while Cliff Robertson in *Charly* wins Best Actor. The first major league baseball game played outside the U.S. is hosted by Montreal. Alexander Dubček is forced to resign as first secretary of Czechoslovakia's Communist Party. The L.A. Free Festival in Venice, California, ends early following a riot. People's Democracy activist Bernadette Devlin, 21, becomes the youngest woman Member of Parliament elected to Westminster. The Who stage the first complete performance of their rock opera *Tommy* during a performance in Dolton, Devon, U.K. At the 23ʳᵈ Tony Awards, Best Play is won by *The Great White Hope* and Best Musical is won by *1776*. N. Scott Momaday wins the Pulitzer Prize for Fiction with his book, *House Made of Dawn*. The Ministry of Defence in London announces that British troops will be used in Northern Ireland to guard key public installations following a series of bombings. Sirhan Sirhan is sentenced to death for the assassination of Senator Robert F. Kennedy. Marshall Lin Biao is named Mao's designated successor as the sole Vice Chairman of the Communist Party of China. Charles de Gaulle resigns as President of France. At the 4ᵗʰ Academy of Country Music Awards, Glen Campbell wins Male Vocalist of the Year and Cathie Taylor wins Female Vocalist, while "Wichita Lineman" wins Song of the Year. New book releases include *The Strawberry Statement* by James Kunen; *Ernest Hemingway: A Life Story*, Carlos Baker; *Bullet Park*, John Cheever; *The Grim Reapers*, Ed Reid; and *What I'm Going to Do, I Think* by Larry Woiwode. *She Loves Me, Megilla of Itzik Manger, But Never Jam Today, Trumpets of the Lord*, and *Coldest War of All* open on stage. New films include *Angel in My Pocket* with Andy Griffith; *If It's Tuesday, This Must Be Belgium*; *Sam Whiskey* featuring Burt Reynolds; *Goodbye, Columbus* starring Richard Benjamin and Ali MacGraw; and the documentary *Salesman* by Albert and David Maysles. New music includes the Beatles' single "Get Back," featuring keyboardist Billy Preston; Van Morrison's *Astral Weeks*; Quicksilver Messenger Service's *Happy Trails*; James Taylor's *James Taylor*; the Beach Boys *20/20*; Bob Dylan's *Nashville Skyline*; Joe Cocker's *With a Little Help from My Friends*; Chicago Transit Authority's double album *Chicago Transit Authority*; Leonard Cohen's *Songs from a Room*; Elvis Presley's single, "In the Ghetto;" and the Guess Who's *Wheatfield Soul*.

The first Tuesday of April was April 1ˢᵗ – April Fool's Day; a day my mom and Gary relished. Mom got us every year, no matter how ready we were not to be fooled. Gary was the same. They both had a knack for making something frivolous and unbelievable seem totally believable. Me, I resorted to the tried and true like, "Hey, your shoe is untied." As did Paul. The girls fell for it. Willy never did.

Up early that morning, I called Kelly. Either she wasn't home, or didn't want to talk with me. I hoped it was the former. Being the negative guy I was, I thought the worst. I was concerned her intuition had kicked in when I had told her about the classmate who'd connected me with the SDS people. Or, mayhap, she was simply playing me for an April Fool.

I invariably chose the path of least resistance. I avoided confrontation at all costs. I would rather allow someone to do what they felt was right, what they needed to do, and figure out a way to let them know, in a way I chose and was comfortable with, that it was a problem. For me, or someone I cared about. Instead of viewing the interaction as a simple, direct, and reasonable way to resolve issues, or differences, I viewed it as a battle – two enemies in mortal combat, where there could be only one victor. If they insisted on continuing what they were doing, or denying that it was an issue, I would sometimes let it go, or perhaps allow them to think everything was okay. I never got mad. I got even. It happened enough with my family. Now it was happening with Kelly. It likely would happen with Luci.

It is said, "April showers bring May flowers." We needed the rain and we definitely needed the flowers. Too many things had been dying. It was time for a rebirth.

I summoned the many symbols of renewal and resurrection I had learned about in my classes, especially English, where we studied how to recognize symbols in literature and how to use symbols in our own writing. In many myths, the primary image of creation and birth was the cosmic egg laid by some primeval creature, which hatched a golden yolk representing the sun. The most well-known was the Phoenix, a mythical bird who died in fire and was reborn from its ashes. The ancient Greeks' symbol was the *ouroboros*, which was represented by a snake consuming its own tail, representing the cyclical nature of life, as we consumed and recreated ourselves. The waxing and waning moon had long been a symbol for renewal. Ancient alchemists associated the moon with silver, which represented purification, cleansing, and rebirth. As the primary symbol for cleansing, water was perhaps the quintessential symbol for rejuvenation.

These images swirled in my head as I packed all the clothes Mom had washed and ironed, said my goodbyes, pointed Ugly Orange toward Davis, and arrived at the apartment late Tuesday night. My first class was first thing Wednesday morning.

I had registered for another sixteen units. "History of England" from the latter eighteenth century to the present wouldn't be too bad. The teacher was an old codger. "Russian History: Soviet Russia" with Brower would be tough, but manageable since we now knew each other better. "Introduction to Historical Thought and Writing" would be rough because I was better with names, dates, and movements, not theory. "Physical Geography" would be no fun. I had to take it as part of the science requirement. Recognizing that science was not my strong suit, I took the class pass/fail.

Luci had talked me into auditing a class that was somewhat off the wall and not part of my degree requirements. She said she'd do most of the work. It was a textiles course offered through the art department taught by José Argüelles. The reading list was counterculture. The final project was to be of our choosing. In his introductory remarks, Professor Argüelles spoke of wanting to stage an "art happening." There would be displays, talks, and skits that explored getting involved, getting healthy, and saving the planet. And music. He hadn't figured out all the details, but it would likely be next year.

A student from my Russian poetry class, who was also taking this class, asked questions and volunteered to help. His name was Roger Davis and he was a friend of Steph's. He was into art, film, and metaphysics, but that was about all I knew about him. From his questions about the event and his contributions in the poetry class, I could tell he was sharp and into some esoteric things.

Argüelles was an intriguing teacher. He was interested in the experience, not the information; breaking down barriers and bringing people together. That first class gave me a hint of what was about to come down when he began the class by playing a Native American flute. When he finished, he stood there in his long hair, tie-dyed caftan, and blue scarf, smiling. Argüelles wanted to subvert the traditional approach to learning, which relied on lectures and testing. He was more interested in learning that stressed cooperation and participation. He made it clear that it was okay to be weird, to create unusual art, and to do things that weren't considered normal. He used slides and music to tell his story and the story of ancient art from around the world. It reminded me of my reader's theater class at JC. I could tell immediately that the journey promised to be mind-altering.

One of the assigned readings was *The Making of a Counter Culture* [sic] by Theodore Roszak. Another was Marshall McLuhan's *Understanding Media: The Extensions of Man.*

The Making of a Counter Culture [sic] was an expanded and revised treatment of articles that had been published in *Nation* magazine in March and April of last year. Argüelles had gotten an advanced copy of the articles and book manuscript thanks to his acquaintance with Roszak. He got permission to copy and distribute the text, promising to buy copies when the book came out in August.

The subtitle said it all: "Reflections on the Technocratic Society and Its Youthful Opposition." Roszak wrote in the opening chapter, "But if one believes, as I do, that the alienated young are giving shape to something that looks like the saving vision our endangered civilization requires, then there is no avoiding the need to understand and to educate them in what they are about." I enjoyed Roszak's writing style. It was energetic, visual, and inspiring.

The book was an academic analysis of what was happening in America and around the world regarding the rejection of technology. He argued that both capitalist and socialist countries had dehumanized the populace through totalitarian technology. Roszak looked at the youth movement, which he felt had been born thanks to a barren Western culture that had forced people my age to seek spiritual meaning elsewhere – in such unorthodox outlets as LSD, wacky religions, comic books, and revolution. According to him, modern society was dominated by science, making it ugly, repressive, and soulless. The "technocracy" was the root cause of problems such as war, poverty, racism, and environmental disaster. The movement reacting to it was organized and consistent enough to be considered a culture. Because it was rebelling against the status quo, Roszak came up with the term, "counter culture [sic]." He theorized that middle class young people had rejected adulthood because they had to give up too much, abandoning pleasure, freedom, and youthfulness for an ordered existence. They – we – wanted something different; something better; something more in tune with who we were, and how we saw the world. It wasn't a political revolution, but a revolution in consciousness.

Roszak theorized that this counter culture [sic] could be the foundation of a new visionary civilization; that it could be the salvation of mankind. But he was concerned that the minds of these "counter culturists" were filled with nonsense. Their instincts were informed and well-intentioned, but their education was not. The seeds germinating and sprouting this future civilization included campus protests, the civil rights movement, love-ins, rock music, psychedelic drugs, and even a popular button that said, "I am a human being; do not mutilate, spindle, or tear." According to him, our generation's quest was as follows: "we are special . . . we are different . . . we are outward bound from the old corruptions of the world." People were trying to figure out what this craziness was that was infecting the country and the world. Roszak defined it and named it.

He made an interesting point about democracy and polling. He was concerned that a random sampling of citizens could incorrectly be interpreted as representing the entire country, especially when the pollsters could " . . . always construe the polls to serve their own ends." For example, if 80 per cent of those polled thought it was a mistake that we "went into Vietnam," but 51 per cent thought we would "lose prestige" if we left, then those who commissioned the poll could say the "people" had been "consulted" and the war could continue with their "approval." It seemed obvious to me that the administration had been doing this all along when it came to Vietnam.

Roszak's closing chapter, "Eyes of Flesh, Eyes of Fire," examined the need for the return of a magical, visionary hero known to ancient civilizations, but now lost to modern ones, thanks to the emphasis on rational thought and technology. This hero was the shaman, who could function as the role model for a new, national consciousness; the "good magic" of the shaman would counter the "bad magic" of technocratic elites. Roszak also discussed the split personality of young people, torn between being political rebels tearing down the walls, or becoming new mystics seeking greater spirituality.

The word shaman meant "he or she who knows." Shamans were the spiritual guides, magicians, tricksters, and visionaries who broke through the monotony of daily existence with songs, stories, dances, magic, or prophecies that presaged the future. They held civilization accountable. They served as intermediaries between the physical and spiritual worlds. Mystics and seers, he or she acted as healers, the keepers of knowledge, and guides. It was they who were called to adventure, suffered trials, and returned with the reward necessary to save mankind. In cultures all over the world, the shaman was that person – man, woman, or child – who had looked death in the face and returned to tell stories that helped the tribe survive.

When I had lost my spleen in 1962, I nearly died. I was beginning to understand the role of the shaman.

One of the sources Roszak drew upon, notably in his exploration of shamanism, was *The Hero of a Thousand Faces* by Joseph Campbell. I had first encountered Campbell over the summer thanks to a seed planted by fellow Modestan, George Lucas, when we were driving to Los Angeles in '62. He had told me that if I was into mythology, I should read the book. It was required reading in his sociology class at MJC. I had checked it out of the library when I returned, but had a tough time reading it. Argüelles had mentioned it in class also, so I bought a used copy. This time I couldn't put it down.

The Hero with a Thousand Faces was published by the Bollingen Foundation through Pantheon Press in 1949. As a book on comparative mythology, Campbell theorized that the journey of the archetypal hero was the same in all world myths. Campbell relied on the work of Freud, Jung, James George Frazer, and Arnold Van Gennep. From Van Gennep, he borrowed the idea that the journey was structured in three phases, which Campbell called Separation, Initiation, and Return. Campbell called this universal structure the "monomyth," which he had first encountered when reading James Joyce's *Finnegans Wake*.

There were several stages in the hero's journey, as laid out by Campbell. It began with the hero in his ordinary world, before he was called to an adventure. He often refused the call at first. Once he accepted the challenge, a mentor helped him cross the first threshold into a supernatural world where he would face many trials, usually assisted by allies. The object of the quest was generally hidden in a cave, or underground. It was here, or not long thereafter, that the hero faced his greatest challenge. If the hero survived the challenge, which was often death or a monster, he received the reward. Having achieved the goal of the challenge, he started his journey home. On his return, he encountered more challenges. He endured one last ordeal before being resurrected and reborn. At last, he arrived where he began and used the reward to improve his ordinary world.

As a history major and non-fiction book reader, this was the type of book I enjoyed. Once I finished, I re-read the myths and stories I knew and had studied, such as Ulysses and King Arthur, to see if the structure worked. It did. I could see how it would influence other writers. It made me think more about my own journey – the road I was traveling now.

Having read Campbell the author, I wanted to know more about Campbell the man. As I was researching him in magazines and books, I stumbled upon an intriguing story. When he had returned home to New York after studying abroad, all he wanted to do was move to Carmel, California, and write short stories for *The Saturday Evening Post*. He acted on his dream, driving west from New York. He stopped briefly in Berkeley to meet with Idell Henning, an old friend he'd met while sailing home from a vacation in Hawaii, who told him that her sister's husband was doing something comparable to what Campbell wanted to do. His name was John Steinbeck. Joe was intrigued. Idell took Campbell to Pacific Grove and introduced him to her sister, Carol, and her brother-in-law, John, who introduced Campbell to Ed Ricketts, who owned a marine biology supply house on Cannery Row and became the inspiration for Steinbeck's character, "Doc." Campbell became part of this small group of Bohemians. At that time, Steinbeck was unpublished and was spending all his time writing. Before long, Campbell and Carol, who were spending more time together, became closer. There was speculation that they may have had an affair which, considering that Carol was Steinbeck's muse, typist, and taskmaster, would have certainly derailed the novelist's career before it started. And it might have, but Campbell, recognizing the greatness in Steinbeck and his talent as a writer, removed himself from the equation and traveled with Ricketts on a specimen hunting trip to the Pacific Northwest. It was a juicy sidebar to a well-known bit of popular culture. It reminded me of Arthur, Guinevere, and Lancelot with "Doc" playing Merlin and the *paisanos* of Monterey forming the Round Table; or Rick, Ilsa, and Viktor, with "Doc" channeling Renault. It was a classic love triangle and an unknown story.

Marshall McLuhan's book was another story. I enjoyed McLuhan. I had never read anything quite like him. His ideas were clear, his writing wasn't. What he said was amazing, the way he said it wasn't. His style was dense, academic, and circuitous. But he challenged me and motivated me to look behind the curtain.

His book was an investigation into media theory, which was the study of the content, history, and effects of various media and mass media, in particular. His phrase, "the medium is the message," which had become the buzz phrase after the book was published in 1964, basically meant that the media, not the content they communicated, should be the focus of study. Another controversial message was the difference between "hot" and "cool" types of media. A "hot" media, like a movie, required less participation because it focused on one sense, such as vision. A "cool" media, like TV or a comic book, required more effort and senses for the participant to fill in the details.

There was much to think about in the book, but what struck me most was his thoughts about leadership, especially at a time when we had a Dick for president. He wrote about how Hitler had used media, particularly the radio, to retribalize the German people. McLuhan pointed out how TV was creating a new type of leader – a man who ruled by "a mass-participational TV dialog and feedback." He was a "tribal emperor," who had mastered their media; a man who governed his country on camera; a man like Castro, or Nixon. Nixon's initial experience with TV had been disastrous, but he had learned to use the medium to his advantage.

McLuhan described how the clash between "the old segmented visual culture" and "the new integral electronic culture" created a "crisis of identity" that would lead to violence. That violence was an identity quest experienced by young people and was acted out in the "theater of the streets." He predicted that the ballot box would be replaced by a simultaneous electronic technology; a technology that would be "a new form of spontaneous and instantaneous communal involvement in all areas of decision making." He continued by positing that a "tribal all-at-once culture" would be supplanted by "a mass society in which personal diversity was encouraged while at the same time everybody reacted and interacted simultaneously to every stimulus."

If I was reading him correctly, he was saying that someday we would all be wired together; we would all be connected; we would all experience the simultaneity of the moment. And that a Machiavellian leader could use this power to his advantage. McLuhan saw the computer as the tool that, instead of selling consumables or solving problems, could lead to universal understanding and unity that could "knit mankind into one family and create a perpetuity of collective harmony and peace." He wrote a line that I highlighted in yellow marker: "Mysticism is just tomorrow's science dreamed today." It echoed something Campbell had written: "Myths are public dreams, dreams are private myths."

McLuhan explained that he wasn't advocating anything. He was merely "probing and predicting trends." I couldn't imagine all the things he was predicting.

After reading McLuhan, I wondered if we would ever face a time when we would have an elected leader as he described, who would manipulate the masses instantly with a word or two simultaneously experienced by all.

The evening news was abuzz when Secretary of Defense Melvin Laird announced that the United States would "Vietnamize" the war effort.

According to the news anchors, the U.S. would now put responsibility for the war on the South Vietnamese army and would begin the withdrawal of American troops.

That was huge news. It could mean the war would be over and the draft would end. If it happened.

In the wake of that news, massive anti-war protests took place in many U.S. cities, large and small, that first Saturday in April, which was the day before Easter Sunday. Appropriate timing for a demonstration of peace.

CHAPTER 25

I took the Easter weekend off and drove home on Friday. Easter was another holiday my family enjoyed celebrating. When we were younger, before Mom and Dad had become disillusioned with the church, we would dress up in our Sunday best and attend. We had fallen out of the habit. The rituals we retained were decorating the eggs, using the PAAS dye kit, and the Easter egg and Easter basket hunt. When Dad was alive, he hid the eggs and baskets, while Mom kept us kids occupied. As we got older, Tim and I took over the duties of hiding things for the younger kids. As the rest of my sibs caught up, it reverted back to Mom and, now, to my stepdad.

There were more eggs and candy than we could possibly consume. We'd cap the day off with a feast of ham, potato salad, deviled eggs, and ice cream, which meant I'd be driving back to Davis in a tryptophan haze come Sunday. Laura often joined us. We had a newcomer this year now that Willy had a girlfriend. Her name was Marilyn. He wouldn't be sixteen until November, but he was growing up fast.

For me, and most of my family, Easter was never about religion or God or church. It was about new clothes and eating candy. Only after taking a "*Bible* as Literature" class and World History course did I look more closely at organized religion.

When the first Neanderthal was able to comprehend abstractions and conjure things that weren't real, he created ghost stories that explained things like the rising of the sun, natural disasters, birth, and death. These stories united the tribes through a common belief system. These ghost stories centered on the concept of a being, or beings, more powerful than the humans. These stories became the God myths that helped explain creation and other phenomena. Different tribes had different ghost stories. One tribe, believing their story was the one true story, would decide it was necessary to convince a different tribe that their ghost stories were wrong. They might even kill members of the opposing tribe to scare them into accepting the existence of the gods and stories of the attacking tribe. Eventually, these stories, gods, and rituals were handed down, written down, and codified into one story and one God.

Each generation was taught their particular story and raised to worship their specific God. Children grew up believing this story and this God and hating the children of other tribes who didn't believe the way they did. The one thing that didn't change as belief systems evolved through time was the willingness of one tribe to kill his fellow man over a belief in something that wasn't physical or real.

I believed the celebration of Christ's resurrection was less about his rebirth and more about the coming of spring and the rejuvenation of the earth. The *Bible* seemed to be a wonderful collection of stories, parables, fables, and myths. It wasn't the word of God. I believed religion was more about love and compassion, not ritual; about how we lived our lives, rather than a higher power that controlled our lives; a guide to living a moral life, rather than a guide to salvation. I believed that doing the right and good thing led to a better world here and now, not a better hereafter. If I was a true believer, I believed in music. If I had religion, it was music. Oscar Wilde made a statement that reflected my view when he said, "Religion is like a blind man looking in a black room for a black cat that isn't there, and finding it." It was Laudanumism. I was probably going to burn in hell for believing that. *C'est la vie.*

Kelly was home for Easter, too. We met at Straw Hat for pizza with Canadian bacon and tomatoes. Our favorite.

"What's wrong," I asked, as she picked at her pizza.

"I think we should see other people."

I felt like I'd been hit in the gut, although I'd been doing the same with Luci since school had started. "Is there someone else?"

"There's always someone else. If you're looking."

"Are you?"

"What?"

"Looking?"

"Not really."

"You seeing someone?" I asked.

"Sort of," she said. "We've gone to a movie, or two"

"You slept with him?" Again, less than honest since I'd done the same thing with Luci.

She glared at me. "I wouldn't do that," she said. "I wanted to talk with you before I did anything."

"I appreciate that. I guess."

"Look, Michael, we knew a long-distance relationship like this might not work."

"Plus, there's all those cute guys at Berkeley."

"I could say the same about Davis," she countered. "I saw Gary at Dunlap's. He forgot I didn't know who Luci is."

"We have a class together."

"Is that all?"

"It is."

"Doesn't matter," she said.

"I guess we've outgrown the high school kids we were."

"I don't know where any of this is going. I wanted to get it out in the open and see what happens."

"Experiment a little," I said, sarcastically.

"Let's not let things get ugly," she said.

"They already are."

"Don't do this."

"What?" I asked, making her do all the hard work.

"Turn on me. We've been together too long. Been through too much to throw it all away."

"I was fine with the way things were," I answered.

"I wasn't."

"Obviously."

"Let's stay in touch," she said.

"Sure."

"Things could change."

"They could," I replied.

"Who knows what the future holds."

"I certainly don't."

"We okay then?" she asked.

"Fine."

She got up and left. I stared at the pizza. The whole thing felt surreal, like I was suddenly transported back to the games we, boys and girls alike, all played in high school – games involving misunderstandings, miscommunication, mistakes, and misery.

CHAPTER 26

Major league baseball's spring training, which had been delayed due to a player boycott, was in the books. So was opening day. It was time for intramural slow pitch softball. Davis had an active and extensive intramural program in all sports, but especially in softball. There were dorm, frat, grad-staff, co-ed, and off-campus leagues, each with multiple divisions. Because I had played football with Wally and FYNC last fall, I was now grandfathered onto their off-campus softball team. League play began the second Wednesday in April with a record-setting 75 teams divided into eight divisions.

I played left and batted first, mainly because I was fast. I could get to anything near me in the outfield and I could beat out anything in the infield and stretch a lazy single into a double. Everybody played barefoot. Nobody wore cleats. A few wore tennies. We wore cut-offs, gym shorts, or sweats. We had matching nylon jerseys that were orange with black trim and lettering. On the front, a black sheep was enclosed by a shield with three black stars above it, and the letters "FYNC."

There were two games scheduled on weekday afternoons from Monday to Thursday. We played on Mondays and Wednesdays at 4:20, 5:30, and a third game at 6:40 once Daylight Savings Time went into effect on Sunday, April 27th. Games were played on the main I.M. field, which was on Russell Boulevard, or at Hutchison, Orchard, or Tercero fields, which were west of campus. At the end of league play, the winners of each division would play each other to crown an all-campus champion.

In addition to slow pitch, there was also a fast pitch league that played on Thursdays, beginning April 17th. Eligibility had been changed from last year. There were no restrictions on who could play, so lettermen, staff, and faculty were all eligible to join students on teams. As far as the competition level, it was an open league. Players could play both fast pitch and slow pitch. We didn't have a pitcher, which you needed to be competitive, so we didn't participate in that league.

Our slow pitch team got off to a fast start, winning our first four games against the Barristers, Barret's Bruisers, the Rippers, and the Stems, which put us at the top of the Southern division. Doug Wilson, our right fielder, was the big slugger against the last two teams, never making an out. In the 10 – 7 win over the Rippers, he got three doubles and a walk. In the 14 – 5 walk over the

Stems, he got a homer and three singles.

Each week, I looked forward to two alternating columns in *The Aggie*. "Underground Sports" with Far Out Fred and Mad John platooned with "Dice's Delights" to provide InforMation and a roundup of the intramural action the week before and predictions for the coming week. They also compiled a top ten ranking of all teams, regardless of the league they were in. We were ranked number six in the first rankings published that season. We'd stay in the top ten for the rest of the season.

It wasn't all good news. In the game against the Stems, I blew out both hamstrings chasing a foul ball along the left field line when I sprinted across a dip in the lawn, hyperextending the hammies. It likely happened because my muscles were exhausted from the tournament. For the next several weeks, I was at third base and the student health center, undergoing ultrasound on the back of my legs. They had turned a dark blue-black, stretching from my butt cheeks to the back of my knees. For each game, I wrapped the hamstrings tightly with Ace bandages so I could field and hobble down to first, where a courtesy runner took over. I didn't need much range at third, only quick hands and a decent arm. I hated being crippled.

That April, things were heating up on the anti-war and resistance front. Harvard students and members of the SDS seized buildings on that campus. Black students occupied buildings at Cornell. Black and Puerto Rican students took over the City College of New York. Things were going to get hotter after the press leaked that the U.S. had bombed, and then invaded, Cambodia in March to stop the flow of men and materiel into Vietnam. The war had been expanded. We, the people, in a supposed democracy, knew nothing about it and had no say in it.

I got a sense of the seriousness of things related to the war when the kid who burned his draft card in the rhetoric class was sentenced to five years in jail. Incredible. Five years in jail for exercising his right to freedom of speech. I was dumbfounded. And freaked.

Studying late one night and listening to Tyree on KDVS, my usual late-night night-light, he made an announcement about an upcoming workday at a park in Berkeley near the campus. The 2.3-acre plot was owned by the university, who had taken over the property through eminent domain in 1967. The area had been occupied by single-family homes and boardinghouses. The university bulldozed the properties. The administration planned to turn the space into athletic fields and student dorms. The residents told a different story. They said the university wanted to root out the cheap housing because that was where many of the radical students lived who had been involved in the Free Speech Movement and, now, the protests against Vietnam.

After clearing the property, the university had run out of money before they could complete the job. The area had remained vacant, collecting dust and old cars. Some students, residents, and merchants developed a plan to turn it into a public park. In an article about the project that appeared on April 18th in *The Berkeley Barb*, an underground newspaper, the story referred to the land as a "people's park." The article had been signed, "Robin Hood's Park Commissioner." That's how KDVS found out about it. Tyree closed the story by saying the workday would be April 20th.

CHAPTER 27

Spring had come. It felt good to see the sun and shed some layers and winter blues. I loved being able to put away all those clothes and shoes filled with dreary. One of the most important annual rites of spring at Davis was Picnic Day. It was a day to showcase the campus and a day to party. Parents and alum came to celebrate the campus. Students came to have a good time.

Picnic Day was the day each spring when anybody who had ever lived in Davis, or attended UC Davis, returned and wandered the campus and downtown, hoping to rekindle a little of that old college magic. It was also the day many locals left town and the students took over. Picnic Day was first held on May 22nd, 1909, when Mrs. Carolee Shields suggested hosting a "Dedication Basket Picnic," to honor the opening of North Hall, the first dormitory on the campus. To promote the event, a cow named Molly walked from what was then Davisville to Berkeley. It took her 97 hours and 11 minutes.

Nearly three thousand people traveled by car, train, and horse-and-buggy for the dedication. They brought picnics, cups, and spoons to go along with the free coffee and cream served by the university in the dairy barn. It was so successful, the faculty started a tradition. The faculty continued to plan and sponsor the event until students took over in 1912. Picnic Day was cancelled five times. In 1924, due to hoof-and-mouth disease. In 1938, because the new gym wasn't done and it was needed to accommodate the growing crowds. And, from 1943 to 1945, as a result of the Army Signal Corps occupying the campus during World War II. Through the years, a number of unique events came and went, including a livestock parade, a jousting tournament, a greased pig race, a water fight on the Quad, bacteria counting, and pigeon races.

It was reputed to be one of the largest student-run events in the United States. In 1969, it was quite possibly the largest. Most departments put on exhibitions, competitions, or presentations to introduce themselves to the public and potential students. Because it was once the University Farm and had a well-known vet med school, Picnic Day hosted exhibitions featuring animals, including the famed fistulated cow, first displayed in 1933, which allowed spectators to view the inner workings of a cow's digestive system live as it ate.

There was a parade, a rodeo, concerts on the Quad and at Freeborn. The theme for this year's event was "Freewheeling & Friendly." The parade marshal was retiring Chancellor Emil Mrak and the concert featured he Youngbloods and Strawberry Alarm Clock. The campus expected 70,000 visitors.

The Youngbloods were a band out of Marin County fronted by Jesse Colin Young. They had a huge hit that became a hippie anthem of sorts called "Come Together." Strawberry Alarm Clock was a one-hit wonder with the song, "Incense and Peppermints."

On the Sunday before the event, thirteen Davis students completed a bike marathon to Berkeley to publicize Picnic Day. The next day, Picnic Day Chairman Roger Klein bested Chuck Turner, Berkeley vice president, in the traditional cow milking contest held at Cal.

The 56th Annual Picnic Day was my first. I invited Luci to join me, but she was visiting family in San Francisco, or so she said. I couldn't tell if she was being straight with me, or had other business to attend to.

The day opened with Ramos gin fizzes at Gator's apartment. From there, we drove Ugly Orange downtown to watch the parade. Starting in front of the library and winding its way downtown before returning to the Young Hall parking lot, the parade featured floats by the various schools and departments, as well as the Aggie marching band and bands from Humboldt State and Cal. We left the truck and followed the band onto campus. We watched a water polo match between students and alumni, checked in on a women's gymnastics meet in the gym, caught a fashion show at Freeborn Hall, hit the main intramural field for the sheep dog trials, and attended a JV game on the baseball diamond. Then off to the Quad for some live music. Gover and Gator planned to get truly and deeply plowed and ride a bull at the rodeo. They staggered off to the horse arena. I walked back to the truck. On the way, I watched bits of a theater production at Freeborn, a tennis match on the main courts, a fencing exhibition in the gym, and a rugby match at Toomey Field. The flag was lowered at 6 p.m. on the Memorial Union patio, closing out the daylight portion of another Picnic Day. There were evening performances yet to happen, including the concert and dance.

That April, it seemed like the only records Slevin played on the communal stereo were anything by Gordon Lightfoot and the new James Taylor album. They were talented singer-songwriters, but hearing them over and over got old fast. In another life, Richard might have been a vagabond troubadour; a minstrel of the dawn like the heroes of Lightfoot's songs.

Gordon Lightfoot was a Canadian musician. His best-known songs included "For Lovin' Me," "Early Morning Rain," and "Ribbon of Darkness." Two of those songs, "For Lovin' Me" and "Early Morning Rain," were popularized when they were recorded by both Ian and Sylvia and Peter, Paul and Mary. My favorite from his *The Way I Feel* album was the "Canadian Railroad Trilogy," which described the building of the trans-Canada Canadian Pacific Railway in the early 1880s.

James Taylor was a musician from Boston, Massachusetts, by way of Chapel Hill, North Carolina. After an unsuccessful stint in a band called the Flying Machine and too many drugs, he pursued a solo career. He moved to London and an old bandmate, Danny Korchmar, connected him with Peter Asher of Peter and Gordon. Asher was the A&R man for the newly formed Beatles' Apple Records. Taylor gave Asher a demo tape. Asher played it for Paul McCartney and George Harrison, who loved his songs, his voice, and his guitar playing. Taylor became the first non-British act inked by Apple. Apple released his debut album, *James Taylor*, in December 1968 in the U.K. and February 1969 in the U.S. *Rolling Stone*'s Jon Landau wrote, "This album is the coolest breath of fresh air I've inhaled in a good long while. It knocks me out."

When I could, I slipped a new album onto the turntable. My infatuation with Joni Mitchell had been supplanted when Tucson native Linda Ronstadt released *Hand Sown ... Home Grown*, her debut album, last March. I had first heard about her in 1967 when she sang lead on *Different Drum*, by the Stone Poneys, a song written by Michael Nesmith of the Monkees. Her solo album included covers of songs by Bob Dylan, Fred Neil, John D. Loudermilk, and Randy Newman. The best song on the whole album for my money was "Silver Threads and Golden Needles," an energetic, fiddle-driven country tune you could really dance to. The album featured a talented group of session players, including Clarence White of The Byrds, Bernie Leadon, Red Rhodes, and Larry Knechtel. With her voice, her smile, and her big hoop earrings, Ronstadt was a performer worth watching. She struck me as a lady who could handle herself in the male-dominated world of rock and country. Joni was ethereal, Linda was earthy. One warbled, the other growled. One wrote songs, the other interpreted them. I was sure they were both going to be around for a long, long time.

During another of my late-night study sessions, KDVS provided an update on the park project in Berkeley. More than 100 people had showed up for the workday. A landscaper donated trees, flowers, shrubs, and sod. The park featured a brick walkway, swing sets, and a garden. Someone provided free food. In the opinion of the people doing the work, "We're using the land better than you, so now it's ours." Near the end of April, the university released its plans for a sports field to be built on the site. The university said they wouldn't do anything without notifying the park's builders. Two days later, the university turned over control of more than one quarter of the site to the people who had built the park. It sounded like everyone got what they wanted.

CHAPTER 28

"All the News that Fits" – May Edition

Jimi Hendrix is busted at the Toronto Airport for possession of heroin. Bill Hartack wins the 95th Kentucky Derby on Majestic Prince. Riots break out during Spring Break concerts in Palm Springs. Bill Russell's Boston Celtics beat Wilt Chamberlain's Los Angeles Lakers 108 to 106 in a thrilling game seven NBA final. John Lennon's visa to visit the U.S. is cancelled. Norman Mailer is awarded the Pulitzer Prize in Literature for *Armies of the Night*. Apollo 10 transmits the first color pictures of Earth from space. President Nixon requests that a draft lottery system be instituted. Prime Minister Pierre Trudeau of Canada offers sanctuary to any Americans fleeing the draft. Activists burn draft board files in Chicago. John Lennon and Yoko Ono begin their second "Bed-In for Peace" at the Queen Elizabeth Hotel in Montreal and record "Give Peace a Chance" live. The movie *If...* by Lindsay Anderson wins the top prize at Cannes. "The Dick Cavett Show" premieres on ABC. The rock boogie band ZZ Top forms in Houston, Texas. Mario Andretti wins the 53rd Indianapolis 500. New book releases include *Ada or Ardor* by Vladimir Nabokov; *The Love Machine*, Jacqueline Susann; *The Goodbye Look*, Ross Macdonald; *The Four-Gated City*, Doris Lessing; *The Andromeda Strain*, Michael Crichton; and *The Day of the Dolphin* by Robert Mele. *We'd Rather Switch*, *Akokawe - Initiation*, and *Fiesta in Madrid* open on stage. New films include *Krakatoa, East of Java*; *Winning* featuring Paul Newman and Joanne Woodward; *Midnight Cowboy* starring Dustin Hoffman and Jon Voight; *Pippi Longstocking*; and Sergio Leone's *Once Upon a Time in the West*. New music includes two singles by the Beatles, "Get Back" and "Don't Let Me Down;" Joni Mitchell's *Clouds*; Neil Young's second album, *Everybody Knows This Is Nowhere*; the Velvet Underground's *Velvet Underground*; Sly and the Family Stone's *Stand*; Phil Ochs' *Rehearsals for Retirement*; Poco's *Pickin' Up the Pieces*; The Who's rock opera *Tommy*; Crosby, Stills & Nash's *Crosby, Stills & Nash*; Merle Haggard's *Same Train, Different Time*; *Last Exit* by Traffic; and the single "Sugar, Sugar" by the Archies.

As the weather warmed, we got more active. We emerged from hibernation ready to get busy.

FYNC continued to win, defeating Manic Depression the last week of April and Jack 'n' the Off Beats the first week in May to go 6 – 0 and remain atop our division. Dan Peavy led the hit parade against Depression with a triple and two singles, while Mike Abbott allowed only 11 hits for the day. On Cinco de Mayo, in a close one against the Beats, the second place team, Abbott gave up 10 hits and had three of our team's six hits. With a win the following week, we moved to 7 – 0 and a ranking of number four, the highest we would get that season.

We were keeping an eye on the other division leaders since we'd be matched up against one of them during the playoffs. In the Western division, the Leper Colony, a pre-season favorite to win it all, was also undefeated. Over in the Northern Division, the Gringo Gorps scored two easy wins over OSP "10" and the Trollers to stand 6 – 0 overall and nail down the number nine ranking. Rick Meade went 5-for-5 against the Trollers to pace the Gorps' hitting attack.

The second weekend in May was one I looked forward to. Not only was it spring and nice weather, but it was the weekend of the 7th Annual "All-Day Tourney"; a one-day, all-campus slow pitch softball tournament. Every on-campus and off-campus team, as well as alumni, were invited to participate in the tourney. The winner would represent Davis in the 7th Annual All-Cal Intramural Sports Tourney, scheduled to be held in Berkeley this year. Davis would host next year. Held each May, the 36-hour festival involved athletes from all nine campuses competing in two sports – softball and basketball.

In last year's All-Day Tourney, the Skellers had beaten Kappa Sigma. On any given day, a frat team could be playing a dorm team, a grad/staff team against an off-campus team. FYNC had never won it all. I had vowed to myself that I wanted to win it all before I graduated and/or left Davis. We had a strong club, so we had a shot. I was healthy again and ready to play.

This year's event had 32 teams. It was a double-elimination format. The entries had been broken down into four pools of eight teams each. The undefeated winner of each pool would move on to the playoffs. Each team would need to lose twice to be knocked out. A control board was set up near main I.M. field 6 with the updated tournament results. The first game was at 9 a.m.

In the end, there was a new campus leader. The Purple Machine from Sigma Phi Epsilon battled against the heat and fatigue to score six straight wins, including the defeat of Theta Xi, who had knocked off Leper Colony in the semi-finals, to take the crown. With the victory, the Eppers shot to the number one slot in the new campus standings. Thanks to our league record and effort in the tourney, we remained ranked number four.

Unfortunately, the All-Cal Tourney was cancelled due to the unrest in Berkeley.

That Sunday was Mother's Day. I was a good son. I never forgot it. I had sent her a goofy card and called.

"Yo, Mom. Happy Mother's Day."

"Thanks, Sweetie. You don't know how much it means." She didn't sound right.

"Everything okay?"

"Everything's fine."

"You sure?" She hesitated. I could hear her thinking through the line.

"I sometimes wonder."

"About what?"

"What it will be like when you're all gone."

"That's morbid," I said, laughing and hoping to lighten things up.

"No, not gone gone. Just no longer here. In the house."

"We're not going anywhere."

"But, you will. Timmy is already gone. We never see him. Willie is always with his friends and now, Marilyn. The girls always seem to be visiting their friends. Paul is at work all day. You're away at college."

"But I come home for the holidays and summer."

"Until you start your own life, then you'll be gone, too."

"I'll always come home."

"It's not the same as having you all here every day. I can't take care of you. Watch out for you. I love being able to do that."

"I thought you liked it when we were all out of the house so you could have it to yourself and get your work done."

"I used to. But, it's lonely. You don't know how lonely it can be."

I had no answer. There was nothing I could say to alleviate the absoluteness of loneliness. I didn't mind being alone. I could handle it. I enjoyed it. Mom didn't and couldn't. Someone once said you could die from loneliness as surely as you could die from heart disease.

A writer once commented that it wasn't possible for two people to truly know each other. No matter how close the husband and wife, the father and son, the lover and beloved, we were all locked inside ourselves. That said something horrible about our lack of knowledge; about our hopeless and terrible and sadly permanent loneliness. It said something about the loneliness of the individual trying to find meaning in their isolation. We were all lonely and we were all going out there again. I hoped Mom was just feeling blue; that there wasn't something more serious going on.

My mom was incredible. She raised five kids in a small house. She cooked, she cleaned, she drove us everywhere. She protected and defended us. Heaven help anyone who attacked, or demeaned, her children. She welcomed our friends and created an extended family. We took it all for granted. We hand-made cards for the holidays and special occasions. We bought her birthday and Christmas gifts. We gave her flowers and hugs. But, we never gave her the gift she wanted, but never expected or asked for, and that was our thanks; our acknowledgement; our gratitude. We assumed she knew and left it at that. After our phone call that Mother's Day, I was convinced that wasn't enough.

I knew there was something else weighing on her mind on this particular day. Another child who wasn't part of our family. Our half-sister, Sarah. Mom was a teenager when she had gotten pregnant by some young man she'd met through a high school friend. They were on a double-date and the guy basically raped my mom. Nine months later, Sarah was born. Mom had met Dad by then through the same high school friend, who was related to Dad. He wanted to get married, but he wasn't prepared to take on a baby. But, he loved Mom and would do anything for her. He told her if she wanted to keep the baby, he would raise her as his own. Instead, they chose to give Sarah up for adoption.

With help from my grandfather and his sister, our great aunt, who mom and her friend had been rooming with, a cousin of Dad's and her husband agreed to adopt Sarah. Mom stayed with the couple during the pregnancy. When Sarah was born, the husband left the hospital with Mom, pretending to be her husband. He took Sarah home with him. Dad took Mom back to Stockton with him. The rest of us were born and life went on. At some point, Mom decided she had made a mistake and wanted Sarah back. She convinced Dad that this was a good idea. She believed because the adoption had never been formalized her idea would work. Sarah had simply left the hospital with the husband and had never been officially adopted. Dad wasn't sure, but he went along because it was important to her.

Early one school day, he packed Timmy and me in the car. We were six and four. We asked what was happening. He said, "We're going to see your sister." We were confused because we didn't know we had a sister. We drove to the foothills where Sarah attended elementary school. It was snowy and cold. We traveled for a while, then Dad told us to get in back and get down. We did. He slowed and opened the car door. Man it was cold. He stopped. We peeked over the back of the seat. We saw a girl somewhat older than me. She was on her way home from school. She was carrying her lunch bag and books.

Dad said, "Hello, Sarah. Remember me?"

She said, "Yes. You're Uncle Tim."

"That's right," answered Dad.

"Would you like a ride home?" he asked.

"Okay, I guess," she replied.

She got in. Dad pulled away. She saw us hiding in the back. We were scared. She said, "Hello."

We got down lower. She got worried.

"Uncle Tim, take me home. Take me home right now!"

"I am," Dad told her.

He sped up. She started to cry. And kick. And hit him. She did that all the way back to Modesto. It was terrible.

The next several days and weeks were uncomfortable and painful for everyone involved. Sarah was returned to her adopted parents, who were the only parents she had ever known. Mom and Dad went to court to get legal custody. The judge determined Mom wasn't a fit mother and legally returned Sarah to Dad's cousin and her husband. We never saw Sarah again. At various times after that, Mom would appear in one of our rooms red-eyed. She would wring her hands, cry, and slowly shred the Kleenex she carried in her waistband and tell us what a horrible mistake she had made by abandoning Sarah and how much she hated Dad for not standing up for her. She wanted us to understand why they had done what they had done and what she had gone through every day since. But, what she really wanted was our forgiveness. We were too young to know that and too naïve to offer it. In time, that deep sadness and guilt shaded into depression, eventually impatience, sometimes anger. Dad shared the same sadness and guilt. It was resurrected each time Mom did this. We never understood or forgave him, either. Then he was gone and we could never say it.

I was thinking about that after I got off the phone. It was impossible to understand how anybody who knew my mother could consider her an "unfit" mother. Her life was her children. I did wonder what her life would be like when her children were gone.

I also thought about Sarah. We never tried to contact her. She never tried to contact us. I suppose that was because we felt we had our own family and she was never part of it, even though she was our half-sister. I tried to look at all of it through her eyes. Did she ever want to know why Mom didn't want her? Why did they leave her there? Why didn't they try again? Why didn't they want to know her better? Of course, once I was born, Mom and Dad had their own family. So, in some weird way, I guess it was my fault. How would her life have changed if she had grown up with us? How much better off would she have been if she had been part of an intact, caring family like ours. I was sure Mom and Dad were also curious what life would have been like if we had all been together. Because she wasn't part of our lives, perhaps we'd never know. Maybe someday.

CHAPTER 29

Anyone of draft age who had not been drafted got some bad news when they read the paper or watched the evening news on May 13th. Tricky Dick asked Congress to reinstitute a random lottery draft system. The reason? The government needed more healthy bodies for Vietnam. The lottery would be used to determine the order of the call to military service in 1970 for men born from 1944 to 1950 – the heart of the Baby Boomer generation. Previously, the government policy had been to draft the oldest man first. The first lottery was held in 1942 to fill vacancies in the armed services which could not be filled by volunteers. It was going to be a nervous time for many of us.

I had spoken with people about the practical and the moral reasons for not serving, but I hadn't talked with anyone about the spiritual reasons. I wanted to speak with someone who might provide insight into that aspect of serving in the military.

Behind Professor Argüelles hung a tall painting – a *thangka* depicting a Buddhist teacher dissolving into a rainbow at the moment of his death. The professor's long hair touched his shoulders. He wore a red scarf and white peasant shirt. Flautist Paul Horn's album, *Inside*, played quietly.

"You're worrying about things you have no control over," he said.

"Small consolation."

"If you're depressed, you're living in the past. If you're anxious, you're living in the future. If you're at peace, you're living in the present. Perhaps you could try to spend more time living in the moment."

I thought of the red orchid, which reminded me of the thought I had last New Year's Eve. That flowers, too, live in the moment. "Easier said than done," I said.

"Do you read Ian Fleming?" he asked, smiling at my quizzical look. "I enjoy pulp fiction. I don't dwell exclusively on higher plains."

"I've watched the movies," I answered.

"In *From Russia with Love*, Fleming wrote: 'Worry is a dividend paid to disaster before it is due.' Worry can be a waste of time. It's squandering energy on a problem you may never have. "

"Ignorance is bliss, but she never pays the bills."

"Is it in you to shoot someone?" he asked.

"I shot a rabbit once. Watching it die was horrible." I told him the story. "I was eighteen. I had never killed anything bigger than a black widow, or a cockroach. I hated those things. A friend talked me into going rabbit hunting in a vineyard owned by his uncle, who wanted us to kill the rabbits because they nibbled on the shoots of the vine.

"The morning of the hunt, I was given a 12-gauge shotgun, some shells, and a few words of caution. Mainly to know where everyone was, point the gun down, and keep the safety on. I was excited, but nervous. The smell of gun metal and wood was energizing. I set off down a row of vines.

"The sun was high and I was sweating. When the rabbit hopped into my row and stopped, I was as shocked to see the rabbit as the rabbit was to see me. I put the gun to my shoulder, aimed, clicked off the safety, and fired. When the blue haze and thunder cleared, I saw the rabbit lying there, twitching. Heart thumping, I raced to where it lay. I nudged it with my tennis shoe. It was dead.

"That was the last time I ever shot a living thing. That night, my father, who had joined the Marines as a seventeen-and-a-half-year-old, told me, 'I will drive you to Canada tomorrow.'"

"He didn't because you're here."

"He would have. It wasn't necessary. Then."

"It's impossible to kill someone in war once you see and know your enemy as a human being. Someone who is a son, a brother, a father. Someone who rises each morning to do the best he can."

"My father never got over the war. He burned everything he had kept related to the military."

"I suspect he was a very spiritual being."

"I don't know. Maybe. But, I'm not."

"Do you truly know what spirituality is?"

"Probably not."

"It is a journey we take from cradle to grave. It is a quest for the divine and the oneness in the universe, a purpose and a way of life. It is who, what, and how we are. Not what we have, or what we do. It's being more concerned about our spirit, or soul, than material or physical things. It's seeking something larger than yourself. It's knowing one's true self and finding peace within.

"It's not something you can buy because you already have it. It's like love or health. We all have it. The question is whether it's good and positive, or bad and negative. Is it self-destructive, or life-giving. Is it something that allows us to reach out to others in charity, or remain isolated in selfishness. It's found in the ordinary, in the everyday experiences of living, both good and bad. Simply put, it's a way of life. A way of be-ing.

"The challenge of spirituality is awakening to the suffering and struggles of all living beings. It's being sympathetic to the intrinsic values of existence. Love, peace, inclusion, contentment, freedom, gratitude, compassion, acceptance, and forgiveness. Gandhi once said, 'Happiness is when what you think, what you say, and what you do are in harmony.' The same can be said for spirituality."

"I've heard it said, and I believe this," I replied, "the day Gandhi is respected as much as Eisenhower is the day we'll have peace in the world."

"'Blessed are the peacemakers, for they will be called children of God.'"

"A state of mind is one thing. Translating it into action is another."

"Hell is full of good meanings, heaven is full of good work. Martin Luther King, Jr. said it in a different way, 'The hottest place in hell is reserved for those who remain neutral in times of great moral conflict.'"

"What can one man do?"

"Stand up to the madness. Stop the runaway train. Make a difference."

"But how?"

"By remaining positive and optimistic. Joining with others who believe the same. Soft is stronger than hard. Water is stronger than rock. Love is stronger than force."

"Those are just words. Platitudes."

"Your father sent vibrations of peace, a message of peace, out into the universe by destroying the mementos and memories of war. You can echo that by taking a stand, protesting the war, refusing to serve. Whatever you are most comfortable doing."

"What if it's not the right choice? What if I make the wrong decision?"

"Take another path."

"It's my life we're talking about."

"I know that. Trust me, I'm not being cavalier about this."

"I get it. The deal is, I'm the only one looking out these eyes."

"It's Uncle Walt's fault."

"Who?"

"Walt Disney. If you study his films, he's giving us permission to rebel. To question authority. To free us from the world as we know it. The *status quo*."

"Be careful. You're threatening an icon."

"Think about it. He encouraged experimenting with drugs in *Fantasia* and *Alice in Wonderland*."

"I was stoned the last time I saw *Fantasia* in the theater."

"Right on. Also, the concept that there are no endings in life, only beginnings, in movies like *Old Yeller*. Or, pacifism. Davy Crockett was an

Indian fighter who hated war. In *Tonka*, as I said earlier, it's difficult to kill someone in war once you know them. Lastly, and most importantly, the message of the film *The Great Locomotive Chase* is that passive resistance isn't cowardly. It takes courage to avoid violence."

"It's too much. I should give up. Just give in."

"Mr. Disney put his faith in youth. In the next generation. To change the world for good."

"That's a lot of pressure. I'm not sure I'm up to it."

Argüelles removed a book from a stack on his desk and showed the cover to me.

"*Tetecan: An Aztec Tragedy* by Howard Muckle," I read aloud.

He opened it to the foreword and read, "Each of us in his destined hour, in hope or extremity, mounts the steps of idealism. In all times and places, fervid youths have climbed in search of idealism, driven upward by sight of the seething plain of life across which the light of brotherhood appears at times to burn fitfully. Too many of them have climbed in vain." He closed the book and placed it on top of the stack.

"It's dangerous being an idealist these days," I said.

"It can be, but I urge you to keep seeking the flame of peace. The like-minded brotherhood. A new hope."

"I hope the climb isn't in vain."

"*Hozho* is a Navajo word. It means harmony, or contentment with the inevitable. You can't control what lies ahead. The best you can do is take the steps necessary to achieve the best outcome, then let it spool out."

"How do you know all this esoteric stuff?"

"I read, I travel, I listen."

"I have a lot to learn."

"Remember this. Everything changes and nothing stands still. Everything flows and nothing abides."

"What does that mean?"

"Nothing is ever as good, or as bad, as one imagines."

The softball season was headed toward the closing stages. In our first league game after the tournament, we struggled to defeat South of Uranus 10 – 9.

CHAPTER 30

It was time to get involved; time to support our fellow students. We were going to Berkeley to find out what was happening with People's Park, as the public park in Berkeley had become known. We planned to attend a rally at Sproul Plaza. It had been Luci's idea. I had talked Gover and Wally into going. And Gary, telling him it would be like the old days when we campaigned for "Clean Gene" McCarthy. Luci and I would drive together, followed by Gover and Wally in the Opel. Gary would come over from Modesto and meet us at Paul Seideman's house. Paul was an old friend, fellow Grace Davis High Spartan, and one of the Mud Bowlers. He was rooming with Dave Henry and Don Hill, two other classmates.

As we drove west on Highway 80, we listened to KSAN's live coverage of the demonstration.

"Ronnie Raygun" was not a fan of People's Park, or the university administrators who had tolerated the student demonstrations on campus. Reagan had been elected governor in 1966, partly based on his campaign promise to crack down on the lax attitude at California's public universities. He had been quoted as calling Berkeley "a haven for communist sympathizers, protesters, and sexual deviants." It was clear the park was his line in the sand, as well as an opportunity to fulfill his campaign promise for the conservatives who supported him.

According to eyewitnesses, who were phoning in updates, the California Highway Patrol and Berkeley PD had arrived before daybreak. Apparently the mayor had asked Reagan to intervene, in spite of the promise by Chancellor Heyns earlier in the month that nothing would happen without warning. They were greeted by protestors who had heard about the raid.

Lt. Robert Ludden of the Berkeley Police Department told the supporters, "You are on university land. If you don't disperse you will be arrested for trespassing. Remove yourself outside the police lines to avoid arrest and any difficulty." They were advised they could take what they built if they wanted. All but three of the supporters dispersed. The three who didn't were arrested without incident and charged with trespassing. The CHP and cops cleared nearly eight blocks around the park. They ripped out a big chunk of what the community had planted. The rest was bulldozed. An 8-foot, chain-link fence was erected around the perimeter to keep people out. Supporters responded by calling for a protest at Sproul Plaza.

KPFA's beat-up Volkswagen bus cruised the area with a sign on its back window saying, "This Event is Being Broadcast Live on KPFA."

Paul's apartment was a short distance from the park. Luci and I pulled up out front first, followed shortly by Gator. Gary was waiting next to his VW bug. He told us Paul had left a note explaining that he, Dave, and Don had already gone to the demonstration. After a pee in the bushes for the boys, the five of us walked toward People's Park.

The rally was set to start at noon. We got there about 11:30. We looked for Paul, but there were thousands of people. We gave up and settled in.

Michael Lerner, chair of the Berkeley chapter of SDS and the Free Student Union, was speaking about the Arab-Israeli conflict. We were confused. We thought it was a rally for the park. Lerner turned it over to Student Body President-elect Dan Siegel, who gave us the latest update on the destruction of the garden and the new fence. He blamed Chancellor Heyns for the "mess at the park."

The crowd was pissed. After he quieted down the shouts, he took a deep breath and yelled: "Let's go down there and take the park!" At that point, there was a scuffle on the stage as the police turned off the sound system. Siegel jumped into the crowd. He pushed his way to the front and marched south on Telegraph toward the park, chanting, "Take back the park! We want the park!"

We followed in their wake.

We had gone a few blocks when I saw Don Hill. He was taller than the rest of us, so he was easier to spot. I didn't recognize him at first because he had grown his hair down to his shoulders. Paul was next to him.

"Si!" I yelled a couple times.

Finally, he heard me and turned. He didn't look the same either with his page-boy length locks. He, Dave, and Don stopped and waited. We exchanged brief brother handshakes and introductions before continuing.

As we moved closer to the park, the crowd got bigger, angrier, and rowdier.

Standing shoulder-to-shoulder across Telegraph at Haste were Berkeley pigs and university cops. More stood flank-to-flank in front of the park. Siegel halted the crowd. The uniform in charge lifted his bullhorn and ordered the crowd to disband. Nobody moved. He yelled the order again. No movement. Suddenly, a fire hydrant gushed water, which forced some of the police to break ranks. At another spot, several protestors rushed the fence and tried to tear it down. When officers pulled them away, others in the crowd threw bottles, rock, bricks, or anything they could get their hands on.

Demonstrators turned on another fire hydrant nearer the law at the corner of Telegraph and Haste. As police moved to turn off the hydrant, they were pelted by more rocks and bottles from the crowd. The commander yelled something to the men behind him. Several lifted tear gas guns from behind them and fired canisters into the crowd. When they exploded, some people scattered, others grabbed the canisters and hurled them back where they came from.

That didn't stop more and more people from streaming into the crowd. It was obvious the 150, or so, officers couldn't contain, or disperse, the crowd. We saw more and more officers from other cities falling in to bolster the ranks. Farther up Haste, we noticed black smoke billowing into the air. Word spread through the crowd that a car had been set on fire. As the confrontation grew, more people gathered on the rooftops of buildings along Telegraph. Witnesses to the revolution.

I had brought along a transistor radio with an FM band so I could get live updates from KSAN. They said the Alameda County Sheriff's Department had sent deputies in full riot gear – helmets, shields, and gas masks. Noting their pale blue jumpsuits, someone shouted, "Watch out for the Blue Meanies," a reference to the bad guys in the Beatles' animated movie, *Yellow Submarine*. The law enforcement presence had grown, but so had the numbers of protestors. We far outnumbered them. But, they had weapons, which they were more than ready to use. The guy in charge made one last attempt to order us to disperse. Nobody moved. He dropped the megaphone and spoke into a radio.

All hell broke loose.

The sheriff deputies waded into the crowd swinging their nightsticks. People went down, many stunned or bleeding. The crowd rolled back toward us. One cop chased a longhair past us. As they flew by, I noticed that the cop had put a strip of black tape over his badge number. They obviously didn't want to be identified. He caught the kid and hacked on him. Other cops joined in, knocking him to the ground and kicking him in the back and stomach, before chasing after other demonstrators.

We moved *en masse* back south on Telegraph away from the park and campus, pursued by the police. In addition to the tear gas, we heard what sounded like gunshots. I caught a glimpse of an officer loading and firing a shotgun at the backs of the running demonstrators. Protestors fell, like they'd been hit.

Somebody on the roof of one of the apartments facing Dwight tossed a rock at the police. A policeman immediately whirled around and, without warning, fired a round into a group on the roof of the building adjacent to the apartment he thought the stone had come from. The group turned and scattered.

It was a nightmare. The smoke from bonfires and tear gas, the noise from helicopters, sirens, and shouts, the anger and panic. It looked and felt like a Hieronymus Bosch painting.

As we reached what looked like a junior high school, our group pushed toward a side street named Derby, trying to separate from the rest of the crowd. We all made it and ducked behind cars parked on the street. All but one. Gover was running as fast as he could, which wasn't that fast because he had blown out a knee playing football at Davis High. As he turned and hobbled down Derby, a sheriff saw him. Being a tall, thin kid, Gover was an easy target. Big enough to be a threat, but too skinny to scare anyone off. That was probably what the deputy was thinking when he went after him.

When the sheriff caught up with him, he swung his club at Gover's gimpy knee, tripping him up. Gover went down face-first. He rolled over and held up his hands. Without hesitating, the sheriff raised his club. A body hurtled through the air and hit the cop mid-section, knocking him on his ass. It was Walt. He grabbed the club from the stunned cop and hit him hard in the facemask. He hit him again and again. The cop went limp, his shield shattered and trickling blood.

Wally raised the club again. I hooked his arm with mine before he could hit again. He spun on me, his eyes hard and crazy. It took a moment for him to realize it was me. When he did, he dropped the club. Gover got to his feet and the two of us pulled Wally away to join everyone else.

When we got back to Paul's house, we all piled inside. Before I went in, I looked back. I could see smoke rising. Police, television, and radio station helicopters circled. Several sirens were blaring. I went in and closed the door.

Paul had the television on. KTVU, Channel 2, was reporting that authorities had claimed nonlethal birdshot was the only ammunition loaded into the shotguns and was used simply to scare the crowd into dispersing. But, when a physician at a nearby hospital was interviewed, he said he had removed "00" pellets from the wounded, which was a lethal load. Alameda County Sheriff Frank Madigan spoke, justifying the use of lethal buckshot by stating, "The choice was essentially this: to use shotguns – because we didn't have the available manpower – or retreat and abandon the City of Berkeley to the mob."

He admitted the possibility that some of his deputies, many of whom were Vietnam War vets, had been overly aggressive in their pursuit of the demonstrators, acting "as though they (the crowd) were Viet Cong."

"Each pellet in that buckshot is about the size of a .38 caliber bullet,"

Wally said. He knew, thanks to being part of a Marine family, a gun owner, and hunter.

Dr. Harry Brean, chief radiologist at Berkeley's Herrick Hospital told an interviewer, "The indiscriminate use of shotguns was sheer insanity."

The drive home was long and dismal. Exiting Berkeley was nearly impossible, between road closures, emergency vehicles flying around town, and police stopping vehicles. Luci and I switched between KSAN and KCBS, San Francisco's all-news AM station. The reports were depressing. And frightening.

The sheriff's deputies had fired shotguns at people sitting on the roof of Granma Books at 2509 Telegraph. One of the bystanders was twenty-five-year-old James Rector. He died four days later, according to the Alameda County coroner's office, from "shock and hemorrhage due to multiple shotgun wounds and perforation of the aorta."

Alan Blanchard, a carpenter, was watching the melee from the roof of the Telegraph Repertory Cinema, where he was working, which was south of Granma Books. He was permanently blinded when a load of birdshot hit him directly in the face.

Another victim caught in the cross-fire was Donovan Rundle, a first-quarter freshman. He was trying to get back to his dorm room when he was hit with buckshot at close range. Mario Savio and others nearby protected him from further harm until an ambulance got there. He survived.

Reagan's reaction to the riot was classic when he said, "It's very naïve to assume that you should send anyone into that kind of conflict with a flyswatter." A spokesman for the University of California Police Department (UCPD) claimed Rector threw steel rebar down onto the police. Others interviewed who had been on the roof with him said they weren't protesting, only observing it all happen.

At least 128 Berkeley residents were admitted to nearby hospitals for head trauma, shotgun wounds, and other severe injuries inflicted by law enforcement. A reporter suggested that the actual number of seriously wounded was likely much higher, because many of the injured probably didn't seek treatment at local hospitals in order to avoid being arrested. Medical students and interns organized volunteer, mobile first-aid teams to help protestors and bystanders injured by buckshot, nightsticks, or tear gas. One Berkeley hospital reported two students wounded with bullets from large caliber rifles as well.

The report of injuries to law enforcement varied depending on who was supplying the stats. One report said five police officers were wounded. The logs of one hospital reported that 19 police officers or Alameda County Sheriff's deputies were treated for minor injuries, but none were hospitalized. UC police claimed that 111 police officers were injured, including California Highway Patrol Officer Albert Bradley, who was knifed in the chest.

It was little wonder the day would later be called, "Bloody Thursday."

Once we had returned to the apartment, Luci, Gover, Wally, and me stayed up past midnight drinking, smoking, and talking about the day's events.

"That was messed up," I said.

"They were doing their job," Wally replied.

"It was a peaceful protest," I countered. "They didn't need guns. Or even clubs."

"They were protecting themselves," Gover chimed in.

"Yeah, those kids were a real threat," I answered. "What were they going to do? Stab a guy wearing a bulletproof vest with the stem of a flower?"

"A cop got knifed," Wally said.

"Hasn't been confirmed," Gover clarified.

"I don't get it," I said. "Why is it that cops go for lethal force. No matter the situation. They've got tear gas. Even clubs are better than shotguns."

"They were outnumbered," Wally defended.

"Why do they ever have to go for the gun?" I asked.

"That's their training," he said.

"You took one out," I reminded him.

"That was different."

"How?"

"I was taking care of a friend."

"Well, things needs to change," I answered.

"So do our tactics," Luci said. She had been silent until then. "Peaceful protest. Nonviolence. The way of Dr. King and Gandhi. Their day is over."

"Work within the system and nobody gets hurt," Wally said.

"It's broken," Luci said. "There's only one way to fix it." She downed a shot of tequila and left.

CHAPTER 31

In the final week of the softball season, although we lost another close one to Pied Pipers to finish 7 – 1, we locked up the league championship and ended the season ranked sixth. The game was a distraction, but no comfort.

The following Tuesday, the Governor called in the California National Guard. They set up camp at the Berkeley Marina and were trucked to campus. Many of the guardsmen were not unlike the protestors, having eluded the draft by signing up. Everywhere you went, they were there. During a vigil for Rector at Sproul Plaza, Guard helicopters tear-gassed the assembly. The noxious fumes drifted across campus and into classrooms, affecting thousands of people, even traveling as far as the ritzy Claremont Hotel. Armed with gas masks and bayonets, Guardsmen boxed protestors inside Sather Gate, arresting 91.

At noon the next day, Associated Students of UC Davis (ASUCD) President Dave Hubin read the following statement, "As representatives of the campus community, we are lowering the campus flag as a symbolic act of protest against violence. We are making every effort to get the facts about the Berkeley situation and will make these available to the campus community as soon as we have them." The statement was signed by Hubin, outgoing Chancellor Emil Mrak, and Walter Woodfill, chairman of the Academic Senate. Woodfill lowered the flag.

Chancellor Mrak sent a telegram to Chancellor Heyns of UC Berkeley and Governor Reagan. It read, "Students, faculty and the rest of the Davis campus community express their deep concern over the continuing presence of outside forces on the Berkeley campus and urge you to exert your influence to bring this episode to a just and speedy conclusion." The telegram echoed what Clark Kerr, first chancellor of the University of California, Berkeley, and twelfth president of the University of California, had once said, "The university is not engaged in making ideas safe for students. It is engaged in making students safe for ideas." That night, students gathered in Olson Hall to discuss what they could do about the Berkeley situation, including a scheduled statewide boycott of classes on Monday and Tuesday.

On Thursday, in what became known as "Operation Box," Berkeley law enforcement corralled and arrested almost 500 people on Shattuck Avenue. Students, professors, and citizens were all taken into custody. The protestors were bused to Santa Rita jail in Dublin, where all charges were dropped. It was later reported they had been physically abused by the guards.

That same day, the Davis campus held a rally, followed by a march on Mrak Hall, which housed offices of the chancellor and the administration.

Rod, Steph, and I walked over to see what was happening.

"Trudeau said Canada would accept any deserters from the war," Rod said.

"Where'd you hear that?" Steph asked.

"It was in yesterday's *Aggie*," I replied.

"Good for Canada," Steph said.

"And the deserters," I added.

"You'll be an outsider there," Rod replied. "And an outlaw here."

"Better than being dead, or crippled for life," I said.

"I've helped Jews escape from the Soviet Union," Rod added. "Their life is better outside Russia. They're not in prison. They're alive. But, it's not the same. They're refugees. They can never go home again. It's painful."

"I get it, but what choice do I have?"

"Proverbial rock and a hard place," Steph said.

"Exactly. Damned if I do, damned if I don't."

"You will always be a stranger, not a native son," Rod continued.

"Better than the alternative. I'll take my chances."

"It's such a shame governments force their people to choose between home and exile," Rod said. "The best we can do is help those who've made the decision to leave."

"Would you do that for me if I asked?"

"Without hesitation," Rod answered.

I knew that would be his answer. He had put his freedom, and perhaps his life, on the line helping Jews escape the Soviet Union. Known as "refuseniks," these people had been denied permission to emigrate, primarily to Israel, by the Soviet authorities. The reason given was they had access to state secrets at some point in their life and thus threatened national security if they left.

The rally was held on the quad. The three of us joined the crowd of almost 5,000. It wasn't a protest, but an informational session about the situation in Berkeley and issues related to UCD. Speakers represented the campus, Berkeley, People's Park, the SDS, and the BSU. The organizer of the rally called on the assembled to march to the admin building and ask for Chancellor-designate Meyer's support.

The crowd migrated, more than marched. We followed. A podium and sound system were set up, which was against campus regulations, and the organizer asked representatives of the administration, preferably Dean Meyer, to state their position on Berkeley. After the initial statements of positions were completed, Chancellor-designate Meyer appeared, mounted the podium, and told the assembled, "I am with you."

He supported the immediate withdrawal of troops from Berkeley and settlement of the dispute over People's Park. We cheered and applauded. None of us expected that, especially from a guy who had recently been appointed chancellor. He read the statement he promised to telegraph to Heyns, Reagan, and other officials. He recommended that classes scheduled for Friday and the coming Monday and Tuesday be boycotted and be used to conduct teach-ins, discussions, and dialogues about Berkeley and the other problems facing the University. He urged the faculty and the public to "listen to the youth; discuss what they have to say and above all respond intelligently to them." We seemed to have someone on our side. We'd have to see how long he would last. And the support would last.

That afternoon, the post-season, slow pitch playoffs began with two dorm teams, Emerson 1 (7-1) and Beckett 2 (5-2). The number one and number two teams in each division were also scheduled to play each other to determine who would represent that division.

On Friday, another rally was held on the quad with students from Berkeley and Davis addressing the crowd of approximately 2000. When the rally ended, almost 1500 students marched in a peaceful, orderly procession through downtown to awaken the community to what was happening in Berkeley. They handed out leaflets, clapped, and chanted, "Free Berkeley!" Troops Out!" and "Join the March!" There was a tense moment when the marchers encountered a line of Black Student Union and SDS students standing in the street facing them. They joined the demonstrators. The march ended at Central Park, where more speeches were delivered, after a moment of silence for James Rector.

That same day, Reagan reacted angrily to Meyer's support of the protest, telling reporters in Los Angeles, "This is the very kind of thing that precipitates more trouble, when those in charge and those with responsibility, adults, can, without any knowledge or understanding of the true facts, further incite this kind of activity."

On Saturday, the 28th annual California Relays were held in Modesto. Events started at 11 a.m. and continued into the evening. The muggy day featured marquee athletes like 1968 Olympians John Carlos and Charlie Greene of the U.S. and Australian Peter Norman, who finished behind Tommie Smith and ahead of Carlos in the 200 meters in Mexico City. Other notables included Bob Beamon, Willie Davenport, Bob Seagren, and Finland's Jorma Kinnunen. Most of the elite universities sent their relay teams, including Villanova, USC, UCLA, and Oregon.

The California State Junior College championships were held in tandem. The meet had its exciting moments and, despite a few meet records being broken, no world records were set, although the relays were known for that, having set twenty-two in past years. Carlos was named Athlete of the Meet after he won the 100 meters, the 200 meters, and anchored San Jose State's 440 relay team. There were 10,000 fans in attendance as the last events unfolded Saturday night. For the first time, the Relays were recorded and broadcast in color by KXTV Channel 10, our local CBS affiliate, on noon the next day. Track and field hall of famer Ralph Boston was the field event reporter.

The next day, KTXL Channel 40 in Sacramento ran a movie marathon in honor of the 62nd birthday of actor, John "Duke" Wayne, who was born May 26th, 1907. Most of the films they chose were ones he had done with director John Ford, including *Stagecoach*, *Fort Apache*, *3 Godfathers*, *The Quiet Man*, and *The Searchers*. They also showed pictures he had done without Ford, which included *The Alamo* and *The Green Berets*.

Like music, movies were a touchstone for me. A time machine. A way to conjure up memories. A way to re-experience past moments in my life. Watching a movie transported me back to who, what, where, when, or why I was. Good and bad. I was lost in the movie and the moment relived.

Joining me for this celluloid endurance run were two other John Wayne fans. Gover, Wally, and I hunkered down on the couch in our apartment. We had the place to ourselves, with plenty of junk food, beer, and a pint of Jim Beam.

"I'm so hungry I'm farting fresh air," Gover proclaimed.

"Keep it to yourself," Wally answered. I passed him the tin of smoked oysters.

As soon as we saw the Duke as the Ringo Kid in *Stagecoach*, holding his saddle, cocking his rifle, and halting the stage, Monument Valley stretching out behind him, we cheered and took a slug.

I had long admired the work of John Ford the director. I had long enjoyed John Wayne the actor, but not John Wayne the politician, who had become Orange County conservative. I would learn one day that Wayne's ultra-patriotism may have been the result of him not serving in World War II, due to his being older than draft age, his work commitments and schedule, as well as being a husband with young children. It was a fact that director Ford, who did serve, never let him forget. Wayne would later admit that America thrived on change; that as laws, ideologies, and mores changed, so did society. And that was a good thing. Over the years, I may have judged Wayne too harshly. He may have been more of a pacifist and realist than what I, or his public, saw.

The second film was *Fort Apache*, another western epic shot in Monument Valley and released in 1948, the year I was born. It was the first in Ford's "cavalry trilogy" that included *She Wore a Yellow Ribbon* and *Rio Grande*. As the end credits rolled, I made the mistake of saying what I was thinking.

"Reminds me of Vietnam," I said.

"Say what?" Wally replied.

"Henry Fonda's Lt. Col Thursday underestimated his enemy. Wayne's Captain York did not. He knew they couldn't win."

"We can win in Vietnam," Wally countered.

"Not if we don't know better who we're fighting and don't adapt better to the terrain we're fighting in."

"You're being too fucking introspective," Gover added, always the mediator.

"York spoke up," I went on. "He told the truth. Thursday didn't listen and paid for it."

"He did his duty," Wally said. "He put his country first. His honor second. His self last."

"Blind loyalty like that is bat-shit crazy. Doing his duty led to his death and the death of all his men."

"He followed orders."

"His by-the-book stubbornness was lethal."

"He obeyed the chain of command."

"It's okay to break that chain and admit when you're wrong."

"He died in service to his country."

"I'm sure that's a great comfort to his wife and daughter."

Gover broke into our debate and said, "I read something, or was told by someone, I don't know where, that the story and his character were based on Little Big Horn and Custer."

"Another man who didn't respect and fear the skill of the 'savages' he was ordered to exterminate," I said.

The movies Ford and Wayne made alone and together were also about what they believed it meant to be a man. I had seen nearly all their collaborations, as well as most of the Duke's films. It seemed like those old black and white war horses were playing all the time on Saturday afternoons on one of the local stations.

Next up was *3 Godfathers*. Also released in my birth year, it was a beautifully shot technicolor film that echoed the story of the birth of Christ and the Three Wise Men – a story of three tough, hardened outlaws trying to protect a mother and her child; three men protecting the weak and defenseless, regardless of the personal risk; three men trying to do the right thing.

"He didn't give up on his buddies," Wally said. "He was loyal to the end."

"He always was. In the movies, or real life," I said.

"They trusted him. And he trusted them," Wally said

"He kept his word," Gover said.

"Even though he could've been arrested, or hanged," I said.

"There's some things a man can't run away from," Wally added. I knew he was talking about more than the movie.

After that was *The Quiet Man*, Ford's homage to his Irish heritage. A western that wasn't a western. A talented cast, including Ward Bond, who was a regular in Ford's acting company.

"Hubba, Hubba," I said, as Wayne dragged Maureen O'Hara across the emerald fields of Inisfree.

"Ding, ding," Gover chanted.

"Chop, chop," Wally added.

"Camp Ti-Wa-Ya-Ee, great!" Gover finished.

"I was talking about Maureen O'Hara, not your Boy Scout camp," I said.

"She was a babe," Wally admitted.

"Ford liked casting strong women," I said.

"And the Duke liked starring with them," Gover said.

"But, he never got the girl," Wally said.

"That wasn't the point," I replied.

"He wouldn't fight the brother," Gover observed.

"Stayed true to who he was," Wally added.

"You don't have to resort to violence to win," I said.

"When he had to, when he had no choice, he did," Wally said. "And won her brother's and the town's respect."

"And the girl. This time," Gover said.

"I understand being strong when it's necessary, but I prefer being kind," I said.

"Wuss," Wally replied.

"Kiss my ass," I said.

"Looks like your face," Gover said. We lifted our cans in toast to the predictably typical exchange and drank.

"Faint heart never won the field," Wally said, surprising me with the mangled English proverb.

"But he sometimes won fair lady," I said, correctly finishing the proverb.

Following that was my favorite movie of theirs – *The Searchers*. The characters Ford created and Wayne portrayed were all about the rugged individualist. In many of their movies, we saw the delicate balance between the individual and the community; wilderness and wildness versus hearth and home. Wayne's character, Ethan Edwards, was the ultimate loner. A man bent on revenge. The last image of the picture was a memorable one. Wayne standing alone in the desert framed by the doorway of the homestead; a man destined to wander the outlands beyond civilization.

"Damn, that was brutal," I said.

"The Duke can act," Gover added.

"He's a different type of hero in this one," I said.

"A lot harder," Wally replied. "More real."

"Reminds me of a character he played in *Red River*, one of his earlier films," I said.

"How come they're not showing that?" Gover asked.

"It was done by a different director," I replied. "Howard Hawks."

"He couldn't be tamed," Wally added.

"He would always be an outsider," I said.

"An avenging angel," Wally observed.

"He was willing to kill his niece, Debbie, to save her," I said.

"But, he didn't. He took her home."

"Even though he was an honorable man, he was a racist," I said.

"They killed his family," Wally countered. "And Martha, his sister-in-law. The woman he loved. No wonder he hated the Comanch."

"The white man killed the sons of Scar, the warrior who captured Debbie," I replied. "No wonder he hated the white man."

"Eye for an eye," Wally said.

"Some reviewers thought Debbie was Martha's daughter, which is why he was so determined to find her," I said.

"Family is all that matters. It's everything," Wally said. "I'd do the same thing."

"Kill her?" I asked.

"Hell no," Wally answered. "Take her back."

"That act saved him," I said. "He found redemption."

"He couldn't save everyone," Wally added.

"He tried," Gover said.

"This time Ford showed both sides in good and bad light."

"It's complicated," Wally observed. "We fear what we don't know, or understand."

"He walked away," Gover said. "From family. From civilization."

"He became the loner," I said.

Then came *The Alamo*. A patriotic epic that nearly bankrupted and killed the Duke. He produced, directed, and starred in it. It was a huge production. As a result, his smoking habit skyrocketed. Even John Ford couldn't save this one, although he tried, without being asked, which created a nearly irreconcilable rift between the two men.

"That was bad," I said. "Too jingoistic for me."

"Those colors don't run," Walt replied. "They were badly outmanned and they failed, but they tried."

"Bad propaganda," I answered. "He probably assumed this movie could get the whole country to rally around the flag."

"His answer to the protestors who are running down our country, hoss," Wally said.

"Thanks, Merle," I replied.

"No different than our fight for independence," he answered.

"It was Mexico's land. We wanted it."

"Manifold destiny," Gover said, chuckling.

"Every fight we've ever been in has been a fight to protect American values," Walt argued. "It's about freedom and a person's right to make their own decisions."

"Study your history," was all I said.

"Up your chocolate speedway," Wally replied and smiled.

"Sure wasn't the story Disney told," I said.

"Sure wasn't Fess Parker," Gover added.

"He was prepared and willing to kill, even die," Wally answered. "Most men aren't. He was."

The last, and certainly the least, was *The Green Berets*. It was even more patriotic than *The Alamo*, which didn't seem possible. It was the Duke's attempt to convince America to remain in Vietnam until we had won. We broke out the Jim Beam for this one.

"Didn't we see this at the Starlight Drive-in?" I asked Gover.

"We did," he answered.

"Didn't we drink Jim Beam just like the Duke?"

"We did."

"Didn't we do some damage to our bodies?"

"We did."

"Didn't you and Gant do some damage to our apartment doing the same thing while watching the same movie last February?"

"I know nothing," he replied, imitating Sergeant Schultz's line from the TV show, *Hogan's Heroes*.

"It's sad," I said.

"What's that?" Wally asked.

"The Duke let his politics destroy his craft."

"Could say the same about Peter Fonda," Wally countered.

"Not in the same class," I replied.

"Big John is balancing out the lefties in Hollywood," Wally said.

"Too heavy-handed."

"Sometimes that's what it takes."

"It's too black and white."

"No, it's color," Gover said.

"Too cut and dried. Too simplistic. Our goal is noble. Their's isn't. We're squeaky clean. They're slime balls."

"He was trying to tell the rest of the story."

"Like Leni Riefenstahl," I said.

"Who?" Gover asked.

"She did films for Hitler."

"Not the same," Wally answered.

"Anyone who's been to war isn't ready to start one," I countered. "That's how my dad felt."

"*Semper fi*," Wally said.

"It's how he would have felt about Vietnam, too. It's not World War II. We're the oppressors. They're dying for their freedom. For their country. For what they believe in. We can't say that. This movie and this war are both about pride and glory. We can't win. We need to admit it and admit we're wrong. That's the right thing to do."

"There's nothing wrong with pride," Wally said.

"*Hubris* has been the downfall of many men better than you or me or the Duke, and countries greater than ours," I argued.

"I'll always be better than you," Gover said.

"Me, too," Wally added.

With that, they both jumped on top of me, kicking off the wrestling match that generally seemed to end these get-togethers.

On Monday, a mass march on the state capital was staged by students from all UC campuses. An informational meeting had been held at Freeborn on Sunday night, laying out the details. Luci and I attended the meeting. She went to the march with one or two of her sketchy friends. I skipped it because I was worried about finals.

All nine UC campuses and many of the Northern California state colleges were represented at the rally. Nearly 10,000 concerned students assembled to confront Reagan and the legislature. Most of the students came from the Sacramento and Davis areas. Linus Pauling was one of many speakers. The march was well-organized and uneventful.

The next day, during an impromptu news conference following a luncheon speech, Governor Reagan made a statement about what Chancellor-designate Meyer had said and done in support of the strike. In barely controlled anger, he said, "I just can't find the words to express my contempt for them and for what they're doing. Some kind of action must be taken." Reagan was all bluster. Meyer would officially become our new chancellor on July 1st.

That Wednesday, Bill Graham hosted the all-day People's Park Bail Ball benefit concert at Winterland. The show featured the Grateful Dead, Santana Blues Band, Jefferson Airplane, and Creedence Clearwater Revival, which was now one of the hottest bands in America.

Winterland Ballroom was the old Ice Capades auditorium located at Post and Steiner off Geary. It was built in 1928 as the New Dreamland Auditorium. In 1936, it began hosting the Shipstads and Johnson Ice Follies. Bill Graham rented the venue for concerts that were too big for the Fillmore Auditorium, which was located at Fillmore and Geary. The first show at Winterland was September 23rd, 1966, with a double bill of Jefferson Airplane and the Paul Butterfield Blues Band. There was always a long line on the sidewalk outside Winterland, with dealers selling a variety of drugs, as people got there early to get good seats on the hardwood floor in front of the stage. There were regular seats above and behind, but they weren't as good as the ground floor.

The Fillmore Auditorium was another concert site Graham used to stage shows. It had been built in 1910 as a dance hall. It was used for socials and balls through the 1930s and became a roller rink in the 1940s. In 1952, Charles Sullivan, the new owner and one of the most successful African-American businessmen in San Francisco, renamed it the Fillmore Auditorium and booked the more popular African-American musical acts, including James Brown and Ike & Tina Turner. In 1965, Graham, who was the manager of the San Francisco Mime Troupe, produced a benefit for the Troupe to help pay the legal bills of one of its founders. The Warlocks, who became the Grateful Dead, opened for the Jefferson Airplane. That benefit launched Graham's career as a promoter. In the summer of 1968, faced with the venue's limited capacity and the deterioration of the neighborhood, Graham bought the old Carousel Ballroom on South Van Ness near Market, renamed it Fillmore West, and continued booking rock acts like the Dead and Airplane, jazz pioneers like Miles Davis, comedians like Lenny Bruce, soul singers like Otis Redding, and poetry. It was an eclectic mix.

Bill Graham was born Wulf Wolodia Grajonca in Berlin in 1931, the son of Russian Jews. His family nicknamed him "Wolfgang." Graham escaped the Nazi purge and landed in a foster home in the Bronx. He graduated from DeWitt Clinton High School and City College. He served in Korea, winning the Bronze Star and Purple Heart. In the early 1960s, he moved from New York to San Francisco, where his sister Rita lived. After attending a free concert in Golden Gate Park, he met the members of the San Francisco Mime Troupe. Following the benefit at the Fillmore, Graham became more actively involved in promoting concerts, first with Chet Helms and the Family Dog and then on his own.

Our first playoff game was the first game that same day. We beat Joxxalott 14 – 10 and immediately played Gringo Gorps, the winner of their division. We lost a squeaker, 3 – 2. Rick Meade, Dan Wettstein, and Emry Allen paced the win for the Gorps, while Pete Champany pitched a great game. Our season was over.

CHAPTER 32

Two days later, we celebrated the Memorial Day holiday.

Memorial Day was originally called Decoration Day, because people would visit cemeteries and decorate the graves of those who had died. It was a way for families to come together to honor the deceased. It was believed that the origin of what we now know as Memorial Day was associated with a desire to honor the Union soldiers who had died during the Civil War, in much the same way that Southern states had honored the fallen soldiers of the Confederacy.

The site of the first of these solemn celebrations was debatable. Some historians have written that the first Memorial Day took place on May 1st, 1865, in Charleston, South Carolina. It was initiated by former slaves who wanted to honor Union soldiers who had died in a Confederate prison camp and been buried in a mass grave. They exhumed the bodies and gave them a respectful burial. When it was done, they held a parade, marching, singing, and celebrating the men who had died so they could be free. Other historians claimed the first day of remembrance was held on April 5th, 1867, in Carbondale, Illinois. The citizens gathered to hear marching bands and speeches honoring soldiers who died in the Civil War on both sides, since the southern part of Illinois had many settlers who fought for the Confederacy. The graves of soldiers from the North and South were decorated to "bind up the wounds of the living."

On May 5th, 1868, General John Logan, national commander of the Grand Army of the Republic, in his General Order No. 11, proclaimed, "The 30th of May, 1868, is designated for the purpose of strewing with flowers, or otherwise decorating the graves of comrades who died in defense of their country during the late rebellion, and whose bodies now lie in almost every city, village and hamlet churchyard in the land." He called it Decoration Day and, when asked, said he chose the date because it wasn't the anniversary of any particular battle.

General James Garfield spoke at the first Decoration Day, which was held at Arlington National Cemetery. It was estimated that 5,000 people attended and later decorated the graves of 20,000 Union and Confederate soldiers. The first state to recognize the holiday was New York in 1873. All the northern states recognized it by 1890. The southern states refused to participate, choosing to honor their dead on different days. Following World War I, the holiday was officially revised to honor all Americans who died in any war or military action. Memorial Day was henceforth to be celebrated on May 30th, regardless of the day of the week. Several southern states still held a separate day to honor the Confederate war dead. In 1968, the Uniform Monday Holiday Act was passed in an effort to use federal holidays to create three-day weekends. Holidays like Labor Day and Memorial Day would be celebrated on a Monday. It wouldn't go into effect until 1971.

This year, May 30th was a Friday. Memorial Day was considered by many, including me, to be the start of the summer vacation season.

It also reminded me of my Dad and the Indy 500. I would always recall him tracking each lap of the race by hand, while he puttered around in the yard, or barbecued dinner. After he was gone, I would listen to the start of the race on the radio or TV to honor his memory.

Berkeley celebrated Memorial Day with another march. "Peace" was the word as more than 30,000 marchers took to the streets. Unlike the other demonstrations, this one was permitted. The flyer announcing the march read, "DEMAND THAT THE FENCE BE TORN DOWN! On Friday, May 30, Memorial Day, come to Berkeley to join the mass protest against the killing, blinding, beating and jailing of our brothers and sisters. Join the march to demand amnesty and the immediate end of bayonet and shotgun rule."

With that announcement, Alameda County Sheriff Frank Madigan and Governor Ronald Reagan promised that they would use whatever force was necessary, including shotguns again, if things got out of control. Fearing more violence, the community helped the march organizers train marshals to keep the demonstration peaceful. Quakers handed out fresh-cut daisies to the citizens who marched to protest the occupation of the city, some on foot and some on bikes. Local women poured glasses of tea and Kool-Aid. Music blared from balconies overlooking the street. The protestors surrounded the park. sticking daisies in the fence, or in the National Guardsmen's rifle muzzles. The march was peaceful. There were a few scattered incidents, but nothing serious. The day ended with live music, as wine and joints floated through the crowd. Spectators cooled off the marchers with garden hoses. The predicted bloodbath became a love-in.

The National Guard didn't leave. Over the next few weeks, they patrolled the streets day and night, breaking up any gatherings of four or more people. Things finally quieted down. Perhaps with summer approaching and school about to end, the fire of People's Park was dying out. There had been no violence or attempts to tear down the fence, so Reagan ordered the Guard to withdraw.

John Lennon added his voice to the noise. He and Yoko were in the middle of a bed-in on the 19th floor of the Queen Elizabeth Hotel in Montreal, which had started at midnight on Monday, May 26th. Police lined the hotel hallway, keeping teeny-boppers and the press at bay. Inside, the suite overflowed with friends and fans, as well as pink and white carnations, empty glasses and plates, and film gear, brought along with two members of a film crew. On a side table sat Vladimir Nabokov's *The Defence* and Jacqueline Susann's *The Love Machine*. Lennon patiently and humorously answered the reporters' questions about their intentions. "The whole effect of our bed-ins has made people talk about peace," Lennon explained. "But it must be done by non-violent means . . . otherwise there can only be chaos."

On the 29th, he spoke by telephone with KYA and with KSAN's Scoop Nisker, who signed off his news broadcasts with the line, "If you don't like the news . . . go out and make some of your own." Nisker had followed Tom Donahue from KMPX, where he had created experimental news collages and gave counterculturists like Allen Ginsberg and Abbie Hoffman access they'd never had. Earlier in May, Nisker had spoken live on the phone with Lennon when John and Yoko were in Toronto. When he asked Lennon if he had anything to say to the demonstrators, Lennon answered, "Tell them all to be peaceful. We don't want any fightin' going on at People's Park."

Nisker had also been wandering the streets of Berkeley with a tape recorder talking to the people. He recalled meeting three longhairs suited up for battle. Each wore a football helmet to protect their head and heavy gloves in case they needed to lob canisters of tear gas back at the cops. Prior to joining the fray, they dropped a tab of acid, did a group hug, and charged into battle. True revolutionaries.

The next day, with the big rally in Berkeley in full swing, Lennon phoned KPFA in Berkeley twice to see what was happening and to urge the marchers to keep it peaceful. "You've got to do it peacefully," he said. "There's no cause worth losing your life for, there isn't any path worth getting shot for and you can do better by moving on to another city." When asked what he would do if he were there, he said, "I'd be urging a music festival to take place. Sing 'Hare Krishna' or something, but don't move around if it aggravates the pigs. Don't get hassled by the cops and don't play their games. I know it's hard, Christ you know it ain't easy, you know how hard it can be. But everything's hard. It's better to have it hard than not have it at all." He told KPFA that people around the world were on the side of People's Park. "But you can't do it with violent means. That won't accomplish anything. Keep it peaceful. Violence is what has kept mankind from getting together for centuries."

Lennon had quoted lines from a new Beatles' single, "The Ballad of John and Yoko," which had released the same day. Although he deeply believed in many things that ran counter to the mainstream, he couldn't resist plugging his new record.

Before they left Montreal and their bed, they would record "Give Peace a Chance." The inspiration for the song was Lennon's constant refrain of "give peace a chance," in answer to questions about what he hoped to achieve with the bed-in. Four microphones and a four-track tape recorder were rented for a spontaneous session. In the room and/or singing or playing along were Timothy Leary, Petula Clark, Dick Gregory, Allen Ginsberg, Murray the K, and Tommy Smothers.

The last day of May was a Saturday. We never needed an excuse to party, but since it was the last Saturday before we had to get serious about finals, we elected to tip a few. Gover went to Wally's to fire it up, while I wrapped up the project for the textiles class. Luci had created this beautiful sunburst tie-dyed wall hanging. I had written a short narrative chronicling the process based on the Tim Buckley song, "Goodbye and Hello." I wanted to make a few changes before turning it in. Anal, as usual.

I stood outside Wally's apartment door, surprised by how quiet it seemed. I knocked and walked in. Silhouetted against the sliding glass balcony doors in the small living room, Wally sat alone in a chair. Gover sat to his left on the couch set against the side wall. I walked through the narrow kitchen and stopped at the edge of the living room.

Wally was staring straight at the wall beside me, where a dart board hung. His face was stone, his eyes obsidian. He guzzled a beer and handed it to Gover, who stacked it on top of several other cans forming a pyramid between them.

"Another one," he said. Gover handed him a Golden Crown, which was the cheap beer we drank because we could afford it. That and Lucky Lager.

"What's up?" I asked Gover.

"He heard a good buddy got hit in 'Nam."

"Shit. He okay?"

"They don't know. They medevac'd him to the Philippines."

"How long he been at it?"

"He heard this morning."

"And he's still standing?"

"He's too pissed to be pissed."

Wally finished off the last one, gave it to Gover, who placed it at the top of the pyramid. "Let's go," Wally said, as he stood. Gover stood, too.

"Where we going?" I asked.

"All the usual places," Gover replied. "He wants to hit something."

"Or somebody," I said.

Wally pivoted left and punched a hole in the side wall. "We're burning daylight," he said.

We kicked things off at The Club, which was an old school bar on G Street, downtown. After that, it was on to the Antique Bizarre. And Blake's. Our final destination was The Silo, which is where all the cowboys and the frat boys from AGR, the ag fraternity, congregated. Two of Wally's buddies were playing in a country band called Powder River. I tagged along because I was the responsible one. I could keep Wally from spiraling too deep since Gover would be right in there with him, shoulder-to-shoulder, which is the way it had been from the first time they met.

The Club had been around since the Fifties. It was where the serious drinkers went to drink. And the bikers. It had two pool tables and a card room in the rear, where the old-timers played poker. The police station was out back across the alley, so things never got too out of hand. The smoke was thick that night. The bikers were running the tables. We moved on.

To the Antique Bizarre, better known as the Antique Bi-arre because the "z" had gone missing. The ground floor was the bar, topped by the Hotel Aggie. Two grad students from the Primate Center drank here. We knew that because we'd played softball against them. Terry Maple and Gary Mitchell were bona fide wild men. That probably came from hanging out with chimps. They tried to calm Wally with shots of tequila. That's the way they thought. Wally got quieter, his eyes darker. I knew this wasn't going to end well. The last time I'd seen him like this was at the Grand National Rodeo at the Cow Palace in San Francisco. He'd gotten totally shit-faced over a girl and we'd decided the rodeo would be a good place to shake it off. It wasn't. I had to get between him and a cowboy, once at the beer stand and once in the bathroom. I pushed him out the door, into the car, and back to Davis. Things were feeling eerily similar.

The Silo was packed. It was an old, wood-shingled building that dated back to the original campus. Built in 1908, it was one of the first built at the University Farm. Located on the south part of the campus near the Physical Sciences and Engineering buildings, it was first used as a dairy barn. In 1965, it was converted to a snack bar and recreation center. It was the place where the cowboys hung their hats. There was no room and even less air. Ripe for misunderstanding. Couples were jitterbugging, doing the swing, or free-forming it.

Powder River was powering through "Swinging Doors" by Merle Haggard, ominous and an omen. Wally wanted to say hello to Burke Tarleton and Dave Hammond, the two he knew in the band, so he shoved his way through the crowd. That pissed off a few bystanders. But, one glance told them Wally wasn't in the mood to say, "Pardon me" or "Excuse me." All but one guy. He was bigger than Wally. He was cradling a long-neck at his waist on one side and a buckle bunny on the other. Alcohol wasn't allowed on campus, but that didn't stop students, or non-students in this case, from smuggling in a few. The frat was supposed to police their own event, but didn't. I'm not sure where the advisors were.

Wally drunkenly waved his arm to get the boys in the band's attention. As he did, he knocked the cowboy's Stetson off his head. If you know anything about cowboys, you didn't mess with their horses, their gals, or their hats. The guy's horse was probably back home in Dixon, his girlfriend was giggling, and his hat lay on the sawdust-covered floor. Wally had found what he'd been looking for ever since he had gotten the bad news. The cowboy slowly released his girl, gave her the bottle, and looked down at what had been a pristine, cream-colored hat. He turned to face Wally.

"Pick it up," he said.

"Sure thing, *amigo*," Wally answered. Wally grabbed the hat by the crown, carefully dusted it off with his hand, stepped in front of the cowboy and placed the hat on his girlfriend's head. I stepped in between them, my back to Wally. Gover grabbed both Wally's arms and spun him around. I carefully removed the hat from the young lady's head and handed it to the cowboy.

"Sorry, friend. My *compadre* here got some bad news from his family today. He's just blowing off some steam."

"Get him out of here."

"Will do." I said and, backing up, turned to follow Wally and Gover out into the cool night air. Gover was having a tough time keeping Wally from knocking him out and going back inside.

"Cool it, dumb shit!" I yelled. "What would your family think?" That didn't stop him. "Or your friend? The one you think you're doing this for." That stopped him cold. The stone face softened. The smoldering eyes dimmed. He spun around and staggered off toward where he thought we left the car.

CHAPTER 33

"All the News that Fits" – June Edition

The last episode of *Star Trek* airs on NBC. Joe Namath resigns from pro football after Commissioner Pete Rozelle orders him to sell his stake in a New York bar. Brian Jones quits the Rolling Stones and is replaced by Mick Taylor. Mickey Mantle's number is retired. *The Smothers Brothers Comedy Hour* broadcasts its last show after being cancelled by CBS. *Hee Haw* with Roy Clark and Buck Owens premieres on CBS. At their graduation, Berkeley students walk out chanting, "Power to the people!" *Oh! Calcutta* opens in New York City. The Students for a Democratic Society (SDS) holds its convention in Chicago, with the radical Weatherman faction gaining control. More than 150,000 attend the Newport '69 festival, which features an appearance by Jimi Hendrix. Georges Pompidou is sworn in as the president of France. Warren Burger succeeds Earl Warren as chief justice of the Supreme Court. The heavily polluted Cuyahoga River catches fire in Cleveland. New York police raid the Stonewall gay bar in Greenwich Village, sparking riots that will last three days. Singer Judy Garland dies. *Life* magazine publishes photographs of the 242 Americans killed in Vietnam during one week in May. New book releases include *The Waves of Night* by Mark Petrakis; *The Death Committee*, Noah Gordon; *Robert Kennedy: A Memoir*, Jack Newfield; *Norma Jean*, Fred Guiles; *The Kingdom and the Power*, Gay Talese; and *An Unfinished Woman* by Lillian Hellman. *Promenade*; *Whores, Wars and Tin Pan Alley*; and a revival of *Oklahoma!* open on stage. New films include John Wayne's *True Grit*; *Che!* starring Omar Sharif; Sam Peckinpah's *The Wild Bunch*; *Chastity* featuring Cher in her first film; and Rowan and Martin's *The Maltese Bippy*. New music includes *From Elvis in Memphis*, Johnny Cash's *At San Quentin*, Three Dog Night's *Suitable for Framing*, the Steve Miller Band's *Brave New World*, and Deep Purple's *Deep Purple*.

The summer issue of *The California Aggie* came out on Monday, June 2nd. It was time to say goodbye to academic year 1969 and wish everyone a relaxing summer. It was at that moment the end of school became real. I would miss the paper's goofy cartoons and the weekly intramural sports updates. We'd meet again come the first Monday in October.

The final game of the softball season took place that afternoon. Sigma Phi Epsilon's "A" team and Leper Colony were the last two teams standing in the post-season playoffs. They met for the all-campus title at 5:30 on I.M. Field 5. The Lepers, the number two team on campus, had beaten a scrappy Gringo Gorps 11 – 10. The Colony then defeated Bixby 4, the dorm champion, 14 – 8, while the Sig Eps' A Team beat the Sig Eps' B Team 13 – 12 to win the fraternity division. Sig Ep repeated what they had done during the all-campus tourney, defeating the Colony to become champ.

My last class was that Friday. It was time to study for finals. I was feeling good about my grades for the quarter, except for physical geography. Although I was taking that class pass/fail, it couldn't hurt to put in a few more hours, especially because I had a GPA to maintain to keep my scholarships and my 2-S.

The Sunday before finals, I'd spent too many hours in Olsen. I needed a break. I needed to smell something other than concrete.

Luci smelled good. I was inhaling her. We'd slept together. She'd showered. We'd both dressed. We sat cross-legged on the bed, facing each other. Something about her was different. Something I hadn't noticed in my horny rush to get her into bed. She didn't look quite the same and I couldn't pinpoint what it was.

"Why didn't you invite me?" I asked.

"Because you're not committed enough." she said. "Mike Walt was."

She was right, I wasn't. She had informed me that she and Walt had attended a meeting of the SDS.

"They're terrorists," I said. "They're doing all kinds of crazy shit."

"You should understand that. You've studied the *Narodnaya Volya* terrorists in Russia."

"That's for a class. Purely academic. I don't plan on killing a Tsar like they did."

"It worked."

"No, it didn't."

"It shook things up."

"That it did. And opened the door for Lenin and the Bolsheviks. I wish people would study history instead of just reading headlines."

"That's all the SDS wants to do. Moderation and conversation aren't working. It's time for action. Time to disrupt things."

"Wally's up for that?"

"He's all in."

"He's from a family of Marines."

"Losing a very good friend changed his perspective."

I stood to go. I turned back. "I really hope you don't plan to do anything stupid. I like having you both around," I said.

"No promises."

I realized what was different. Her hair. It wasn't dyed anymore. It was short. Twiggy-short. The fringed, Earth Mother look had been replaced by militant black Levi's, T-shirt, and jacket.

When I returned to the apartment that evening, the boys were watching the news. Nixon had flown to meet South Vietnamese President Nguyen Van Thieu on the island of Midway. In their joint press conference, the President said 25,000 U.S. troops would leave Vietnam by the end of August. Thieu looked like someone had kicked him in the nuts. He knew this was the end. Of his regime and possibly him. Without the United States backstopping his corrupt government, he wasn't long for the world. I suspected he had already calculated where he would seek asylum and had stashed enough cash to live comfortably the rest of his life. Nixon and Thieu went on to emphasize that South Vietnamese forces would replace American forces. Nixon said we would "increase the combat capability of the Republic of Vietnam Armed Forces so the South Vietnamese would eventually be able to assume full responsibility for the war." More troops out, more money in. I wondered if we'd ever escape the mire.

The other story that night that was significant to me because it involved my childhood hero. Mickey Mantle had given a "farewell" speech at Yankee Stadium earlier that day. Mantle's wife, mother, and mother-in-law were in attendance and received recognition at the ceremony held to honor him. The day was declared "Mickey Mantle Day" by New York's Mayor John Lindsey, and the Yankees retired the number seven worn by Mantle. The only other numbers that had been retired were three, four and five – for Babe Ruth, Lou Gehrig, and Joe DiMaggio. Ruth and Gehrig were assigned those numbers because that's where they hit in the batting order when numbers were first added to uniforms in 1929. When DiMaggio came up in 1936, he was assigned number nine because number five was worn by Frank Crosetti. The next year, DiMaggio was given number five, which he would wear the rest of his career, and Crosetti was given number one.

Mantle's teammates were introduced and milestones from his career recounted. Frank Messer, the Yankees broadcaster and the event's master of ceremonies, introduced Mel Allen, the "Voice of the Yankees," who Introduced Mantle, "Ladies and gentlemen, a magnificent Yankee, the great number seven, Mickey Mantle." An ovation lasting several minutes followed. "When I walked into this stadium 18 years ago," Mantle said in his speech, "I felt much the same way I do right now. I don't have words to describe how I felt then or how I feel now, but I'll tell you one thing, baseball was real good to me and playing 18 years in Yankee Stadium is the best thing that could ever happen to a ballplayer." It was a day to remember.

When the news broadcast ended, I went to my bedroom cell and flipped on KDVS. Tyree was playing a set of Rolling Stones' music. The reason became apparent when he announced that a guitarist named Mick Taylor had replaced Brian Jones, who had been kicked out of the band he founded and named. Taylor was a young, hotshot guitar slinger, who had previously been a part of John Mayall's Bluesbreakers. Mayall's band was an incubator for British musicians. Eric Clapton and Jack Bruce of Cream, as well as Mick Fleetwood and John McVie of Fleetwood Mac, all played with Mayall. Tyree added that the Rolling Stones were gearing up for a tour of the states. I was a Beatles fan, but Kelly and Luci loved the nasty boys of rock. The Stones were rehearsing to roll.

When I put together my class schedule at the beginning of each quarter, I did it with an eye toward finishing finals as early as possible. I wanted to be done and gone. This year that was especially important. I wanted to get home for a number of reasons. It was summer. My little brother Willy had a Babe Ruth game on Thursday. And Father's Day was on Sunday.

The historical thought course, as well as the Soviet and English history classes, went well. Physical geography was a bear. I didn't feel good about that one. The textiles class wasn't graded because I'd audited it. I left self-addressed postcards for all but textiles; reluctantly for geography.

Another reason I scheduled early classes was so I could be back at the apartment for *Jeopardy*. Hosted by Art Fleming, it aired at noon each weekday. The show was originally conceived of and developed by Merv Griffin. I was a trivia freak, so I never missed a show if I could help it. I also tried to watch *Concentration*, with host Bob Clayton; *Hollywood Squares*, emceed by Peter Marshall; and *Match Game*, hosted by Gene Rayburn. All four shows aired on NBC. I tried to wrangle Gary or Gover to watch it with me so we could duke it out. As I got to know Steph better, he and I would watch it together. We had some heroic battles.

CHAPTER 34

Thursday morning I was up, packed, and out the door. Threlfall was at his girlfriend's, so I'd had a good night's sleep. Slevin's door was shut. Gover was sitting on the couch, chain-smoking, drinking coffee, and looking rough. He had two finals to go, with chem being one of them. I did not envy his next two days. I waved and headed for Ugly Orange. He'd catch a ride with one of our Modesto friends when he was done.

It was a beautiful summer's drive along the delta. Very different from my trip last January. Everything was in bloom. The air was balmy. The river flowed gently onward. The road ahead was empty. The song playing on the radio was "All Summer Long" by the Beach Boys. I should have been feeling nice and mellow. But, I wasn't. There were many things swirling around inside my head. I needed to figure out where things were with Kelly. I had no idea what was going on with Luci. Walt was freaking me out. My draft status was up in the air. Decisions, or at least choices, needed to be made.

I got home in time to dump my dirty laundry, which made Mom happy, I thought, toss my things on the bed, call Gary to meet me at Willy's game, and jump back into Ugly Orange. I'd say hello to my stepdad when I got there because he was the coach.

The game was at Enslen Park. Foster Farms sponsored the team, which competed in the National League division. When I had played and Dad coached Tim and me, we were sponsored by Gene Thomas Trailer Sales. Paul had become coach when Willy turned 13 and was eligible to play Babe Ruth. He was now 15 and in his third and last season. He would turn 16 in November.

Several of Willy's high school friends were on the team, including Jon Rowland and Tim Venn. Mom was at the game. She never missed one and never let the opposing team get away with anything. She was generally dogging the coach, the players and, especially, the umpires. One of her favorite phrases to yell at the other team's pitcher or batter was, "Your mother wears army shoes." The phrase originated during World War II when prostitutes followed American troops, dispensing sexual favors and sometimes receiving shoes, boots, or other items in return. Rather crudely, it meant your mom was a whore and you were a son of a bitch. Probably was something Mom shouldn't have said, but it rattled the poor kids. She got some help from Gary's sister,

Ken White

Lucy, who made a few games.

Tim and Laura sat at the top of the wooden bleachers. Gary and I sat below them. Jeff Bellotti, a neighborhood kid and younger brother of a classmate, was umpiring. Jeff's father had tried to get me tickets to see the World Series in 1962, when I was trying hard to connect Dad with Mickey Mantle. Mom was teasing him mercilessly. Between innings, Rowland and Venn goofed around for the crowd. They were both good athletes, but enjoyed playing grab ass, as much as they enjoyed playing ball. Willy played short and batted third. He was having a good year. He was batting .714, a Cooperstown number. He ended up going three for three, Paul Lehfeldt pitched a no-hitter, and Fosters won. We celebrated with bottles of RC Cola and Orange Nehi.

Friday night, Gary and I went to see John Wayne's latest movie, *True Grit*, at the Briggsmore Theatre. The Duke was back. He had returned to the complicated loner he had played in *Red River* and *The Searchers*. It was a role that combined many of the characteristics of the best Ford and Wayne creations. This time, there was an added dimension. He was able to make fun of himself. The scowl had been turned upside down. He was more like Falstaff than Henry IV, Bottom rather than Richard III. He was taking direct aim at his iconic macho image. His character, U.S. Marshal Reuben J. "Rooster" Cogburn, even wore an eye patch. A salute to his old friend and mentor, the Coach – John Ford.

The cast also included Dennis Hopper, who had co-starred in *Easy Rider*. In casting, Wayne may have been following the old adage about keeping your friends close, and your enemies closer. The screenwriter was Marguerite Roberts, who had been blacklisted when she refused to testify before McCarthy's House Un-American Activities Committee. The old Reagan Republican was mellowing. *True Grit* was a movie about persistence and trust, loyalty and forgiveness, even stubbornness, which Wayne's characters were sometimes known for. As he did in *3 Godfathers* and *The Searchers*, Wayne's character risked his own life to protect and save the life of the young girl, Mattie Ross, played by Kim Darby. Mattie had hired Cogburn to find the man who killed her father. There was a memorable bit of dialogue between Cogburn and Lucky Ned Pepper, the leader of the outlaw gang, played by Robert Duvall.

Rooster Cogburn: I mean to kill you in one minute, Ned. Or see you hanged in Fort Smith at Judge Parker's convenience. Which'll it be?
Ned Pepper: I call that bold talk for a one-eyed fat man.
Rooster Cogburn: Fill your hand, you son of a bitch!

True to Joseph Campbell's hero's journey, Wayne had most often played the reluctant hero, refusing to leave his ordinary world and embark on the adventure he had been challenged to take. This was true in *Stagecoach* and again in *True Grit*. He had come full circle. There was some serious Oscar buzz about his role. I thought liberal Hollywood might finally award the archconservative Wayne for this role specifically and his body of work in general. Stranger things had happened.

On Saturday night, as I pulled away from the house, I heard a deuce coupe rumbling out Paradise Road far, far away. School was done for the summer. The mechanized, mobile mating ritual known as cruising had begun.

I was feeling nostalgic. I wanted to hit the streets and join the cruisers. Ugly Orange would fit right in. I was needing to revisit the places that reminded me of a time when cruising was king, the world was simpler, and the music was sweeter. I had dragged Tenth Street and cruised McHenry many times since hearing the history lesson about the ritual from Mr. George Lucas back in '62 and then getting my license to finally experience what he was talking about. It was just another slow night in Modesto. I was chasing blondes in white cars. The Wolfman was on the radio, live from XERB in Tijuana, Mexico. Me and The Wolfman had met before. At Burge's Drive-in, while my father lay dying in his hospital bed. I wanted to send a dedication to Dad, hoping it would inspire him to keep fighting. The Wolfman made it happen. It didn't work. But, the Wolfman did what he did best.

The history of "dragging Tenth" and "cruising" dated back to the end of World War II. The GIs came home. They had time and energy. They needed wheels to get around. The rations on fuel, rubber, and metal had been lifted. Gas, tires and cars were available so the young men could drive. For no reason at all.

California played an important role in the birth of a national "car culture" after the war. GIs moved west, suburban housing boomed, and freeway construction expanded. This all fueled greater mobility and freedom for residents of the Golden State. In the '50s, the stylings of cars reflected the new wealth and confidence of a growing, prospering America. The tailfins, the chrome, and the flash were seductive and cars became an important status symbol. By mid-century, powerful and flashy automobiles became vital aspects of a regional youth culture that emphasized being "cool." They were badges of working-class and middle-class prosperity, mobility, and freedom. Like Kerouac, for them there was something hallowed and righteous about the open road, driving, and speed. It was freeing. There were no responsibilities.

No destinations. No end point. The world couldn't touch you, even if it could catch you. Rods and customs made them rebels with a cause – mutinying against conformity.

The '50s were also a time when cars were built not bought; chopped, rebuilt, and modified as a hobby. Motorheads who were into cars did their own customizing, rebuilt the engines, and transformed these labors of love into showpieces. They stripped anything unnecessary and hopped up the engines. Some found old jalopies, chopped-and-channeled them, tuck-and-rolled them, and hit the strip to show them. Others found motorcycles and tricked them out. Deserts and flatlands provided the perfect environment for many to strut their "souped-up" Model T's and Model A's.

Teenagers in California had disposable incomes, leisure time, and cars, so they cruised. The streets of Central Valley towns like Fresno, Bakersfield, and Modesto were popular places for the nightly rituals of drag racing, cruising, or simply hanging out.

A writer for *The Modesto Bee* described "the Drag" in 1956, "A night on the drag begins sometime between 7 and 8 o'clock. It starts slowly with just a few cars. The momentum picks up by the minute. Soon there are between 100 and 200 cars 'dragging.' On Saturday nights, maybe 300. The scene has a weird and almost hypnotic effect. Hundreds of cars loaded with even more teenagers running in merry-go-round fashion over the same path . . ."

The commonly accepted source of the word "drag" had to do with where the race took place, which was the "main drag" through town. "Drag racing" was born in the dry lake beds of the California deserts. Following the war, as engines got bigger, better, and faster, a bunch of kids with cars, hanging out with nowhere in particular to go, turned the hobby of drag racing into something more serious. Although it became more popular, it remained underground. Abandoned military runways, or dry lake beds like Muroc in the Mojave Desert, became popular locations for informal races, usually for boasting rights, occasionally for money, and sometimes for pink slips. The first official event took place sometime in 1949 at the Goleta Air Base near Santa Barbara, California.

The name "draggin' Tenth" originated in Modesto as drivers would drag race from one traffic light to the next on Tenth Street. Hand-signals were used at the intersections – one finger for a first gear race to the next light, or two for a second gear race. Most of the people that drag raced downtown never really experienced the real drag racing that occurred on the deserted straightaways on the edge of town.

The original cruise route started at Burge's Drive-in on Ninth Street, which was also Highway 99, and O Street, up to Tenth, a right, out Tenth, then a turnaround at the Modesto Fire Station block between F and G Streets, back down Tenth, a left on O, and back to Burge's.

Before 1957, Tenth and Eleventh Streets were two-way streets. Drivers could stop and give a hard time to the driver of the car in the opposite lane. In 1957, because of the congestion and to discourage cruising, the city made Tenth and Eleventh one-way streets, with Tenth heading south and Eleventh heading north. It didn't work. All it did was create a large loop. Cruising became even more popular.

Back then, the boys filled up their cars with 30-cent a gallon gas and hoped their girlfriends had enough money to get some food at the drive-in. People would come from across the region to drag. Boys and girls motored in from Oakdale, Turlock, Hilmar, and surrounding areas to see and be seen on Tenth and Eleventh Streets in downtown Modesto.

You didn't need to be a driver, or even be in your car, to enjoy the drag. Many parked their cars in one spot and watched. One of the most popular places to hang out was the Lucky Grocery Store parking lot on Tenth between L and M, which was perfectly positioned to see everyone driving by. Others walked up and down the strip. All witnessing the show and waiting for the cruise to draw to a close at the end of the night.

For a handful of daredevils, the true dragging occurred on deserted straightaways around the Modesto area. Although drag racing was illegal and dangerous, it was still regularly practiced on the long straight roads and streets on the outskirts of town, outside police jurisdiction. The proximity of downtown to country roads made it easy to arrange a quick pick-up race.

There were also a variety of service stations where the cars would get tuned up before the races, and many of the car clubs had their own workshops, where the cars were readied for the race. Blue Gum Road was one of the main drag strips since it directly connected to North Ninth Street. The racers would meet at the intersection of Poust and Blue Gum, out past the old Hammond General Hospital, now the State Mental Hospital. Paradise Road was also popular because it had long, straight stretches with limited intersections, as did Rumble, Claribel, and Ladd Roads. Other streets in the Modesto area that were home to regular races included Rose Avenue near Locke Road, Santa Fe, and Terminal. Drag racing was a dangerous sport and, unfortunately, some of these races ended tragically.

Along with the open road came the drive-in. Across the busy highways of America, carhops served up burgers, fries, and shakes to the hungry motorists. Drive-ins like Burge's were where it was happening. Following the opening of Thomas Downey High School in 1951, Downey students adopted Al's and Felix's Drive-ins on McHenry. Al's was located at McHenry and Francis Avenues. A cruiser was once overheard saying, "You went to Burge's on a date, you went to Al's to fight."

A long line of other hangouts would follow. Web's on Seventh and G and Orangeburg and McHenry. Sno-White at McHenry and Morris. Warren's on Washington Street near Modesto High. The Orange Julius on McHenry. The Scenic Drive-in on Scenic Drive. Ricky's Drive-in on Coffee Road. The Dairy Queen and Dan's Foster Freeze on H Street. MOAB (Meal on a Bun) on Tully Road. The Knights' Round Table was across from Downey High School, while the A&W Root Beer Drive-in was the first "fast food" restaurant in town.

In the mid '60s, the downtown was dying and most of the growth was migrating out McHenry Avenue. McHenry Village was built in 1953, which provided another reason to abandon downtown. The cruise route changed. It still started at Burge's and then over to Tenth. It followed Tenth, but instead of continuing to the fire department, it turned left on J Street and followed J to Five Points, which was the intersection of McHenry, Downey, Seventeenth, J, and Needham, then veered onto McHenry. The northern turn-around was Al's Drive-in, just north of the canal. The cruise route became a T-shaped loop that traveled J Street and McHenry, with cruisers circling around Al's to head back the other way, looping through Felix's parking lot on the way to check out the scene, and back to Burge's to do it all over again.

After 1962, as Grace M. Davis High School began to influence the cruise, coupled with the fading of Burge's and Al's, the cruise extended all the way out to Sylvan/Standiford Road, where there was a Frosty Top Drive-in and, on the north-east corner, the Sylvan Clubhouse. One of the major turnaround points was the parking lot of the Briggsmore Theatre at McHenry and Briggsmore, across the street from where a second A&W Drive-in was located. When Burge's closed in 1967, the route changed once more. The cruise then began at Five Points, traveling McHenry out to McHenry Village, where the drivers turned around and motored back toward town.

Modesto became home to some of the most legendary street rod builders and car customizers. Car customizing, or kustomizing, evolved out of necessity. Kids couldn't afford new cars, so they had to repair and rebuild the ones they had. These cars were built to race, to display, and to spotlight the talents of the builder. For many, a cool car was a surefire way to get a date for Saturday night.

Beginning in a chicken coop converted into a garage on Modesto's west side at 1309 Figaro Street, Gene Winfield honed his skills at lowering, chopping, and hammer welding to create enhanced body parts and dreaming up vivid, shiny, world-changing paint finishes like Candy Apple Red and Pearlescent. He opened a shop on 451 Tully Road near MJC, where his latest creations could be seen in the display window. He lived on our bike route to Davis High. When we rode to school our freshman year, we'd always see a wild, customized creation in his driveway.

Gene was assisted by many other cruisers, including Marvin "Bart" Bartoni and Pete Hischier. Bart had a ringside seat on the cruise and saw many of their creations drag Tenth because he owned the Bartoni Jewelry Store located in the middle of Tenth. "Go See Bart, the Jeweler with a Heart" was a popular radio jingle for years. Gene and Bart started the first custom car shows in California. Pete Hischier was a regular at Gene's shop. He had a rare, modified 1950 Mercury he would later sell to Gene, who further customized it. To the classic car customizers, it was all about the cars – the lowering, the wheel shrouds, the polish, the Appleton spotlights, the chrome, and the "flicker" wheels.

Police officers on the beat regularly ticketed the cruisers for every possible infraction, from the cars being chopped and lowered too close to the ground, having tinted windows, or hanging items on the rear-view mirror. It was pretty harmless and most of the infractions weren't serious even though a few ended in chases out into the orchards and along canal banks. Modesto was still a small town, so the police knew most of the regular cruisers by name and there was a semi-friendly relationship between the law breakers and the law enforcers.

The most common ticket issued was for an "illegal left turn." The city posted a temporary sign during the evenings to prevent cruisers from making the left turn off Eleventh at O Street to get back to Burge's to start the round trip again. The other most common ticket issued was for the excessive lowering of cars. Everyday items like a pack of cigarettes, or a can of beer, were used as gauges for the appropriate height off the ground. Another way to confirm the correct height was to ask the driver to deflate their tires. If anything touched the ground, the car was too low. Most of the tickets issued cost two or five dollars. Since the tickets weren't that expensive, cruisers collected them like confetti. A key nemesis of the draggers was Officer Leroy Applequist, a motorcycle cop who issued thousands of tickets to the young car drivers for anything he could find or dream up.

There were frequent pranks pulled around town, many of them in front of Burge's. Some of the most common ones involved setting car oil on fire or pouring old crankcase oil inside a Model A muffler with the tops of the tailpipes cut open to blanket the street in smoke. Another gag was emptying a drum of oil to create an oil slick at corners and intersections. Many people had stories to tell about the night the rear axle of a police car was yanked loose, or some version of it. But, most of all, cruising was always about hanging out for some harmless fun, going on dates, and showing off your car.

Both the car guys and the motorcycle dudes formed clubs. Many of the clubs started as high school "athletic" organizations, such as the 36'ers and the Regs. Some were more social and others were started by car enthusiasts. All these clubs had custom logos, jackets, patches, and other items to show club unity.

Two of the first car clubs in Modesto were the 36'ers and the Century Toppers. Founded by Winfield, Bartoni, and Hischier, the Toppers got their name from the fact that their cars went over 100 miles an hour, or the "Century" mark, thus the Century Toppers. The FAROS was a car club at Modesto High, until the dean banned it from the campus in 1958. It was restarted in 1960. The Road Rebels and the Modesto Street Rods were true car clubs whose members were gearheads devoted to rebuilding, restoring, and racing cars around the Modesto area. These clubs were a bit rowdier than the others and were known for some of their pranks and parties. The Road Rebels had a white '32 Ford truck with a keg in the back, which was featured on their logo and jackets.

The emergence of rock 'n' roll in the late 1950s and the popularity of AM radio created a common soundtrack for us kids. Music had always been a big part of Modesto history. Country radio disc jockey and musician Chester Smith was the voice of the Central Valley. Buck Owens and Merle Haggard began their musical careers in the Central Valley and, at one time, called Modesto home. The music of the Maddox Brothers and Rose helped forge the rockabilly style that paved the way for the rock 'n' roll bands that followed.

The Maddox Brothers and Rose were billed as "America's Most Colorful Hillbilly Band." The Maddox family grew up and worked as sharecroppers in Boaz, Alabama. They escaped the Dust Bowl and migrated to Modesto in 1933. Tired of working in the fields, they thought they'd give music a try. It worked. They first appeared as the "Alabama Outlaws" on KTRB's morning show in 1937, sponsored by Rice Furniture. They were known for their raucous performances, colorful costumes, and bawdy jokes. Their music made you want to dance.

Brother Fred Maddox pioneered a driving, slap-bass style because he didn't know how to play and was basically slapping random notes in rhythm with the music. His boogie-woogie, backbeat style was credited as being the foundation of rockabilly and rock 'n' roll. The band had recorded at Sam Ratliff's Associated Studio on Watts Avenue in West Modesto. Johnny Cash had recorded there, too. My hometown could rightly claim that it was the birthplace of rock 'n' roll.

There were dance halls in the '50s and '60s that were magnets for rockabilly and hillbilly music, which were the commonly accepted origins of rock 'n' roll. The Riverbank Club House drew national performers like Hank Williams and was always jumping as a dance hall, attracting people from across the Central Valley. The Oakdale VFW Hall, AKA the Cloverland Ballroom, was also a popular dance and music spot, and featured local country band, Glenn Stepp and His Western Swingsters, who also got local radio play. During the late '40s and into the '60s, the Rendezvous Club on Ninth Street played hillbilly music. The Red Barn, also on Ninth near the Grange building, featured a bar, a stage, and music by the "Okie" singers. Other venues included the Bamboo Room, the Tack Room, and Jack's Club.

The California Ballroom on Sixth Street, Merry Garden Skate Rink at Sixth and I, the Uptown Arena at Tenth and G, and the Fable Room in the basement of the Hotel Covell downtown were the most popular dance hall nightclubs during the '50s and '60s, featuring bands like Kent Whitt and the Downbeats, as well as Roddy Jackson and the Merced Bluenotes. Also appearing on these stages was Ceres' own Jim Burgett, who had a string of hits in the early '60s. Other touring artists included James Brown, Bobby Blue Bland, Ike & Tina Turner, Dick and Dee Dee, the Safaris, Bobby Freeman, Duane Eddy, and many other top acts of the day.

Playland on Kansas Avenue, next to the Borden Dairy, had a dance hall that was a local favorite until the owner, Mr. Albert Basmajian, was murdered by a jealous husband in 1958. During the '60s, the Playhouse in downtown was a trendy nightspot and regularly featured the Julian Brothers and Earl Knight. Michael Allsup, a local boy whose first band was the Chancellors and who was lead guitarist for Three Dog Night, often performed with Earl at El Patio, a dinner club on McHenry near Orangeburg.

Later in the '60s, the Purple Turnip on Tenth Street was the place where many of the local bands played, including the Ratz. The Strand Theatre hosted concerts showcasing well-known performers like Them with Van Morrison, Arthur Lee and Love, the Grass Roots, the Golliwogs, who later became Creedence Clearwater Revival, Peaches & Herb, and the Sir Douglas Quintet with Freddy Fender. The Modesto Skate Rink on Tully Road held concerts headlined by the Doors and the Grateful Dead, with home-grown favorites like the Kitchen Cinq opening. Modesto was on the way to everywhere, so many bands booked extra dates in town on their way to someplace else.

AM Radio was the soundtrack of the '50s and '60s. As the teenagers dragged Tenth, KFIV-1360 AM would play the popular songs of the day. Since there was only one rock station, everyone shared the same music. The nights were filled with doo-wop, rockabilly, soul, and rock 'n' roll.

Boys and girls purchased the records they heard on the radio at Harley's Records, located at 1218 J Street. North and across the street, there was another store simply called "Records" at Fourteenth and J, where keyboardist Bob DeLeon of the Downbeats worked. This store had listening booths so kids could check out the new tunes before buying, many times gathering as a group to listen.

Wolfman Jack, whose given name was Robert Weston Smith, howled out to cruisers in Modesto beginning in 1963, but only after the local AM radio stations had signed off for the night. It was then that the 50,000 watt "border blaster" transmitter of XERB located in Tijuana, Mexico, broadcast the Wolfman's program over Los Angeles, California, and beyond, even reaching Modesto in the late night air.

The first radio station to go on the air in any community between Sacramento and Fresno started broadcasting in Modesto in 1933. Bill Bates, a 33-year-old radio engineer, who owned and operated a radio service shop in Modesto, applied in late 1932 for a commercial radio broadcast license and went on the air June 18th, 1933. The station was called KTRB and was located on Norwegian between McHenry Avenue and Coffee Road. It became home to Chester Smith and hosted country and rockabilly greats from all over the USA. Chester would later give advice to Buck Owens, then working at a local cannery, to move to Bakersfield to get on the radio there.

KMOD became Modesto's second radio station in 1950 under the ownership of Jud Sturtevant. The transmitters were located on East Orangeburg Avenue and broadcast on 1360 KHz AM. In November 1956, the station was acquired by the Kilibro Broadcasting Company and the call letters changed to KFIV, serving Modesto and the surrounding communities with the rock 'n' roll Top 40 format. "K-5" continued as the station of rock for the '60s, and the on-air personalities became well-known in the area, promoting concerts and special events. I remembered listening to disc jockeys like Nelson Eddy and Lloyd Walters and Gene D'Accardo doing the news. KFIV's weekly Top 30 "Tune Dex" flyers became the last word for the local music fan.

KFIV also had a small remote studio inside Burge's Drive-in where DJ Dwight Case would sit at a booth, play records, and send out song dedications. You could request a song dedication and, since everyone in Modesto was listening to KFIV, the person you dedicated the song to would likely hear it.

In 1951, KBOX was started by former attorney, assemblyman, and speaker of the California House of Representatives, Ralph Brown. The KBOX studios were located on Tenth Street behind Burge's Drive-in. KBOX had the first rock 'n' roll DJs in Modesto when Pete and Mike Pappas started there in 1953. The brothers first presented the rock 'n' roll idea to KTRB, who declined, so they went to Cecil Lynch, who was general manager and program director at KBOX, and he put it on the air. When KBOX was purchased by the McClatchy Broadcasting Company in August 1956, the call letters were changed to KBEE-970 AM and the studios moved to a building behind *The Modesto Bee* on I Street between 14th and 13th Streets. It was part of the former Capitol School Building, which had a distinctive Spanish-style architecture.

The local area's last radio station to begin broadcasting was KLOC, licensed in nearby Ceres. Chester Smith, formerly a country disc jockey on KTRB, received FCC approval for "Clock Radio" in 1963, and launched his format of country-style music on 920 AM as a daytime-only 500 watt station. The broadcasting studio and transmitter towers were located off Paradise Road, on Iowa, near dairy farms, vineyards, and orchards.

That Saturday, I thought about how it all felt like an uncomplicated, gentler, and more peaceful time. You could dance to Kent Whitt and the Downbeats at the California Ballroom. Whether you had a Gene Winfield Candy Apple Red paint job, your car was lowered and chopped, or even if you drove the family car, downtown Modesto was where it was happening. Whether you were in a car club like the FAROS, Road Rebels, or Century Toppers, or one of the fraternities or sororities, or just enjoyed a night out with your date, there was something magical, mysterious, and memorable about the cruise in Modesto. It was all about having time, gas, a car, music, a place to hang out, and, of course, a date, or the hopes of getting one.

However, I didn't have one and wasn't looking. Things with Kelly and Luci were unsettled. I was flying solo. I approached Five Points from Needham, following in the wake of a posse of vintage roadsters. It was all a bit surreal. On the radio, I heard the Wolfman say, "Ain't nothin' gonna stop us now. 'Cause tonight's the night. We gonna cruise, baby. We gonna cruise."

The cruise was like a 4th of July parade, a street dance, a carnival, a county fair, a concert, and a drive-in all rolled into one.

"Check it out, 'cause yuh got a ticket to ride. I'll be seein' yuh all. Out on the boulevard," the Wolfman continued.

At Five Points, both sides of the avenue were jammed. The cruising was going full throttle. The human barbed wire lined both sides of the streets.

"Everybody knows yuh live and yuh learn, uh-huh. But, the lessons just go on and on. Yuh gonna have to wait for all the pages to turn. To find out if it's right or wrong. Have mercy!"

This was the head end of the cruise. As I turned left onto McHenry, I could see through the windshield an intricate graffiti image spray-painted on a wall ahead, next to the Denny's Down Town. A classic, rocket-finned Cadillac convertible traveled up a snaking, red river toward an ancient temple silhouetted by a blazing sunset. A pair of eyes peered out of the crimson sun. The Cadillac's driver and his fellow traveler passed through nine concentric rings en route to the end of their journey.

"The Wolfman gonna lay a little philosophy on yuh all now. Regret is a powerful thing, children. Dreams are all we got. But, regrets are what we live with. Do it today so's yuh won't regret it tomorrow. Don't give up somethin' yuh got for somethin' yuh think yuh need."

As I straightened out and chugged down McHenry, a glossy blonde in a classic white '56 Thunderbird floated by. She turned toward me and mouthed the words, "Carry on." When I tried to find her in my side-view, she was gone. Evaporated.

The diesel-driven procession rolled down the strip. Keeping pace alongside me was a maroon, '51 Mercury lowered and chopped with slitted windows. In the small back window was a metal plague that read: "FAROS."

"Some day, some day. People always talkin' 'bout some day. Some day never comes, yuh all. Today's all we got. This, here and now. So, get on with it."

I watched the faces and places flash by as the moveable feast carried on. A white, decked-and-channeled, tuck-and-rolled '58 Chevy Impala with a flamed hood glided by in the oncoming lane. It was sharper than Darryl Starbird's superfleck moonbird.

"'Freedom's just another word for nothin' left to lose.' Freedom, freedom. Everybody always talkin' 'bout bein' free. Freedom don't mean much if yuh can't do nothin' with it. Can yuh dig it."

At Modesto Avenue, a seedy, something-wicked-this-way comes carnival had set up camp in the empty lot next to the Inselman Texaco. An evil-looking, midway Mephistopheles was hustling people to take a few potshots at his shooting gallery. Heading toward me was a perky, dark-haired girl driving what looked like her parents' Edsel.

"Every moment of every day yuh got to make choices. Only one choice of all the choices is the right one at that time, uh-huh. Your instincts will tell yuh what it is. Always trust your gut."

Sucked along by the power glide *paseo*, I glanced out the passenger window in time to see a red-tailed hawk snag a mourning dove in the empty sky. Below it, in the flatlands, a Vespa crashed into a cigarette vending machine outside a steak house.

"Storm warning, yuh all. Weatherman says a storm's a-brewin'. Better batten down the hatches. Gonna be a rough ride."

The fossil-fueled parade snaked on, passing an abandoned building just past Don's McHenry Union Gas Station on Roseburg, which was temporary sanctuary for the homeless. The driftwood people of all ages included mothers, fathers, and children. There were vagrants and hobos, alcoholics and druggies, young and old. A gang of football jocks approached, mayhem on their minds.

"Gots to stop worryin' now, yuh all. It's always darkest just before the dawn. Yes, it is."

The chopped-and-channeled caravan creeped past a Brazil's Chevron Gas Station at the corner of Orangeburg and McHenry. A short shit of an ancient hard guy tried to pick a fight with the father of five. The punk was able to get away with mouthing off because he had a bunch of bigger bad asses backing him. They all wore frayed and undersized gang jackets with the name "Little Okies" stitched across the back. They scattered when a battered, bug-eyed, faded grey Citroen *deux-chevaux* careened through the station.

"Wishful thinkin', ah wishful thinkin'. It can take yuh only so far, my friends. Hope needs somethin' real to keep it alive and kickin'."

The high octane armada inched along, passing Granger. Pulling onto McHenry from the quiet side street, I heard an eardrum shattering rumble and turned to see a yellow, '32 Ford deuce coupe chopped and lowered with a monster Hemi-V8. The roaring chariot was piloted by a cat in a white T-shirt dragging on an unfiltered Raleigh.

"Slow down now, yuh all. All dem wheels on fire are lightin' up the night. Ain't livin' long like this, baby."

The rolling thunder remuda was gathering steam. Even if I wanted to stop, I couldn't. The procession of gleaming cars traveled through the hot night.

"It's bad on the avenue tonight, children. The blues be makin' people crazy. Ev'rybody knows what they want, not what they need. What they want to do, not what they need to do."

Far out in summer country, I heard the drumming of steel wheels on metal tracks. The hellish midnight special spat sparks into the dark night.

"Got's to watch out for each other now. There ain't nobody else gonna do it. Put a little love in yer heart, yuh know what I mean."

The petroleum powered procession rushed past Briggsmore. It seemed to be dragging me along to some inexorable ending. Rushing up behind me was a devilish looking black, '55 Chevy Bel Air tricked out with a blown engine, scooped hood, and slicked tires. It swung around and pulled up next to me on my right. A cowboy turned to look, tapping the brim of his straw hat in acknowledgement. He put the Chevy in neutral, revved it, smiled, popped the clutch, and shot off after the deuce coupe, tires smoking and car fishtailing.

"We only get one chance at this life. Let's make it a good one. Have to help each other make it through the night. Listen to The Wolfman. Be true to yerself and everything's gonna be just fine."

At Bowen, I stopped behind the Ford and the Chevy. Side-by-side. T-shirt and cowboy hat. The two drivers were eyeballing each other. The Chevy revved again. The deuce coupe idled. The light changed. The two cars blasted away. I jumped ship. I turned left on Bowen and pulled away from the circus, headed to Gover's house. I glanced in my rear-view at the receding carnival on wheels. I turned back around to face the road that lay ahead of me. I escaped the sultry summer night haunted by the ghosts of the kids and their rumbling machines wheeling through the darkness looking for something, anything.

"We keep retellin' our stories cuz we can never seem to get 'em right, uh-huh."

CHAPTER 35

Sunday was Father's Day. Since Dad's passing, it had been a tough day for us. Paul was such a good guy and tried so hard to fill Daddy-O's shoes, that it had become almost the same thing. We tried to make it easier on him by doing many of the same things we did when Pater was alive. I barbecued chicken slathered in Woody's BBQ sauce. We played pinochle, listened to Al Martino, and jitterbugged. We pooled our money to buy Paul a tie and after shave. Your typical Father's Day. Until I saw the New York Yankees hat that Mickey Mantle had signed when Dad was in the hospital. It all came rushing back. I called Gary.

There was a free concert at Mancini Bowl in Graceada Park and we checked it out. A DJ at KBEE named Tom Romano had put it together. It featured two bands, Canyon and Poor Richard's Almanac. We knew a few of the band members in Poor Richard's Almanac. Both bands played cover tunes and original tunes. They both sounded like many of the local bands emulating the San Francisco acid-rock bands, like Jefferson Airplane and Quicksilver Messenger Service.

Gary had been noodling around with the flute, so he brought it. We sat at the back of the amphitheater so he could play along.

"Not bad," I said.

"I don't know what I'd do without music."

"Me, either."

"It's a safe place to go. No judgments, no expectations."

"It reminds me of things. Good and bad."

"Funny how it can change your frame of mind in an instant. You can go from happy to sad to excited to angry all in a heartbeat."

"It's like a soundtrack to a movie."

"Or a radio playlist."

"Only it's our life."

"Profound, dude," he commented.

"Up yours."

"No, I get it. I really do."

"Well, the soundtrack in my head is playing an anthem one second and something totally weird the next. It's all jumbled up."

"You thinking about the draft?"

"That. The demonstrations in SF and Berkeley. And some crazy stuff going on at school."

"Like what? Maybe something to do with Luci?" That caught me by surprise.

"Maybe, I guess," I answered.

"Really? I was taking a wild guess."

"She's gotten out there all of a sudden. Real radical. Changed her look. Changed her mind."

"I liked the way she looked," Gary replied, grinning salaciously.

"Back off, hound dog."

"Just kidding, but not really."

"You remember Mike Walt?"

"Sure. You've talked about him. Lives in the same apartment complex, right?"

"Right. I think she's got him going along. It's weird."

"What, she gonna blow up a bank?"

"Maybe."

"Damn. Again, I was guessing."

"I think she's pissed enough to do something out there like that," I replied.

"Where's that put you?"

"I don't know."

"But, you dig her, right?"

"I did, uh, do. But not this new stuff. Not what she seems to be into," I said. "I don't like what's going on in Vietnam. I don't trust Reagan or Nixon or the rest of them. Something needs to change and I want to be a part of that. I want there to be hope and peace. But, violence isn't where it's at."

"But, Canada is."

"We'll see."

We cut out early and went to Beard Brook Park to watch some fast pitch softball. Gary had turned 21 in January so he was able to buy alcohol. We sprawled out on the sloping banks above the diamond, popped open two quarts of Burgie beer, and watched the game.

"I miss Dad," I confessed to Gary.

"I do, too," Gary replied. "He was the best."

"Paul's a really good guy, but it's not the same."

"I can't imagine not having my dad around."

"It's good for Mom, so I guess we shouldn't be so selfish."

"How's the rest of the family handling it?"

"They're all good. Willy thinks he might even be a better coach than Dad was."

"How about Tim, Jr.?"

"He's usually at Laura's."

"Makes it easier that way, I guess."

"How was your dad's dad's day?" I asked.

"Probably the same as yours. Breakfast, some greeting cards, and BBQ. He had some beers and started snoozing early. Your call was perfect timing."

"I don't know if it's Dad being gone, or she's getting older, but Mom is different."

"She still gives me a hard time."

"She seems tired. Less patient. More judgmental. She's smoking and drinking more."

"We all are."

"She's no fun to be around sometimes."

"Losing your husband will do that."

"I wonder if Dad's keeping an eye out on us."

"The *Bible* says he is. And all those good Christians."

"I'm not sure I believe in an afterlife."

"You'll rot in hell for that."

"Another place I'm not sure I believe in."

"I'll send you a fan."

We both laughed and took another slug of beer.

Larry Warburton, the ageless father of a high school classmate, sliced a line drive down the third baseline off Darryl Top, one of our Davis High teachers, to win the game for the Stanislaus County Employee Association team. I had a flashback to my Garrison Little League days. Coach Leach also played fast pitch softball. His team was the Sportsmen of Stanislaus (SOS). They had these cool black and white uniforms with gold piping that featured an Indian hatchet that looked like the Atlanta Braves. Overlapping SOS letters like the Chicago White Sox were embroidered on their black hats. When Coach Leach's team played a game at the State Hospital south of Highway 99, several of us players and our parents would attend. Some of the patients would join us in the stands. One in particular I remember was named, or we called, Mr. House. He would sit quietly in his white pajamas and robe, intently watch the action on the field, and chatter non-stop. Another patient would walk around the bleachers dragging a wooden toy car behind him. It was sad to see what the world had done to these poor souls.

At times like this, I would go to Dad. I wasn't quite ready to go there with

Paul. But, there were other adults who had helped me in the past; answering questions, offering advice, or listening. Men like Coach Leach and my old neighbor and college professor, Mr. Gordon.

We sat in Mr. Gordon's study, which was to the left of the front door of his home. The office was filled with books, photographs, and World War II memorabilia. He had a Nazi flag and German helmet he had liberated while Patton's army occupied Germany. Research material and documents covered his desk. He wasn't teaching summer school at Modesto Junior College, so he was free to concentrate on his study of the American Civil War.

He swiveled around in his chair, scanned a bookshelf, and selected a volume. He opened it and read, "It is only those who have neither fired a shot nor heard the shrieks and groans of the wounded who cry aloud for blood, more vengeance, more desolation. War is hell."

"William Tecumseh Sherman," I said.

"You were a good student."

"You were a good teacher."

"It's unconscionable that old men continue to dream up ways for young men to die," he went on. "Unconscionable."

"It's hard to stop them."

"The men, or the wars?"

"Both."

He closed the book and said, "I can't tell you what to do. My best advice is to listen to your gut. Intuition is a better guide than information. At least I've found that to be true. Use your own good judgment."

"That's what my dad always said."

"He was a good man. And that's sound advice."

"I don't want to go to Canada. I don't want to hide in Europe. I don't want to be branded a coward."

"General Patton had a quote I heard many times. 'If we take the generally accepted definition of bravery as a quality which knows no fear, I have never seen a brave man. All men are frightened. The more intelligent they are, the more they are frightened.'"

"He didn't like cowards."

"He did not. I saw that firsthand."

"He paid for it."

"Yes, he did."

"I don't believe this war is right. We don't belong there. I don't want to die," I said.

"The General also said, 'Better to fight for something than live for nothing.' If you believe in something, stick to your guns. If you believe this war is wrong, then fight for your beliefs."

"They'll throw me in jail."

"Perhaps. One more thing Patton said. 'If a man does his best, what else is there?' Do your best. That's all you can do.'"

"I'm afraid."

"So is my son."

"What's Robbie going to do?"

"He's eligible for the draft. We've discussed it. His mother doesn't want him to go."

"And you."

"I don't want to lose my son. But, he has to decide. I served. I did my duty. We had good reasons to win that war. We were fighting for survival. I'm not sure why we're in this one. I'm not sure we can win."

"That's not really the point, is it?"

"No, I suppose it isn't."

Friday night was one of the nights we played softball in Modesto. I was too old for the traditional hard ball leagues, so I'd turned to softball. I'd played in Davis and wanted to keep playing when I came home for the summer. I got some people together and we helped start an informal recreational league. The city had fast pitch leagues, but no slow pitch.

Our team was sponsored by Laura's parent's real estate firm, Carrasco Real Estate. Marco had quit his job as a milkman. It was killing his back and knees. He went into real estate with his wife, Elaine. She handled sales. He handled renovations. All the players on our team were family, friends, and kids we'd played with in Little League and Babe Ruth. Tim played, so did Laura's brother, Vito, as well as some high school friends of Tim's and Vito's. Gary, too. Willy was 16, but we lied about his age and let him play. He was that good. We were competitive.

There were six teams. We played at Downey High School. The diamond was basically a corner field with loose bases measured off. No backstop. We paid an umpire to keep the games under control. Our biggest rival was a team sponsored by Dunlap's Department Store. A few of our buddies and teammates from grade school played for them. Another tough team was named the A-Wonders, after the name of their sponsor, A-1 Carpets. The Bethel Church also fielded a team.

We weren't a power hitting team like Dunlap's, or the A-Wonders. We hit singles and we were fast. We played solid defense and had a pitcher, Gene Guptill, who was loco. He kept the batters off balance with his antics on the mound.

Our sidelines were filled with fans. Wives, girlfriends, parents. And beer.

We were good, but not as focused and intense as the other teams. It was a good league. And a great distraction.

Unfortunately, I was too competitive to make it as fun as it could have been. If someone booted a ball and we lost, I'd come home totally pissed. I'd pop a beer and sit by myself in the family room stewing over the game. Nobody would come near me when I was feeling that way. I'd even dream about it. Paul had to have a heart-to-heart with me from time to time to remind me that it was a game. Pure and simple. I disagreed, but I listened. I tried to change, but I enjoyed being pissed too much to stop. Dad had unsuccessfully had the same conversation with me many times.

CHAPTER 36

Saturday, June 21st was the Summer Solstice, defined as: "the sun standing still." The longest day and shortest night of the year. It was a good day to get out of town – to go somewhere and get my head straight. Not with alcohol or drugs, but the best cure of all: Mother Nature. I borrowed Gary's VW bug since Ugly Orange couldn't make the grade. At sunrise, I tossed my sleeping bag and backpack into the VW and drove south on Highway 99 toward Yosemite.

I cut over at Merced and went through Mariposa. I took that route instead of the Oakdale/Sonora/Groveland route because it was easier and because I wanted to stop at the Mariposa Grove and Glacier Point before dropping down into the valley.

The Mariposa Grove of Giant Sequoias was the largest sequoia grove in Yosemite and was home to over 500 giant sequoias. They were the most massive trees on the planet. The concept of state and national parks was started when President Lincoln signed legislation on June 30th, 1864, deeding Yosemite Valley and Mariposa Grove to the state of California, "upon the express conditions that the premises shall be held for public use, resort and recreation." The legislation was important enough to Lincoln that he did it even though the nation was in the middle of the Civil War. It was the first time the government had taken steps to protect scenic areas.

The grove was located before the old Wawona Hotel on the Wawona Road/Highway 41. One of the major attractions in the grove, and the first place I stopped, was the Grizzly Giant, which was the oldest tree in the grove, estimated to be between 1900 and 2400 years old. Standing at the foot of the massive tree, it put things in perspective, considering that this tree was already standing when the Roman Empire ruled the known world. At that moment, my issues didn't seem to amount to much.

I continued up the Wawona Road and took the turnoff to Glacier Point. It was a beautiful, if winding, road. The bug chugged right along. Parking wasn't bad. I found a spot and walked toward the overlook.

Glacier Point was located on the south wall of Yosemite Valley. It measured 7,214 feet high. The views of the valley, Yosemite Falls, Half Dome, Vernal Fall, and Nevada Fall were spectacular. Directly below was the entire valley spread out like a natural map. I could see Curry Village, the Ahwanhee Hotel, and Camp 4, which was my destination.

A trail wound more than four miles from the summit to the valley floor. It was here on the Overhanging Rock that President Teddy Roosevelt posed with naturalist John Muir in May 1903. The two men camped in a nearby hollow that night and awoke to five inches of snow. Roosevelt had written Muir asking to meet him in Yosemite telling Muir, "I want to drop politics absolutely for four days and just be out in the open with you." It was during that outing that Muir convinced Roosevelt that the federal government needed to take full control of Yosemite and the Mariposa Grove and make it part of the National Park Service. Roosevelt did exactly that on June 11th, 1906. One of many incredulous things about the President's visit was that Roosevelt dismissed his staff and security and rode off to be alone with nature and Mr. Muir, even though his predecessor President William McKinley had died from an assassination attempt in 1901.

The sun was dropping as I pulled into the lot across from the dusty and boulder-speckled Camp 4, which was located a little east of Yosemite Village at the foot of Yosemite Falls. I found a secluded spot beneath a pine tree, unrolled my foam mat, spread out my bag, and opened it to air out. It hadn't been used in some time. Camp 4 was the campground that all the climbers called home when they were in the valley. It was where the serious rock jocks lived, survived on next to nothing, and climbed almost full-time. There was a two-week per year camping limit. It was a tough rule to enforce because the rangers never knew the date a camper actually arrived. When asked, the person would stretch the truth, saying they'd only been there a few days. But, when the same faces were seen in the coffee shop or campground time after time, the rangers had no choice but to do something. The climbers then had to find clever ways to avoid the rangers so they could extend their stay without getting busted. The rangers were being pressured by the Curry Company to control the rule breakers. Sometimes they'd leave for a few days, or camp behind the boulders, and quietly sneak back into camp. Most of the rangers were cool. Some were not. But, that was the case with any troop of officials. Serious enforcement would always begin in late May when the weather got nicer, the climbers were preparing for big climbs, and more tourists were visiting.

The last time I had been in the valley floor was senior ditch day in 1966. The third graduating class of Grace M. Davis High School had taken two busloads of soon-to-be graduates from Modesto to Yosemite. We hiked and rode bikes, laughed and sweated, teased and flirted. By the time we loaded back onto the buses, we were pleasantly exhausted. Compared to the trip going in, the trip going out was achingly quiet.

Like Jack Kerouac and Gary Snyder, I had come to the mountains for healing. Kerouac had written in *The Dharma Bums* that he had taken his wounds to the wilderness for a cure. I was seeking the same.

I was confused. And concerned. Violence wasn't the answer. It never was, or would be. But, things had to change. Guys I had grown up with were getting shot, messed up, or dying in Vietnam. My best friends and my generation were being clubbed in the streets for waging peaceful protest – for doing what our country was founded on and known for. Freedom. Democracy. Individualism.

I wanted to speak with someone who also came to the mountains to seek solace, inspiration, and guidance. Another valley refugee; a fellow Modestan. His name was Royal Robbins. He was perhaps the world's greatest rock climber. He had made first ascents of many of the big wall routes in Yosemite, including Half Dome and El Capitan. He was a true believer in clean climbing. He disliked using bolts and pitons. When he wasn't climbing, he sold paint in Modesto. I had first met him when some high school friends took me climbing our junior year of high school. Bill Magruder, John Decker, and Dave Threlfall had fallen under the spell of granite. Magruder more than the other two. Decker preferred caving and Threlfall was a skilled amateur photographer. I hadn't enjoyed the climbing. It was hard work and scary. But, I did like the evening gathering of the rock-climbing clan. There was wine, weed, and good conversation. That's where I'd first met Royal and his wife, Liz.

That Saturday evening, I knew they'd be among the boulders at Camp 4, philosophizing and solving the world's problems. I wasn't disappointed. The "dirtbags," as they now affectionately referred to themselves after being called that by so many rangers and tourists, were huddled around a campfire. Someone was playing a guitar. A few were singing. Another group was passing around a doobie. Others were sipping Teton Tea from tin cups. Teton Tea was a mixture of tea, lemons, sugar, and port. As Royal once said, "it kept us awake and relaxed at the same time."

I found Royal and Liz away from the group. I approached, gestured to sit, and Royal nodded. After I got comfortable on the rock, he stuck out his hand.

"It has been a while, Mikey," he said.

"I wasn't sure you'd remember me."

"When you pull someone off a rock wall after they've frozen, you don't forget them."

"That was not a good day. Sorry about that."

"Happens all the time," Liz said, also extending her hand. "You weren't his first," she smiled. We shook hands. Liz offered a cup of Teton Tea. I shook my head.

"Have you returned to see who's tougher, you or the rock?" he asked.

"No, I'm done with climbing and caving and all that other lunatic stuff. I want to be on flat ground and out where I can see the sun."

"Level-headed and practical," Liz said.

"I'm here because I need to clear my head. Think some things through. I wanted to get away from it all for a while."

"It's good to do that on a regular basis," Liz added.

"People who need that usually have some things on their mind," Royal said.

"Maybe I will take a hit of that," I said, pointing at the tea. Liz passed the cup over and I took a drink. It tasted good for bad wine. "It's the war. And the draft," I continued. "I've got some friends who're thinking about doing something stupid. It's all a muddle."

"I'm sorry to hear that," he said. "I did my time in the service. It was good for me. It's not good for everyone. I'm not a 'my country right or wrong, love it or leave it' patriot. I don't believe in this war. We're in it for the wrong reasons. We're not hearing the whole story. I know how the military works."

"I feel the same way. I feel bad for the soldiers who are fighting and dying over there. They're doing their duty for the right reasons, but for the wrong people and the wrong war. Like you, I don't believe the government is being straight with us."

"So, what's the problem?" he asked.

"What I'm going to do about it."

"And what's that?" Liz asked.

"I'm not going, but I don't know yet how to make that happen. I'm not religious, so the CO route isn't going to work. I don't want to leave the country. I'm not thrilled about joining the reserve, or National Guard. Cutting off a finger, or going to jail is crazy. I wish they'd end it."

"That won't happen right away," Royal said.

"What things are your friends considering?" Liz asked.

"Radical stuff. SDS, Black Panther. Like that."

"Violence," he said.

"I'm afraid so."

"That won't work," he said.

"I know. That's why I've gone the non-violent route, like letters and protests, but that doesn't seem to be making a dent."

"Maybe you're too impatient," he said.

"Slow and steady wins the race," Liz said.

"Think Grand Canyon," he said. "The Colorado just kept going."

"They'll draft me before that happens. "You don't know that for sure," Royal said.

"I don't want to take any chances. It's my life we're talking about."

"You should have faith in many of your fellow citizens, some of your leaders, most of the rest of the world. They know it's wrong and they will end it," he said.

"The clock is ticking," I answered.

"Keep doing what you're doing," Royal continued. "A critical mass of public opinion will be reached. As Martin Luther King, Jr. said, 'The arc of the moral universe is long, but it bends toward justice.'"

"If it's inevitable, why do anything?" I asked.

"It becomes preordained by the weight of our work. It's not a chemistry experiment that needs to remain undisturbed. Peace is not a Sunday walk in the park. We need to get our hands dirty to make sure that arc doesn't straighten out, or bend in the wrong direction," he went on.

"I'm curious," Liz said. "If you're worried, and you obviously are, why haven't you made a decision? Why haven't you done something, anything, already?"

"Inertia. Fear of making the wrong mistake."

"I understand that," Royal answered. "It's so much easier to stay as we are, even if it's hurting us. Right up until it hurts too much. People don't change unless it's too painful to stay the same. It seems like some people don't do the right thing until all other options are exhausted.

"For me, there are no options. There's a right way to do something and there are all the others. Right is right."

"I'm not you," I said. "I wish I were that certain."

"Nobody is," Liz observed.

"Think of it this way," he replied. "Remember the fable, 'The Tortoise and the Hare?'"

"Sure. Read it as a kid. Heard it any time anybody wanted to make a point about the race going to the slow and steady versus the fast and careless."

I glanced at Liz. She smiled.

"That's the point," he said. "We all arrive at the same destination eventually, whether we're the tortoise or the hare."

"Sure. Like that butthead who tailgates and whips around me to get wherever he's going faster than everyone and we end up sitting side-by-side at the next light."

"Exactly. Different people travel through life at different speeds and on different paths. One isn't better than another, just different."

"Well, I need to take more time to figure things out. I like to have all the information before I decide. If it's worth doing, it's worth doing right."

"If you are uncompromising in your commitment to do what is right, you will die well," Royal said.

"Slow and steady," Liz repeated.

"I'll get there eventually," I said.

"And know it for the first time," Royal added.

CHAPTER 37

I got back to Modesto on Tuesday. The boys were ready to do something that night after a hard day's work. Gover was working for his dad cleaning out silos at the Foster Farms feed mill in Livingston. Gary was grading peaches for the Cling Peach Advisory Board, which was a terrific job for college students. Steve Gant was also grading. They were bored. Phone calls were made. They were horny, so they picked a strip club in Ceres called the Green Door. It had opened recently, so we thought it was time to look it over. Gov, Gary, and Steve were all 21. I was a few months away, but with my receding hairline, scruffy beard, and fake ID, I was able to get past the bouncer.

The Green Door was not your upscale gentleman's club. It was a working-class bar with strippers. The inside was hazy from cigarette smoke and smelled of stale beer, body odor, and cheap perfume. It was catnip for twenty-year-old innocent punks like us. We found a table near center front. The club wasn't that busy, likely due to it being a Tuesday night. I looked around at the faces and tried to figure out a story. They looked so damned bummed out, no stories came to mind. I did want to know why they were here and why we were here because I didn't get places like this. The fantasy world of the strip club never made any sense. The dancers didn't want to be there. The patrons didn't want to be there. None of them wanted to be doing what they were doing. For the ladies, it was a way to make a living. For the patrons, it was a way to avoid reality. For everyone involved, it was a way to be less lonely and isolated.

Round after round came; song after song played; girl after girl danced; minute after minute passed. Steve was wasted. He was drinking his own plus mine, when he realized I wasn't going to match everyone drink for drink.

"Gotta piss like a racehorse," Steve mumbled as he lurched to his feet and staggered off to the john.

"He's toast," I said.

"He's fine," Gover said. "We're all fine." Gary didn't say anything. He was too busy singing along with a Beatles tune.

"He's going to get us all tossed on our asses," I pressed.

Gov was about to reply, when we heard a ruckus by the bar. Sure enough, Steve had pissed someone off. Words were being exchanged. Gov and I hustled to the bar and dragged Steve away.

"I was merely complimenting his girlfriend's tits," Steve whined.

"I'm sure they were lovely, but they're not yours," Gover said.

We staggered back to the table, stumbling a few times, as we hauled our heavy load. Gary drained his beer and stood. Steve reached to finish his.

"Whoa, Trigger," I said. "Let's – "

"Why don't you dicks come with me before you get nutted," a voice growled. We all swung around. It was Motown the Angel.

"I'm gettin' real tired of savin' your necks," he said. He turned and pushed toward the door. The crowd parted like the Red Sea in DeMille's epic *The Ten Commandments.*

Outside, he hopped on his hog, fired it up, and yelled over the pipes, "Follow me!" then roared onto the road. We jumped into Steve's Volkswagen and chased him.

Motown had told me after he crashed his ride on New Year's that he had a place on Victoria in south Modesto near Paradise Road. It was a tidy, post-World War II bungalow. Two bedrooms, one bath, and a tiny kitchen. It was incredibly clean and tidy. A black lab greeted us with a cautionary growl.

"That's Zeus. Bark is nothin' compared to his bite, so don't piss him off. Make yourselves comfy," he said as he went into a bedroom.

We did. The living room looked like a college apartment – black light posters, ferns and wandering Jews, tie-dyed fabrics on the couch and chairs, a beanbag chair, an expensive stereo with massive speakers, an aquarium. Nothing indicated a Hells Angel lived here. Or a female.

Gary thumbed through the LPs. "Nice collection," he said as he pulled *Disraeli Gears* by Cream from the stack. He slipped the disc on the turntable and started it. "Strange Brew" filled the room.

"Turn it up, man," Motown said as he came back. "Give it some air. Let it breathe."

"What about the neighbors?" I asked.

"You really think they're goin' to say somethin' to me?" he replied.

"Guess not," I said. Gary pumped up the volume. It sounded incredible.

Motown went into the kitchen. We all kicked back and grooved. He returned a few moments later.

"This'll straighten you up and let you fly right," he said, as he handed around glasses of a murky liquid.

Steve drank his without hesitation. Gover followed suit. Gary and I, the sheep in the flock, looked at each other.

"'Every party needs a pooper, that's why we invited you,'" Gov and Steve sang. "'Party Pooper! Party Pooper!'" Gary and I were shamed into downing our drinks.

It didn't take long for whatever it was to kick in. It made me incredibly mellow and dreamy. Everything seemed so clear and crisp. I smiled. I looked at the boys. They were all splayed out around the room smiling like beatific loons.

"What is this?" Steve asked.

"Secret formula."

"Where can I buy it?"

"I'll send you home with some."

"Sweet," Steve exhaled.

"Enjoy the trip," Motown replied. As I stared at him, I swear I could see a vibrating halo encircling his head.

"I'm gonna crash," he said. "It's been a rough one. Let yourselves out," and with that our personal Captain Trips disappeared into the bedroom and softly closed the door.

We had all been here before. Not here-here, but in a similar situation. It was during the summer after we graduated from high school. We were at Chuck Horne's house. "Round and Round and Round" spilled from the speakers of the stereo console.

Round and round and round we spin,
To weave a wall to hem us in.
It won't be long . . . It won't be long.

Sex, drugs, and rock 'n' roll. Rock 'n' roll we got. Sex we were starting to get. Drugs we didn't have a clue. We were the virgins, the newbies, the rookies. Gary and me. He was cautious. I was curious. We both had a strong sense of self-preservation. And fear.

We went to Berkeley to change that. To score some mescaline from a high school classmate who'd chosen Cal over JC. While he collected the contraband, we listened to Neil Young's solo album. He sang "The Loner," as our connection explained the ins and outs.

How slow and slow and slow it goes,
To mend the tear that always shows.
It won't be long.
It won't be long.

Back home, we rendezvoused at Chuck's house. That is, his parent's house.

The pros from Dover dropped by. The gang of addicts in training. The ones with no fear. To show us the do's and don'ts. They left us to our own devices.

We locked ourselves in, closed the shades, and took off on a magic carpet ride. Joyriding to the edge. Drag-racing to the cliff. Lying on my back in the backyard, the edges of the trees spun like pinwheels on fire. Starry, starry night. Van Gogh trippin' on LTD, our clever, letter-scrambled code for acid. Back inside, I popped Buffalo Springfield's "Greatest Hits" into the 8-track. The metallic silver-blue guitar of "On the Way Home" punched holes in the walls.

It was a fine line between here and there, this side and the other. A very fine line.

How the hours will bend
through the time that you spend
till you turn to your eyes,
And you see your best friend
looking over the end
and you turn to see why,
And he looks in your eyes and he cries.

The next day, Tim and Laura came by. They were going to the City and wanted the Buffalo Springfield 8-track I'd promised and forgotten about. I slipped it through a slight crack in the front door, wondering why they were there so damned early. The sun, burning directly overhead, scorched my dark-adjusted eyes.

Gary went home. He came back. He couldn't face his family. He freaked out. The pros were called back to talk him down. They did. Eventually. We never looked at things the same again.

Round and round and round we spin,
To weave a wall to hem us in,
It won't be long.
It won't be long.

It could have been seconds, minutes, or hours later. I didn't know. I opened my eyes. It took a moment to realize we were still at Motown's house. The last thing I remembered from the night before was staring unblinking at a fish spitting rocks in the aquarium. Everyone was zonked out. The needle was rhythmically scratching against the inside hub of *Surrealistic Pillow*. I got up, replaced the needle, shut down the turntable and amp. I went to each of the guys and shook them awake.

"Time to split," I said.

Groggy, they all groaned to their feet and we did.

Outside, the sun was coming up. A rooster crowed to greet the new day. We had places and people to be.

CHAPTER 38

Paging through *The Modesto Bee* the day after I'd returned from Yosemite, I read an article, buried inside, that the Weatherman offshoot group of the SDS was now in charge of the entire organization. It had happened during their meeting in Chicago on June 18th. I was sure that wasn't going to be a good thing for the government. Or anyone associated in any way with them.

Although the splinter group originally called themselves "Weatherman," they soon became known as "the Weathermen." Their goal was nothing short of overthrowing the government. They took their name from the Bob Dylan song, "Subterranean Homesick Blues," which included the lyric, "You don't need a weather man, To know which way the wind blows."

The escalating Vietnam War, black militancy, clandestine activities of the FBI, and government repression led to the Weathermen becoming more radical and reckless. Inspired by revolutionary movements in Latin America, Southeast Asia, and China, they believed they could use violent confrontations to bring the war home. By starting a violent domestic revolt, they thought they could force the U.S. government to abandon Vietnam to deal with the violence at home. Their tactics dredged up the Russian terrorist movement I'd been studying. There were many similarities.

Gary and I had a softball game that night. We were both tired from our experience with Motown. But, tired as we might be, we loved playing ball. We certainly weren't going to let our team down. The game ended with a few beers. But, Gary and I were too damned tired. We went straight home after squeaking out a one run victory over the A-Wonders.

That Friday was a night I had been dreading. Kelly and I were going to meet at the MoBand concert at Graceada Park. It was the Modesto Band of Stanislaus County's 50th season. Kelly and I hadn't seen each other, or talked, since school had gotten out. She was busy with summer school, working at J.C. Penney's downtown, and family travel. I was avoiding her, so her being busy wasn't a problem.

I rode my bike. She drove in from the westside. I was sitting in the swing in the sand box where we had met the last time we had attended a concert, a little more than seven years before. I heard her approach. She walked around to face me. We looked at each other. Familiar strangers.

"Good to see you," she said.

"You, too," I replied.

"You look good," she said.

"You, too."

"Still the man of many words."

"Sorry. You still make me tongue-tied."

"Glad to be home?" she asked.

"I am. You?"

"Very much," she answered.

"Miss me?" I asked.

"A little," she responded. She was pissed. I couldn't blame her. But, we had too much history to let it go. I wasn't going to give up easily. We talked about school, our families, our summers. We danced around what was really on our minds.

"You okay?" she asked. "You look worried."

"I am."

"About what?"

"Us."

"I don't want to talk about that now."

"Okay, then school. I'm worried about school. I can't mess up my scholarships. Or my deferment."

"Ah, 'The Monk.'"

"How'd you know about that?"

"Your roommate."

"Which one?"

"I only know Gover."

"Big mouth."

"A friend. Who likes to share."

"When did you talk with him?"

"I've seen him around."

"My 'friend' have anything else to say?"

"That you're doing well in school and they never see you and you're never any fun."

"I am the 'no fun guy.'"

"That you're concerned about the draft, which has got him concerned about you. Seems you've been keeping some strange company."

"Sounds like you didn't just pass the time of day."

"Like I said, he's a friend."

"He's right. I am freaking out about the draft and the war. About what it is. About what I might have to do. I'm not in a good place right now."

"You'll work it out."

"Easy for you to say. Girls don't get drafted." That stung her, but she was determined not to let it bother her.

"I want you around for a while," she said.

"You don't act like it."

"I guess that's on you."

"And you."

"I want to make sure you don't do anything silly."

"Like go to Canada?"

"Maybe."

"Join the reserves."

"Another thing I hope you don't have to do."

"Shoot off a toe."

"That would be dumb."

"Go underground and fight this thing measure for measure."

"That's the one." I stood and brushed past her.

"Look, my head is all messed up. I don't believe in this war. I don't trust our government. I don't want to shoot anybody. I don't want to be shot by anyone."

"I don't want you to die, either."

"I hope you mean that."

"You'll figure something out," she said. "You usually do."

"I can only hope."

"You can do more than hope. You already are."

"Then I hope it's enough."

"Regardless of where we go from here, regardless of what you think, you need to know that I will always care about you. I will always worry about you."

As I stared at her, I believed her. It wasn't enough. I wanted more. "Is that all I get?" I asked.

"For now."

The following Monday was league night. Gover, Gary, Decker, and I had joined a bowling league at downtown's Modesto Bowl. We enjoyed bowling and it kept us inside on hot summer nights. The bowling alley had several pinball machines, which occupied me before our matches started. I wasn't bad, but I was an amateur compared to Doug Baldwin, an elementary school classmate and Little League teammate, who had lost his leg to cancer. He was a wizard on the pinball. Another kid we saw regularly was Lee Renner, who worked there. He was a year younger. He had worked at Modesto Bowl for years and had made enough money to buy his own car. Pretty impressive.

Gary and Decker were scratch bowlers. Their good averages carried mine and Gover's inconsistent averages. Except for one night when Gover got hot. He was in the zone and on his way to rolling a "300." The rest of the bowlers, the waitresses, and the bar flies drifted down to our lane as the word spread. Gov kept knocking pins down. He couldn't get the ball back fast enough. Unfortunately, in the ninth frame, he managed to bang the ball against his calf as he released, and threw a gutter ball. That was it for the perfect game.

Everyone but me had their own shoes and ball. Gover had gotten into the game because his dad, Cal, had bowled in Buffalo. Cal had quite a collection of bowling shirts he'd worn in various leagues. Instead of buying our own matching shirts, we all picked one of Cal's. Of course, they all said "Cal" on the front of the shirt, which confused our opponents. Another unorthodox thing we did was smuggle beer into the alley in our ball bags. Our justification was that it would save money, but we also did it simply to do it. A couple matches into the season, we were called into a league meeting, which took place in the Turtle Creek Saloon bar. The president of the league told us they knew about our smuggling and had agreed to kick us out of the league. We toasted them with our contraband beer and left. That was the end of our summer bowling.

CHAPTER 39

Another way we kept cool during the summer was to drive to the coast on our days off. The last time I'd been to Santa Cruz was following our senior year, the summer of '66. It was a salty-aired, refreshing memory.

The Beach Boys' 8-track whirred in the tape deck, propelling us over the hill to Santa Cruz. "Surfin' Safari" and "Surfin' U.S.A" filled our ears and minds. We were escaping the hot, dry, suffocating valley. We were seeking the cool, clear, cleansing Pacific Ocean. And the blonded, bikinied surfer babes.

Terry Shaw drove his '55 Chevy with the two surfboards hanging ten for dear life, while Mark Peterson snoozed, swaddled in his Block "D" jacket. Jim Haub tail-gated in his '55 Chevy Nomad station wagon with its own boards. Robert Zeff, with me riding shotgun and white-knuckling it, power-drifted his canary yellow '65 Mustang through the Santa Cruz mountains. Dave Bengston and Jim Coito hunkered down in the back seat. Roberto's customized stereo echoed off the redwooded canyons.

We were the Valley Boys, the Sissified Surfers, who skateboarded and belly-whomped the Curve because the ocean was a lifetime and lifestyle away. We wore Pendletons, or striped surfer shirts, baggies, *Huarache* sandals, and our semi-long, bushy blonde hair with sweeping bangs resembling the Banzai Pipeline.

Zeff had tucked pints of brandy and sloe gin in the Mustang's air cleaner so we wouldn't get busted if the CHP stopped us. For us high school graduates, the legal drinking age was a few years off. We never got to toast the setting sun at the beach because some loser surfer hoods spied the liberated bottles on the back-seat floor and got to them first. We found the dead soldiers lying on the sand near the parking lot.

We cruised Beach Street and the Cocoanut Grove because that was where the action was. Shaw, Peterson, and Haub found the girls because they knew what to say and how to say it. Bengston and Coito looked for trouble because it came looking for them. Roberto fiddled with his stereo because that's what he knew and how to do it. I walked alone along the beach because I didn't know any better and had no place else to go. The cool, salty air and screeching gulls were comforting.

Jan and Dean serenaded us as the sun sank into the ocean. And we journeyed home. Back to dusty reality.

The dented, copper-colored Opal sat in front of 1532. Gover, Gary, Wally, and I sat inside the dining room playing pinochle and drinking beer. Wally had driven down from the family ranch in Fort Bragg to see what Modesto was all about. He'd never been. We gave him the twenty-five-cent tour. The landmarks: The Arch, Mancini Bowl, the McHenry Mansion and Library. The Schools: Garrison and Beard elementaries, Roosevelt Junior High, Grace Davis High, Modesto Junior College. The Hangouts: The Curve, Nunes Drop, the pool hall, Phil's Smokehouse. The Bars: Straw Hat Pizza, H&L Tavern, Voyage East, Manjo's, The Fable Room, The Sandalwood. The Parks: Pike's, Graceada, Mellis, Beard Brook, Kewin; the places where we played softball and The Mud Bowl.

I mention that the Opal was dented because, as Wally was taking the curve on Orangeburg before Garrison Elementary School, someone coming the other direction didn't make the curve and plowed into the Opal. Wally was pissed, but resigned. "A remembrance of my visit to Modesto," he said.

Hank Williams played on the stereo. The pyramid was becoming monumental. Like we had the night of The Silo incident, each time we played cards and drank beer, we built a beer pyramid. It drove Mom crazy. She was a meticulous housekeeper and the thought of sticky beer on her clean floors was almost more than she could handle. But, the four of us were a force she was willing to tolerate.

Gary and I were partners. Gover and Wally teamed up. Gary and I had been winning steadily, mostly because our opponents were sloshed. I could tell because Wally would get this crooked, shit-eating grin when he was toast. His lip was definitely curling.

"You're set," I said, subtracting their "39" bid from their dwindling total.

"Thought I could sneak that club through at the end," Gover said.

"Nice try," Gary said.

"How's the ranch?" I asked Walt.

"Keeping me busy," Wally replied. "Clearing acres of dead wood."

I was hoping the question and his inebriation might loosen him up enough to talk about the friend he'd lost in 'Nam. Or Luci. It wasn't working. She was gone and Gover said Wally was pissed. Luci hadn't come up.

"When you going back to Davis?" I asked.

"Mid-September probably," he answered. "Fall quarter starts end of September."

"September 29th," Gary chimed in. "First class on Monday, October

16th," Gary clarified. He knew because, after a year at CSU Stanislaus, he was transferring to Davis in the fall and would be our roommate.

"Any other plans for the summer?" I asked, trying to get more specifics on what he'd been up to after school ended.

"Help on the ranch. Ride a little. Work out a little. Drink a little," he replied, toasting us all and draining his Gold Crown.

"You heard from Luci?" I asked.

His eyes narrowed. "No, have you?"

"No," I answered.

"Jealous?"

"Hell, no. I've got a girlfriend."

"For now," Gary added.

"She's called. I asked her to stop," Walt said.

"Why?"

"I've got some things to figure out."

"Like?"

"Easy, cowgirl," Gover warned.

"Like why my buddy had to die. And for what? Like what am I going to do about it? Like I'm a Marine through and through and I'm beginning to doubt that. Like there's people out there doing shit I don't like. So, all's I want to do is drink beer, play cards, and listen to some country."

"How about some Cash?" I suggested, knowing it was time to move on.

"That works," Wally said. We listened to "A Boy Named Sue" from Johnny's new album, *At San Quentin*.

Wally rolled out early the next morning. I received my postcard grades that afternoon. Two "As" and a "pass." I guess I knew geography better than I thought.

CHAPTER 40

"All the News that Fits" – July Edition

Brian Jones of the Rolling Stones dies. The Stones hold a free concert in Hyde Park. The Atlanta Pop Festival, featuring Janis Joplin and Led Zeppelin, draws 140,000. The first troops are withdrawn from Vietnam, as a battalion from the 9th Infantry Division are sent home. The 16th annual Newport Jazz Festival experiments with its traditional format, showcasing jazz, soul, and rock acts like Dave Brubeck, Miles Davis, Jethro Tull, Ten Years After, and Led Zeppelin. Apollo 11 is launched. Neil Armstrong and Buzz Aldrin walk on the moon. Joe Namath sells his interest in a New York bar in order to play for the NFL. Mary Jo Kopechne dies under mysterious circumstances involving Senator Edward M. Kennedy. Eddy Merckx of Belgium wins the 56th Tour de France bicycle race. Francisco Franco names Juan Carlos as heir to the Spanish throne. Blind Faith plays a free concert in Hyde Park. In the wake of the Orange Day parades and "marching season," rioting breaks out in many cities in Northern Ireland, including Derry, Belfast, and Dungive. The National League wins the 40th All-Star baseball game and Willy McCovey is named Most Valuable Player. Senator Kennedy announces he will not run for president in 1972. Chicago police engage in a gun battle with the Black Panthers. The first gay pride parade is held in New York City in reaction to the Stonewall riots. New book releases include *The Three Daughters of Madame Liang* by Pearl S. Buck; *You Must Know Everything*, Isaac Babel; *The Pill*, Robert W. Kistner; *Sons*, Evan Hunter; and *The Making of the President* by Theodore H. White. *Man Better Man*, *Take One Step*, and *Hoofers* open on stage. New films include *Castle Keep* with Burt Lancaster, *How to Commit Marriage* featuring Bob Hope and Jackie Gleason, *Putney Swope*, *The Stewardesses*, and *Easy Rider*. New music includes Tim Buckley's *Happy/Sad*, It's a Beautiful Day's debut album, *Led Zeppelin II*, The Doors' *The Soft Parade*, Leslie West's *Mountain*, and "Give Peace a Chance" by John Lennon and the Plastic Ono Band, which is released in the U.S. on the Fourth of July.

Although I wasn't a Stones fan, I was shocked and saddened to hear of Brian

Jones' death on July 3rd. He was found by his girlfriend, Anna Wohlin, at the bottom of the swimming pool at his home in England. Rumor had it that drugs were involved. Jones founded the band and was the original leader. Bassist Bill Wyman was quoted in a later issue of *Rolling Stone*, "He formed the band. He chose the members. He named the band. He chose the music we played. He got us gigs. He was very influential, very important, and then slowly lost it – highly intelligent – and just kind of wasted it and blew it all away."

Two days later, the Stones hosted a free concert in Hyde Park. The concert had been scheduled for a few weeks, so they could announce that Mick Taylor had replaced Jones as guitarist. The Stones dedicated the concert to Jones. Jagger read excerpts from "Adonais," a poem written by Percy Bysshe Shelley about the death of his friend, John Keats. Stagehands released hundreds of white butterflies, which promptly died from the heat. It was a grand, but empty gesture.

It was the Stones first public concert in two years. Estimates ranged from 250,000 to 500,000 people in attendance. The British version of the Hells Angels provided security. The resemblance was in name alone. Their payment was in cups of tea. They were basically worthless. Several bands opened, including King Crimson. The Stones played fourteen songs, a mix of familiar tunes and some from a new album they were working on. Their performance was ragged and raunchy and rockin'. The Stones were back. And the good old U. S. of A. was on their radar.

Sandwiched between those two Great Britain news stories was an annual event caused by Great Britain. Our nation's birthday fell on a Friday this year. That was the best day for the Fourth of July. You got a paid holiday and the next day was Saturday. I went to the parade and sat alone. In the same spot Kelly and I had sat in since attending our first parade in 1962. The 95th edition of the parade was no disappointment. There were cars, bands, flags, equestrians, and politicians. I wondered what it would be like to sit on the back of one of the convertibles and wave to the crowds. Fortunately, there wasn't a horrific accident like the one we'd witnessed seven years ago.

In 1969, the patriotism and number of military-related parade entries were legion, on full display, and full-throated. There were no counter-protestors, but there was a lot of cheering for the red, white, and blue and some grumbling from those who opposed the war. I didn't like seeing my hometown divided like this.

I was a patriot. I loved my country. I loved the American flag. But, the flag was a piece of cloth. I wouldn't burn it, but I wouldn't drape myself in it, either. I didn't believe in "my country right or wrong." Blind patriotism was blind. Our founding fathers had established this country to fight tyranny, subjugation, and blind allegiance. We were continuing that fight.

Following the parade, I joined Gary, Gover and Nancy, and several old friends from the schools we'd attended together for some burgers, dogs, and beer at Enslen Park's Little League diamond. We played some co-ed softball. Decker was there, having gotten the holiday off from Phil's Smokehouse, where he and Gover worked part-time during the summer. The Smokehouse made beef jerky and had a plant between the Tuolumne River and Crows Landing Road. One of the fun things about Phil's was the daily poker game that took place at lunch. Nothing high stakes, but always well played. John was a good player and won regularly. Gover didn't do as well. I sat in a few times, but never won.

At the park, Decker set up a ping-pong table for some competitive table tennis. Willy brought along his Babe Ruth teammates. Stepdad Paul was manning the grill, flipping burgers and spinning dogs. Bob Buzbee and some musician classmates were playing guitars and singing folk songs. Mom was making sure everyone had a full glass.

Creatures of habit, that night we watched fireworks sitting on the fairway at the Municipal Golf Course next to Del Webb Field. It was a beautiful evening and a spectacular show. It was good being with friends; with people who knew what you were going through. I missed Kelly.

I spent the weekend kicking back, swimming, hanging out, and trying not to think about Kelly; about what I'd done to screw it up.

That same Independence Day, in a parking lot in Vallejo, a stranger approached a young couple sitting in their car. The man fired into the car, killing the woman and injuring the man. Later, Vallejo police received an anonymous call reporting a murder.

The following Tuesday, the media reported the first flights home of U.S. troops from Vietnam – 814 soldiers of the 3rd Battalion, 60th Infantry of the 2nd Brigade of the 9th Infantry Division boarded flights to McChord Air Force Base in Tacoma, Washington. For once, Tricky Dick hadn't lied. Our soldiers were coming home. It was about time. Now, if we could get them all out before any more died.

Just about a week after that, I heard on KSAN that a crowd had cut down the chain-link fence at People's Park. Demonstrators had attacked the fence with bolt cutters concealed inside bread loaves. The four guards on duty summoned help. By the time it arrived, several holes had been cut. As police drove the activists from the park and toward campus using clubs and tear gas, they were showered with rocks, bricks, cherry bombs, and other projectiles. Participants on both sides were injured. Once the attackers were pushed back, repairmen restored the fence.

The demonstration was staged in observance of Bastille Day, the French "Fourth of July." which was celebrated July 14th. On that day in 1789, a mob of French peasants stormed the Paris prison, as part of their revolt against King Louis XVI. The mob cried "bread" as they charged because Queen Marie Antoinette, when informed the peasants had no bread, replied, "Let them eat cake." Pieces of cut chain-link were handed out as souvenirs, symbolic of the Bastille bricks that were distributed to the mob in Paris 180 years before. A group of singers, accompanied by a flute, a guitar, and a harmonica, performed the "Marseillaise," the French national anthem, and also sang, "This Land is Your Land."

On Wednesday, July 16th, Apollo 11 was launched by a Saturn V rocket from Kennedy Space Center. On board were Commander Neil Armstrong, lunar module pilot Buzz Aldrin, and command module pilot Michael Collins. The lunar module was named *Eagle*. The command module was *Columbia*. The whole world was watching. For the next several days, their progress was tracked and broadcast live as they traveled toward the moon. Transmitting images of the earth back home, many observers, including Michael Collins, noted that there were no boundaries, no countries, no races or religions visible from space.

Many of the NASA personnel involved, as well as journalists and broadcasters, commented that perhaps this stunning accomplishment would bring people together in what had become a bitterly divided country and world. Maybe it would provide a brief time out from all the rancor and distrust. I know I was entranced and proud of what my country had accomplished.

It was time to work to pay for my next year of college – what might be my last year. I'd been hired for the summer by Hunt-Wesson Foods to be a sample puller, or "box boy," at the Del Rio weigh station. This station was one of many locations owned by the canneries, like Hunt's, Tri-Valley, and Del Monte, where farmers could bring their varieties of peaches for weighing and grading. The grade, or quality, of the peach determined its value. During the peak of the season, there were usually two graders at each station.

Most of the graders were teachers, or college kids. They moved from station to station, so they wouldn't get to know a weighmaster, or farmer, too well. The weighmaster was also a teacher, or college student. Their job was to tag the bins with color-coded, paper tags that indicated the name of the grower and the variety of the peach. They would weigh the peaches as they came in and weigh the tractor and trailer, or small truck, once the peach bins had been offloaded on the concrete slab by the trailer, or lifted off the flatbed truck by a union forklift driver, who had been supplied by another company. Most of the fruit came into our station in four bin lots on a trailer pulled by a tractor, or truck. Each station had a weighmaster and an assistant weighmaster. I had gone to school with both of ours. Jerry Bird was the weighmaster and Dale Muratore was the assistant. The forklift driver was a guy named Bob Ubaldi, who lived in Patterson.

As the box boy, it was my job to pull a sample from a bin that had been randomly marked in chalk by one of the graders. The forklift driver would put the bin on a Blackwelder sample puller. The bin would slide down rollers on a short track and into a hydraulic, metal-framed "box." I operated the hydraulic lift, which would raise the bin and dump the peaches onto a rubber conveyor belt. The belt had staggered holes with slotted strips of rubber that would allow peaches to randomly drop down into a chute, which would fill a large, gray plastic bin.

When full, I would weigh it, dump the bin onto the wooden grading table, which was illuminated by an overhead light. The rest of the peaches would run off the conveyor belt and fill an empty bin sitting on a track at the other end. I would transfer the tag from the sample bin to the new bin, the forklift driver would stack the newly-filled bin with the rest of the fruit bins it arrived with, or load it onto a waiting semi-truck for shipment to the cannery. Before the summer was out, I'd also been hired part-time to drive the forklift. The percentage of good and bad peaches, based on uniformity of size and free of defects, like scab, worms, scale, split pits, or brown rot, would be calculated against the weight of the sample to assess the quality of the load.

It was a dirty job. Even on the hottest days, you wore a long-sleeved shirt, Levi's, hat, and bandana because the peach fuzz was everywhere. Your biggest concern was that the bin didn't get jammed in the sample puller; or that the bottom or sides of a damaged, or old bin, didn't pop open; or that the conveyor belt would run too fast to get a good sample. I sometimes had to pull and push the start lever to slow the belt to get an acceptable sample.

The Del Rio station was located near the country club along the Stanislaus River. It was a long drive to the edge of town. The office was on the south end of the station. It was a green painted cinder block with two ancient wood desks, a bathroom, and a screened window looking out on the scales. The mechanical sampler and the grading area were on the west side under a corrugated shed. Everything sat on a concrete slab that was big enough to hold the weigh station, the grading area, stacks of empty bins, and at least one double-trailer semi.

Each morning, I parked Ugly Orange under a walnut tree that stood between McHenry Avenue to the east and the huge stacks of empty bins to the west. It was cool and quiet, so I could snooze on those days when it was slow, or I'd had too much to drink the night before. I'd also prop two wooden lug boxes against one pole of the grading shelter and snooze there when it was quiet. I spent time talking with the graders, many of whom I knew, and reading.

That summer, I read Hermann Hesse, including *Siddhartha* and *The Glass Bead Game*. That was also the summer that J.R.R. Tolkien's *Lord of the Rings* was popular. I read *The Hobbit*, as well as the trilogy. Stretched out on my lug box in the middle of an orchard in the middle of the valley, I was transported to Middle Earth. It was one of the most interesting and exciting books I'd ever read. It was on a par with my other favorite authors, Ray Bradbury and Ernest Hemingway. I re-read Bradbury's *Dandelion Wine* and Hemingway's *A Moveable Feast*, which I did ritually every summer.

Bradbury's coming-of-age book was the one book I read regularly because it evoked the magic of summer. The wine made from dandelions picked from the front yard was a metaphor for summer – all the magic and memories of summer captured in each bottle. As the twelve-year-old protagonist, Douglas Spaulding, said, "Dandelion wine. The words were summer on the tongue. The wine was summer caught and stoppered." Following Doug's joys and heartaches reminded me of my growing up. Instead of Green Town, Illinois, it was Modesto, California. Instead of best friend John Huff, it was Gary Rawlings. Instead of Cream-Sponge Para Litefoot sneakers, it was Adidas. Along with Douglas, I experienced a happiness machine, the Lonely One, a time machine, the Green Machine, his best friend's leaving, a Tarot Witch, Mr. Jonas and his wagon full of miracles. The book was a simply and wonderfully written chronicle of small-town America and a simpler yesterday.

There are those who might have considered my love of this book a wallowing in nostalgia – a sentimentality for the past, a yearning for the "good old days," or a "warm childhood." Nostalgia came from the Greek word *nóstos*, or homecoming, and *álgos*, meaning "pain," or "ache." *Nostos* was the central theme of Homer's *The Odyssey*, the epic which followed the hero Odysseus, as he returned home from the Trojan War. Nostalgia was once considered a disease. A Swiss physician applied the phrase to the condition seen in soldiers fighting far from home. Because the "good old days" weren't always so good, nostalgia could simply be considered bad memory. For me, especially now, the book and the nostalgia it evoked, provided comfort. I was happy to immerse myself in it.

I enjoyed *A Moveable Feast* because there was a part of me that dreamed of being a novelist like Hemingway. I appreciated his spare, masculine prose. Paris in the 1920s was exotic. His interactions with James Joyce, F. Scott Fitzgerald, Gertrude Stein, and the other writers, artists, and Parisians were fascinating. Living hand-to-mouth in a garret seemed so bohemian. If I ever made it to Europe, Paris would be a priority.

The Glass Bead Game was the last novel written by Hesse. It was published in Switzerland in 1943 and translated into English in 1949. Hesse was awarded the Nobel Prize in Literature for his body of work in 1946. It was a tough read, compared with his other books. The game and its rules were not easy to follow. Playing it took many years of studying music, mathematics, and cultural history. The game synthesized all aspects of the arts and sciences. The goal of play was for each participant to make some connection between seemingly unrelated topics. It was much too cerebral.

I had read nearly all of Hesse's works. The romanticism of his early novels was especially intriguing. I had enjoyed *Peter Camenzind, Rosshalde, Narcissus and Goldmund, Demian,* and *Steppenwolf.* There was something about the loner in the last novel that felt close to home. There were elements, including the "magic theatre," which were almost psychedelic, helping explain its current popularity.

Quitting time at the weigh station depended on the last load of the day, which, most of the time, came in between five and six. Some growers would try to sneak in a load of slop at the end of the day, hoping to get a break, thanks to a tired crew of graders. It rarely worked. When the peaches were ripening, we might be there as late as eight, or nine. Mother Nature always made the final call.

Once or twice a week, Gary, Gover, Gant, and me, would gather at Straw Hat on McHenry for pitchers of dark beer and pizza. I was underage, but the kids behind the counter, some of whom we knew and most of whom were as young as us, having recently turned 21, rarely checked my ID. If it was somebody we didn't know, I'd use my fake ID, or order a Coke, because it looked enough like dark beer, and we'd sit in the back. I'd drink the Coke, dump the ice in an empty pitcher, and fill the plastic glass with beer. There was nothing better than that first slug of icy cold beer after a long day of pulling samples, grading peaches, or shoveling silage.

CHAPTER 41

Around the middle of July, I read about the plans to build a drain that would allow the large factory farms owned by the Westlands Water District to discharge irrigation wastewater into the Kesterson Reservoir, located in the Kesterson National Wildlife Refuge, which was part of the San Luis National Wildlife Refuge. The massive amount of irrigation done on these farms, some of which were as big as 2200 acres, was leading to a rise in the groundwater level. The excess water was pooling, largely due to the fact that there was a layer of clay below most of the topsoil, which acted like a massive bathtub. The crops were being damaged by the pooled water. It struck me that this was a recipe for disaster. All those chemicals being used on the farmlands to kill pests would be collected in a toxic stew. It didn't make any sense, but the farmers were convinced they had no choice, since their livelihood depending on feeding most of the world.

Thank goodness it was a slow day at the grading station when the two men in dark suits, sunglasses, and shiny shoes walked toward me. I was doing my usual mindless job of sweeping up the endless mounds of dirt the tractors and trucks dumped on the slab when unloading their bins. It was like shoveling shit against the tide. I didn't see them until I swept dust onto their shoes. I stopped.

"Michael Wright?" the shorter of the two asked, although they were both over six feet.

"That's me," I replied.

"I'm Special Agent Mullens," the speaker said, as he pulled his credentials from an inside coat pocket and displayed them in a motion he had obviously been trained to do and had practiced many times.

"This is Special Agent Rieger," he introduced the second man, who also flashed his creds. "We need to ask you a few questions."

"How'd you know I was here?"

"Your mother gave us good directions."

"You were at my house?"

"Yes, sir."

"I hope you didn't scare her."

"We didn't give her many details," said Agent Rieger.

"What can I do for you?" I asked.

"Is there someplace we could sit?" Agent Mullens asked.

"Everyone's at lunch. We can sit in the office." I sat in the wooden chair next to the massive oak desk that filled one corner. The two agents sat on creaky wooden chairs facing me. Agent Mullens removed a small, lined, spiral notepad from his inside coat pocket and flipped it open.

"Do you know a Lucius Zinaida Dolgushkin?" he asked. I was stunned and hoped it didn't show. She had never told me her middle name.

"Why?" I asked.

"Not your concern," said Agent Rieger.

"I guess it is 'cause you're here," I remarked.

"Answer our questions, please," Agent Mullens prompted.

"Yeah, sure. I know her from college. We took some classes together."

"You do anything else with her besides classes?" Agent Mullens asked.

"A little personal, aren't we?"

"I meant, have you been involved with any of her extra-curricular activities?"

"We attended a march, or two. That's about it."

"You ever join her for meetings on– or off–campus?"

I hesitated, then said, "No."

Mullens jotted a note and asked, "Did she invite you to?"

"A couple times."

"To meet with whom?"

"SDS. Black Panthers. Weather Underground." The two men glanced at each other. "The usual social clubs," I added, trying to be funny.

They weren't amused. "Why didn't you go?" Agent Rieger asked.

"I wasn't interested."

"Why?"

"Too radical for my tastes."

"What are your tastes in radicals, Mr. Wright?" asked Agent Mullens.

"I don't have any."

"Our records indicate otherwise."

"Okay, I've listened to some speeches and gone to some rallies. I never blew anything up."

"That's not funny, Mr. Wright."

"You two really don't have a sense of humor."

"We do, but not about that."

"Has Miss Dolgushkin been in touch lately?" Agent Mullens asked.

"Not since school got out."

"Do you know her whereabouts?"

"Probably in Davis, or home in San Francisco."

"We've tried those places, but have been unable to locate her."

"I'm sorry to hear that," I said.

"Not likely," said Agent Rieger, who was turning into the bad cop in this scenario.

"Do you have any plans to travel?"

"No, sticking close for the summer."

"Your home address and phone number are good in case we need to reach you?"

"Haven't changed since you asked my mother," I answered, again being the smart-ass, although I wasn't feeling real smart.

"Good," said Agent Mullens. Thank you for your time." He extended his hand, which I shook.

"Good day," Agent Rieger said, as we shook.

"See you around."

Both men exited the side door. I followed them and watched them get into a black Crown Victoria sedan and slowly pull onto McHenry Avenue and drive south toward town.

I had lied and they knew I had lied.

The big news that weekend was the death of a young woman on Chappaquiddick Island off Massachusetts. She had drowned when the car she was riding in had plunged off a small bridge. What made it newsworthy was that the driver was Senator Edward M. "Ted" Kennedy of Massachusetts, brother of an assassinated president and an assassinated senator and a potential presidential candidate himself.

On Sunday, July 20th, the United States made history. Mission commander Neil Armstrong and pilot Buzz Aldrin landed the lunar module Eagle on the surface of the moon. Armstrong became the first person to step onto the lunar surface. Aldrin joined him twenty minutes later. They spent over two hours outside the spacecraft, collecting lunar material to bring back to Earth. Michael Collins piloted the command module *Columbia* circling in lunar orbit.

The landing was broadcast on live TV to an international audience. We watched as a family. My little sisters stared at the screen from the outside patio, where they stood knee-deep in a wading pool. When Armstrong stepped onto the lunar surface, he said, "One small step for man, one giant leap for mankind." We would learn later that, in his excitement, Armstrong omitted a word, which changed the meaning of the sentence. He was supposed to say,

"One small step for a man, one giant leap for mankind." It would create a minor public relations nightmare for NASA and Armstrong. I liked what he said better than what he intended to say.

The next day was an unusually slow day at Del Rio. I was able to knock off at 2 o'clock. I hopped into Ugly Orange and pointed it toward Davis. I needed to see Luci. Face to face.

CHAPTER 42

Luci was crashing at a friend's trailer at the mobile home park across the tracks from Larry Blake's. I was able to find her because I talked her old apartment manager into giving me the address. It wasn't difficult. She believed in young love.

Luci and I sat in the long, narrow living room of the trailer. She hadn't changed much. She retained that militant look.

"It's quite a web you've been weaving," I said.

"What makes you say that?" she replied. She was being coy. A trait I hadn't minded before, but now found annoying.

"The FBI visited Mike Walt, too."

"How do you know?"

"I called him."

"I hope their visit wasn't too painful."

"Scared the crap out of me."

"Oh, my tiny scaredy-cat," she pouted, resurrecting the undeniable attraction I'd felt when we first met.

"I don't need the feds keeping a file on me."

"They already are."

"Thanks to you."

"You're welcome."

"I don't need them thinking I've done something. I've got enough other shit going on."

"There's no turning back now."

"That was your plan all along. For me, for Wally, for anybody else you've seduced."

"Recruited," she corrected me.

"Once we're compromised, there's no escape."

"Fruit of the poisoned tree." I stood. "Study your history, son," she added.

She stood and came close; close enough I could smell her breath.

"You could stay the night," she said. "It's just little old me." I looked into her eyes. The hardness there said a different story.

"I'll take a rain check," I said and left. It was an unpleasant drive home.

I sat alone on the slab waiting for the next load. I was listening to the All-Star baseball game through the earpiece of my white Sony transistor radio. Three days after man had landed on the moon, Willie McCovey of the Giants hit two moon shots to lead the National League over the American League 9-3 at RFK Memorial Stadium. The game was played on Wednesday afternoon instead of Tuesday evening because a torrential downpour in the Washington, D.C. area forced postponement.

My somber mood was lifted Friday night when Kelly and I met. For old time's sake, we went to Hob Nob Pizza. It was quiet for a summer evening.

"Where were you Monday?" Kelly asked.

"I was around," I said, trying to cover the fact that I hadn't told her about my trip to see Luci.

"Not according to your mom. Or Gary. Or Gover. Do you have some new friends I don't know about? Or, maybe some old friends I'd rather not know about?"

"I had to get something straight with her."

"Is that all you got straight?"

"Now, you're being crude."

"Really. When my supposed boyfriend drives an hour, or more, to see another woman in another town, I'm not supposed to be the least bit concerned?"

"She's a classmate."

"Get real," Kelly hissed. "Take me home."

Reluctantly, I did. As I drove home, I kept flashing on the image of the Greek god, Narcissus, who basically lost what he had by wanting something he didn't have. Not satisfied with his own beauty, he fell in love with the beauty of his own image reflected in the stream. He drowned trying to kiss it.

The news over the next few days was mostly about Ted Kennedy. He had pleaded guilty to causing the accident that caused the death of the young woman, whose name was Mary Jo Kopechne. A few days later, he announced he would not be running for President in 1972. He had been expected to challenge Nixon. With the Kennedy name and the work he'd done in the senate, he had a decent chance of beating the incumbent. Now, our best hope of kicking Tricky Dick out of office had made a truly bad decision, which seemed to continue the Kennedy curse. I was pissed. I wanted Nixon out. It has been said Republicans get in trouble over money, Democrats over sex. Unfortunately, Kennedy proved the cliché true by thinking with something other than his brain.

I was able to take a break and not think about Kelly, Luci, or the FBI when I went to Willy's Babe Ruth playoff game at Enslen Park. Foster Farms had finished first in the National League East. Unfortunately, they lost and were eliminated. Salas Brothers would win it all and would face Lodi in the regional playoffs.

July ended with letters arriving at the *San Francisco Chronicle*, the *San Francisco Examiner*, and the *Vallejo Times-Herald*. The letters revealed details of the July 4th murder in Vallejo that only the killer could know.

CHAPTER 43

"All the News that Fits" – August Edition

It is a month of rock concerts, starting with one in Atlantic City; followed by Woodstock; Isle of Wight, which features Bob Dylan's comeback performance; and the Texas International Pop Festival, where 120,000 people rock out. Civil rights marchers are attacked in Northern Ireland. President Nixon continues the work initiated by previous administrations to guarantee equal employment opportunity by initiating the "Philadelphia Order." Don Drysdale retires from the Los Angeles Dodgers due to shoulder issues. More clashes are reported on the Russia-Chinese border. A ticker tape parade is held in New York for the Apollo 11 astronauts. The Wild West Festival in San Francisco is called off due to the threat of violence. Hurricane Camille causes damage and destruction across much of the Gulf Coast. The Gap opens in San Francisco, selling record albums and Levi's. Mick Jagger is accidentally wounded while filming *Ned Kelly* in Australia. Taichung City, Taiwan, defeats the Briarwood Little League of Santa Clara, California, in the Little League World Series. TWA Flight 840 is hijacked after departing Rome and diverted to Damascus, Syria. New book releases include *The Wolfling* by Sterling North; *Dona Flor and Her Two Husbands*, Jorge Amado; *Fat City*, Leonard Gardner; *The Poseidon Adventure*, Paul Gallico; and *Mile High* by Richard Condon. *Butterfly McQueen and Friends* and *Arena Conta Zumbi* open on stage. New films include Haskell Wexler's *Medium Cool*, Woody Allen's *Take the Money and Run*, Arlo Guthrie's *Alice's Restaurant*, *De Sade*, *The Cycle Savages* starring Bruce Dern, and Francis Ford Coppola's *The Rain People*. New music includes Creedence Clearwater Revival's *Green River*, *The Association*, supergroup Blind Faith's debut album, *Boz Scaggs*, *Touch of Gold* by Johnny Rivers, *The Stooges*, and *Santana*.

The first Friday of August was the last MoBand concert of the season. I skipped it. I didn't want to see anybody. Instead, I drove around town, eventually ending at Dad's grave at Lakewood Cemetery, which was down the road in Hughson. It was a beautiful setting along the Tuolumne River. The site had been chosen because explorer John C. Frémont buried members of his scouting party there during his second expedition in the west. Florence Owens Thompson, the woman who was photographed by Dorothea Lange and became known as "Migrant Mother," would be buried here in 1983.

I squatted cross-legged in front of the bronze plaque where my father's ashes had been interred.

"I'm not you," I said. "I didn't sign up at seventeen-and-a-half. I didn't fight in Saipan and Tinian. I didn't see all the things you saw and never talked about. I'm not brave like you. I don't think I'm a coward. I hope I'm not.

"I'd like to think I'd do what I had to do. I can't even shoot a bird, how am I going to kill a man? I will serve honorably if that's what I have to do. I wish you were here. I need to talk with you. Paul is great, but he's not you."

"I wasn't brave, either," said a familiar voice behind me. I wasn't surprised. I was expecting him. I stood and faced my father, who was dressed in the same clothes I had seen him wearing on New Year's Day standing on the side of Carpenter Road.

"I don't know that I could do what you did."

"You'd be surprised."

"Grampa Owl served. You served."

"Those wars weren't the same as this one."

"You never talked about it."

"They weren't good memories. Except for my buddies."

"Who you named us after."

"To keep their memories alive."

"The only things you kept were the ceramic sculpture of the Japanese man and a book about the war in the Pacific."

"Interesting the things you remember."

"He was a scribe. He had a tiny pen that fit in his hand. Mom was worried we would lose it. I think the book was called *Follow Me*."

"I kept a few medals."

"Which we never saw."

"They were in a box with my yearbooks and some other things from the past."

"We used to go through that book. I kind of remember that Tim scribbled in it."

"He did."

"It looked amazing."

"It was. But not the way you think."

"I guess not. We were kids."

"I hate war. I'm against this one."

"A lot aren't."

"They've never been there."

"A lot of veterans support it."

"They're fools. Or, they've forgotten."

"Mom's against it."

"She doesn't want to lose her sons."

"Paul, too."

"He's a wise man."

"Good for Mom, too."

"I'm glad. For her. And you kids."

"Like you, he told me he'd take me to Canada if that's what I wanted to do."

"I hope it doesn't come to that."

"I don't understand why people and the government believe in this. All of it. Why don't they stand up to the bullshit?" I asked.

"Language."

"Sorry."

"They don't have the guts. They want to keep what they've got."

"What about the greater good?"

"They've lost sight of it."

"That's why we're in the streets."

"That's democracy."

"I don't think this is a democracy anymore. Maybe it never was. It's really an oligarchy. A small group of wealthy people controlling the country. The founding fathers were rich white men telling everyone else what to do. Nothing has changed in almost two hundred years."

"There's more people. More like you. Smart, concerned, involved, and vocal."

"Hasn't made any difference."

"I think it has. You've got their attention."

"But not their hearts and minds. Or their balls."

"Patience and perseverance."

"I'm running out of time."

"You'll know what to do. You'll make the right choice."

"How?"

"Use your own good judgment." I smiled, recalling the familiar words he used when one of us kids tried to manipulate him, or Mom, into making a tough decision for us.

"People will think I'm yellow."

"I don't like that phrase."

"A coward then."

"There are too many of you for that to happen. You're all good kids."

"I don't understand how people think war is the answer. I've studied history. War never solves anything. It may change something for a while, but it's never permanent. And always seems to lead to another war. There's never an issue, or a disagreement, that can't be negotiated by reasonable people."

"Unless they're crazy."

"They never last, either."

"Power to the people." I smiled at my square father using this hip jargon.

"People need to study their history," I continued. "War destroys lives. It destroys places. I look at paintings, or photographs, of the destruction that follows in the wake of a war. Of all the things that have to be rebuilt."

"Anybody who has been to war would never send anybody to war."

"I wish you, and people who think like you, were in charge."

"Every day, I'm reminded of the war. Of what we lost, what we all lost, when I see this." He raised the sleeve of his jacket and shirt to reveal the tattoo on his left arm.

It got to the point where we didn't see it anymore. I guess that's the way it was with tattoos. My father's arms and my arms were much the same. Except for the faded ink. I recalled sitting on his lap and staring at the bulldog with the spiked collar and the furled banner that read: "United States Marine Corps." It took some serious prodding, or alcohol, to get him to tell stories about the war in the Pacific. He never liked talking about it. He went in at seventeen-and-a-half and came out much older. His father accepted his high school diploma, while he was in a foxhole in Saipan.

"This is my rifle, this is my gun," he would repeat the chant he learned in basic training to distinguish between the two. "This is for shooting, this is for fun." He would chuckle, as he remembered his fellow recruits forced to walk through camp holding their penis when they forgot and called their rifle their gun. He wouldn't smile as much when he talked about going on patrol with those in his squad who wanted to do some souveniring. My dad was a natural leader and was soon called upon to lead others. He would frown when he told us about one of his men puking his guts out when the bloated corpse of a Japanese soldier, who had been burned alive by a flamethrower, cracked open and oozed yellow goo, as the peach-fuzzed grunt tried to remove the dead man's samurai sword.

My father was a rookie member of the greatest generation. Young men who were called upon to do things that were less than great. The tattoo was cool, but not what it represented. He wasn't always proud of what he had done. He was reminded of it every day as we stared at the pale stain of the Devil Dog.

"Take responsibility for your actions," he continued. "That's all you can do."

"I will. I don't expect special treatment. I'll handle whatever comes my way. Whatever it is. Whatever it takes."

"Every father wants his children to be better than he was," he said.

"That's a heavy load."

"You are. I'm proud of you." And he was gone.

CHAPTER 44

I was feeling paranoid. I kept seeing men in dark suits, sunglasses, and shiny shoes driving unmarked cars everywhere I went. It was time to get out of town.

That Sunday, which was my next off day, I was asked to go caving with Threlfall, Decker, and Magruder. They had gotten into spelunking, or exploring caves, while we were in high school. They had formed a club as seniors so they could collect dues to pay for equipment and outings. The real reason was to lampoon the rest of the campus clubs. Their advisor was the librarian, Zarah Virgin.

The club was called the Stanislaus Speleological Association. The president of the club was an experienced caver named Marshall Bryden. He had been the janitor at Garrison, my elementary school. He had a bomb shelter on his property. We had ridden our bikes out to see it during one of Mr. Leach's field trips. I realized that a major attraction of caving for my friends was that they could grow pot in a relatively secure place. The soil was perfect, the temperature was right, and it was hidden. They soon were smoking "Cave City Tops." I didn't partake during our trips because I didn't like being out of control. I couldn't imagine being stoned in a cave.

We traveled to Moaning Cavern in Vallecito, which was in the gold country near Angels Camp. The cavern held the largest vertical chamber in a public cavern that you could visit in California. It was big enough to fit the Statue of Liberty.

There were four of us. The lead guy and the guy bringing up the rear wore headlamps. We wore beat-up clothes because we were going to get filthy. The last time they'd been here, Magruder found a new chamber off one of the smaller chambers. But, to get there, you had to wriggle through an impossibly narrow tube connecting the two chambers. As I looked at the hole, my latent claustrophobia tapped on my shoulder. But, the last thing I wanted to do was chicken out in front of my peers. Magruder lead the way. Threlfall went next, followed by me and Johnny D.

The tunnel was damp and humid. The only way you could navigate was to tuck your arms close to your sides and squirm forward like an inch worm. I could barely see Threlfall's feet in front of my face and I could hear Decker giggling behind me. He was ripped. I wished I was.

The thoughts raced through my panicked brain, ricocheting around like stray bullets. Thoughts of Luci and what she was mixed up with; images of Kelly and how badly I had treated her; memories of my father; but mostly worries about the draft and the war. None of the alternatives were appealing. Being classified a conscientious objector seemed unlikely. Both Mom and Paul would support my exile to Canada. Cutting off a toe or finger, which sounded horrible, was against the law. Joining the reserves, or the National Guard, wasn't realistic. I could see if another doctor would write me a letter about my jaw, or my spleen. I could claim economic hardship, but we were lower middle class, so that wasn't going to fly. If I became a father, that would exempt me, but I wasn't ready for full-time fatherhood.

Someone suggested shooting a bald eagle, which was a felony, but I wasn't sure where I would find a bald eagle, I had no rifle to shoot it with, and my history of killing live things was checkered. If I could afford braces, rumor had it that would disqualify me. The chances of being rejected by wearing a dress and claiming I was homosexual were as slim as mutilating my body. Acting bat-shit crazy like the kid from Downey did was nuts. Someone suggested I could rob a bank and go to jail, because that's where I was destined to go if I told them to go to hell and resisted induction. Supposedly losing weight would rule you out. Unfortunately, I wasn't that disciplined. I loved chips and beer too much. Lastly, I could try to get my student deferment extended with the hope that, in time, something insane would happen, like the draft being abolished, or the war ending. They all seemed like extreme long shots. It was a jumble.

As I writhed forward, keeping an eye on Threlfall's heels and Magruder's dim light, I swore to whatever God was listening that if I got out of this hole, I would get my shit together, get the information I needed, and do something. Make a decision and get on with it. Whatever it was.

As someone told me, if you weren't the lead dog, the view never changed. It didn't for the rest of the trip.

We did many stupid things growing up. As teen-agers, as young men, as young adults. We were adolescent and arrogant. Nothing could touch us. The stories were too numerous to recall. There had been so many opportunities to bite the bullet. We rode box cars out to Del Rio to fish golf balls out of water hazards. We drove through 4-way stops in the country with our headlights off. We paid a bum to buy us sloe gin. We took good and bad drugs. We had safe and not so safe sex. We drove drunk. Got into fights. Partied with lowlifes. Played the daredevil. Taunted Lucifer.

Our survival stories were often hilarious; if they hadn't been frightening. Case in point. The shit-wagon incident. When the Johnson family moved west, they drove out in a 1958 Buick Century Caballero Estate Wagon. A monster with a half-ton of chrome. When they bought a new Buick Electra to be the family car, Gover got the "way-gun" and immediately stripped the chrome, Bondoed and primed it, with the goal of customizing it, which never happened.

Johnson had become good friends with Hal Flesher, another tall, gangly, flat-assed guy he had some classes with. They also both competed on the swim team. One Saturday in the summer following our senior year, they were shooting and missing swallows on a canal bank near Claribel Road and the railroad tracks. Finished hunting, having never hit a bird but possibly wounding a few cows, they came up with an absolutely absurd idea. Hal would climb on the roof of the Buick, lay spread-eagled on his stomach, and grab the luggage rack on each side. Gov would start driving. The plan was to see how fast they could go before Hal signaled it was time to stop. A new sport would be born. Car belly whomping. The signal to stop would be Hal banging the roof of the wagon with his head.

Hal climbed aboard and off they went. The dirt road along the canal bank made a sweeping left-hand curve before it intersected with the pavement of Claribel. Gover punched it. They slid through the curve going too fast, barely missed plunging into the canal, and locked up the brakes before hitting the pavement. They cruised down Claribel, coasting to a stop at Claus Road. Johnson checked both ways, as he had been taught in driver's ed. Hal considered tapping out at that point. Before his brain could calculate the risk versus reward, Gov was accelerating, hell-bent and flying east on Claribel. The speedometer climbed – twenty-five, fifty, seven-five. There may have been a moment, or two, of doubt or concern, but Gover kept rolling, figuring all was well because Hal hadn't signaled differently. When he hit one hundred, which wasn't a stretch for the behemoth Buick's V-8, he decided it was better to be safe than sorry. Good plan.

Gover rolled to a stop and opened the driver-side door. As he stepped out, Hal, who was white as a sheet, sat up on the roof and took a deep breath. The boys hadn't studied their aerodynamics. As the car accelerated, the rush of air up over the windshield and across the top of the car increased to gale force. To the point where Hal couldn't move his head, which was locked in an upright, face-forward position, the wind not just blowing his head back, but making it impossible to breath, let alone yell. If Johnson hadn't stopped when he did, Hal would have passed out and gone flying off the back of the car. They were lucky. Someone had been watching out for them. There but fortune and all that. They never pulled that stunt again.

The Stanislaus County Fair started the following Tuesday. I briefly considered calling Kelly to see if she wanted to go. We had spent such a memorable evening there seven years ago and a few times after that. I decided she was probably still upset and wouldn't be interested.

Solo, I made an efficient tour of the fairgrounds. I began at the barns, watching as the junior high and high school kids showcased their animals. I stopped briefly at the main stage to listen to Paul Revere & the Raiders. It was on to the exhibit halls with their collection of informational and commercial tables, artwork, photography, and crafts of every description. I followed that with a brief tour of the floriculture exhibit. I was hungry so I purchased my obligatory corn dog and beer, which I worked on as I toured the carnival. I tried my hand at the horse racing booth and added a small metal horse to my collection. I was far from the bronze horse with the clock in its belly. I ended the evening watching the destruction derby in the arena. It wasn't much of a county fair, but it was ours.

The next day, I met Coach Leach at Shakey's for pizza and beer. My treat. It was odd drinking beer with my elementary school teacher and Little League coach, but the topic at hand overshadowed any discomfort.

"I'd be happy to write you a letter, Michael," he said. "Or appear before the draft board and speak on your behalf. But, keep in mind, you have to build quite a case in order to qualify for conscientious objector status."

"I understand that," I replied.

"You'll need to go before the draft board to plead your case."

"I'm not looking forward to that."

"You'll have to convince them why you should not be drafted based on religious, or moral grounds. Being against the Vietnam war by itself isn't reason enough. You need to be against all wars and killing."

"I consider myself a pacifist."

"Until you're not."

"I guess."

"When was the last time you went to church?" my old coach asked me.

"Last Easter."

"Before that?"

"Last Christmas."

"That won't look good."

"I was afraid of that."

"Our draft board does not look fondly on COs."

"I've heard that, too."

"If your request for CO status is denied, you can appeal."

"I've been told that never goes anywhere."

"If you should happen to be approved, you'll need to do alternative service, usually in a noncombatant capacity, or in a job that contributes to the betterment of the country, like conservation, education, or health care."

"I've read about those and they don't sound that bad."

"I don't like seeing you, or any of the other kids I taught or coached, having to go through this."

"It's not fun."

"Do you remember Bill Halvorson? He was two years older than you."

"Sure. He had a good voice. Played Dick Deadeye in our production of *H.M.S. Pinafore.*"

"He applied for CO status and was denied. He appealed, so they granted him a hearing. I wrote a letter of support and appeared before the board with him and his father, Bill, Sr., who was Catholic. Though he didn't believe in what his son was doing, he supported him and thought speaking up as a Christian would help Bill's case."

"What happened?"

"His appeal was denied."

"That's too bad."

"Their reasoning was that being a Catholic didn't qualify him. If he were a Quaker or Dunkard, he might have won his appeal."

"I guess the Catholics weren't peaceful enough for them."

"He was prepared to refuse induction. But, when he took the physical, he was reclassified 4-because of a bad back.

"Glad it worked out."

"I wish this war would end. For all your sakes. For our country's sake. It's insane losing our best and brightest to a war that makes no sense."

"Too bad Nixon and his crew don't feel the same way."

"War will exist," he continued, "until that distant day when the conscientious objector is as celebrated and honored as the warrior is today."

"I've heard the same thing before," I replied, recalling the words I'd said to Professor Argüelles, which seemed so very long ago.

He rubbed his hands together, opened them, and looked at them. "It saddens me," he said.

"What's that?"

"You're all much too young to be carrying this weight."

"Dad was seventeen-and-a-half."

"He was too young, too."

"He never forgot it."

"I'm reminded of something someone said following the assassination of President Kennedy. *Washington Evening Star* columnist Mary McGrory told Daniel Patrick Moynihan, who was a Kennedy aide, 'We'll never laugh again.' Moynihan replied, 'Heavens, Mary, we'll laugh again. It's just that we will never be young again.' I would add to that. We will never be innocent again. Or trusting."

On August 7th, a follow-up letter arrived at the same San Francisco and Vallejo newspapers that had been contacted about a previous murder. "This is the Zodiac speaking," it began. It was the first time the killer had identified himself.

CHAPTER 45

The weekend papers were filled with two horribly dark stories. Actress Sharon Tate, who was married to film director Roman Polanski, had been murdered, along with four other people. Tate was eight months pregnant. The next day, the police found the bodies of supermarket executive Leno LaBianca and his wife, Rosemary. A statement by the LAPD said there was no connection. They thought it might be a drug deal gone bad. Horrible drug incidents were epidemic in the country these days, especially in southern California. The descriptions of the crime scenes were grisly. Someone had written the word "pig" in blood on the front door, which led some to believe it might be political, perhaps involving the Black Panthers.

From the radio, TV, and newspaper reports, it sounded more like some drug-crazed Hollywood party. The dark side of the LA party scene, perhaps because it involved someone like Sharon Tate. She was an actress and model with a promising career ahead of her. She received a Golden Globe Award nomination for her role in *Valley of the Dolls*, based on the novel of the same name by Jacqueline Susann. In 1968, she had married Polish director Polanski, who had directed her in *The Fearless Vampire Killers*. She was 26 when she was murdered. Polanski was ten years older than Tate. He was known for films like *Knife in the Water*, which was nominated for Best Foreign Language Film at the 1962 Academy Awards, as well as *Repulsion* and *Rosemary's Baby*.

This incident totally bummed me out. It was so brutal and seemed absolutely senseless. It felt like all the wonderful things that had been happening the last few years were going south fast. Violence was never the answer. To anything.

It was time to make some serious, practical plans. Once the peach season was over, I would schedule a time to speak with our National Guard. Oakland and Berkeley had organizations that counseled men on draft resistance and evasion. Davis also had a group in South Hall. I considered speaking with Dr. Robinson, my pediatrician, who was my doctor when I ruptured my spleen. Perhaps he could make a convincing case for my missing spleen. I also thought about planning a trip to Europe. And the possibility of not coming back.

The one thing that kept me, and maybe all of us, optimistic and able to cope with all the madness was the music. I listened every day. One song I played over and over again was "Four Days Gone." It was written by Stephen Stills and was on Buffalo Springfield's final album, *Last Time Around*. I wasn't sure what he meant it to be about but, for me, it was a song about a draft resistor on the run. It was a tremendous song and provided some comfort because there were others out there facing the same decision and possible outcome.

KSAN, KFIV, the TV stations, and *Rolling Stone* were abuzz with word that a huge rock concert was being planned for upstate New York in a town called Woodstock, where Bob Dylan had been living after his motorcycle accident in July 1966. It was promoted as being the biggest rock concert ever. As much as we wanted to, there was no way Gary or me, or anybody I knew would be able to afford it, or get back to New York in time to attend. It was shaping up to be a strictly East Coast gathering. Gover said his little sister Robin was visiting relatives in Buffalo and introducing Annikki Vanamo, their foreign exchange student from Finland. They were thinking about attending.

Gover had been born and raised in Buffalo. When the Johnsons arrived in California, they moved into a house on Bowen Avenue. Gover and Jan attended Davis, while Robin attended Beard Elementary. Mrs. Johnson's maiden name was Gover, thus Michael's middle name and nickname. Cal and Mary had met while attending college at Oklahoma State University which, when they were attending, was known as Oklahoma Agricultural and Mechanical College (Oklahoma A&M). He was studying engineering, she was studying home economics. He was from a large family in Buffalo. She was from a large family in Temple, Oklahoma. He was raised in the city. She was raised on a hog farm. The damned Yankee had fallen in love with a Southern belle, who promised to bake him a pie a week once they got married. He would have to wait for those pies because she wouldn't get hitched until she finished her degree. When she did, they did, and they set up house in Buffalo.

In 1969, Robin was a junior at Davis High. Through the high school's International Cultural Youth Exchange (ICYE) program, the Johnsons were connected with Annikki. She came to Modesto from a small village called Valadamo near the Soviet border. Her family included two younger brothers, a pharmacist father, and a science teacher mother. Annikki had arrived in Modesto in July to get acclimated to the warm weather. The family told stories about how they thought they had killed her when they took her to our annual Fourth of July parade and she nearly died from heat stroke. Adding insult to injury, in August, they all piled into the Buick Electra and headed for

Buffalo, which wasn't all that far from Bethel, New York, where the concert was being held.

The "Woodstock Music & Art Fair – An Aquarian Exposition" was scheduled to take place from August 15th to August 17th. It would spill over into Monday due to the number of acts, the number of people, and the weather. Joel Rosenman and John P. Roberts financed it. Michael Lang was the promoter, having co-organized the Miami Pop Festival the year before. Bill Graham was consulted. Woodstock would feature 32 bands, including The Who, Jimi Hendrix, Santana Blues Band, Creedence Clearwater Revival, Janis Joplin, the Airplane, and the one band I wanted to see: Crosby, Stills & Nash, with special guest Neil Young. It would be a mini Buffalo Springfield homecoming, which I would have given anything to see. The Beatles, Stones, Led Zeppelin, The Doors, and Dylan were all invited, but passed for a variety of reasons. Creedence was the first act to sign, agreeing to play for $10,000. Lang asked my hero Roy Rogers to close the festival with "Happy Trails." Unfortunately, he declined.

Following successful gigs and a suggestion by Atlantic Records president, Ahmet Ertegun, CSN had become CSNY. Stills said Young was brought onboard because "we wanted another life force. I wanted another rhythm section. But instead of a keyboard man, we thought why not a guy who could do other things – write songs, play guitar, be a brother and stuff." Plus, they had some history.

Since I couldn't be there, I had to rely on the TV, radio, and newspaper reports to provide the details, including my main source, *Rolling Stone*.

The venue for the concert changed a number of times, most located in upstate New York, including Saugerties and Wallkill. The organizers were introduced to Max Yasgur, a forty-nine-year-old dairy farmer. His 600-acre farm formed a natural bowl that rolled down to a pond, where the stage would be set up.

Woodstock was the cover story of the September 20th *Stone*. Quoting from a *New York Times* editorial, author Jan Holenfield wrote, "with Henry the Fifth, they could say at Bethel, 'He that outlives this day, and comes safe home, will stand a-tiptoe when this day is nam'd.'"

At one point during the event, Yasgur was farmer-honest when he said, "I don't know how to speak to 20 people, much less all of you . . . you are the largest group of people ever assembled in one place at one time . . . we had no idea there would be this many . . . and you have proven something to the world . . . that half a million kids can get together for fun and music and have nothing but fun and music." It was an event to be reckoned with wrote Max Lerner in the *New York Post*. And it was a generation to be reckoned with.

The organizers expected 60,000. They got between 400,000 and 500,000. At its height, it became the third largest city in New York state. There was no way to tell the exact attendance. Tickets were priced at $7 per day, or $18 for the weekend.

Once the organizers had the site and the performers, it was time to set up the venue. Gates, ticket booths, a stage, concessions, bathrooms, and medical facilities had to be built. Before most of it was complete, people arrived. Michael Lang later said, "You do everything you can to get the gates and the fences finished—but you have your priorities. People are coming, and you need to be able to feed them, and take care of them, and give them a show. So you have to prioritize." They did. The show, the audience, and their well-being became the organizers' first priority. Woodstock was suddenly a free event. Many people stayed for the duration, but many more left when they couldn't get through, or the number of people or the weather were too much. When the books were closed, the partners owed more than they made, but they promised to honor all debts. They were counting on sales of the movie that was shot, records, and books to cover their losses. It would be a while before they would see that money.

Woodstock was a far from perfect event. There were traffic jams, rain and mud, not enough food or water, bad trips, garbage piles and not enough garbage cans, long waits between acts, injuries, theft of nearby produce, overflowing portable toilets, and lack of security. Even if you had a way to replenish what was used, you couldn't get in, or out, through the mass of humanity. The Hog Farm, a commune led by Wavy Gravy, agreed to help. They cooked much-needed brown rice and bean soup. When that ran out, they cooked a filling oatmeal-raisin-sunflower concoction. *Rolling Stone* described it as a "tribal gathering," complete with skinny dipping, dancing, handicrafts, camping out, impromptu jams, and drug deals. Local residents and law enforcement were pleasantly surprised by how polite these kids were.

Bill Hanley handled the sound, building huge speaker boxes mounted on towers, which created some scary moments when the lightning flashed. A guy named Chip Monck was the production manager and supervised construction of the 80-foot stage, as well as managing the lighting. His real name was E.H. Beresford Monck. Chip rolled off the tongue more easily than E.H. Beresford, so it stuck. Most of the lights he rented were too heavy to mount on the make-shift stage roof due to the late change in venue. Those lights sat under the stage while Monck relied on follow spots. When somebody realized they didn't have an emcee, Lang drafted Monck. He made announcements all weekend long, trying to connect people, lost friends or children, and warning about bad drugs. It added a personal touch to what was basically an impersonal event.

Richie Havens kicked things off around 5 p.m. on Friday night. He was asked to do an extended set when Sweetwater, the opening act, got lost in traffic. He did nine songs that set the tone for the rest of the festival. Dressed in an African tribal gown, missing the top row of teeth, and wildly strumming his acoustic guitar, Havens fired up the crowd with anti-war songs like "Handsome Johnny" and an improvised spiritual called "Freedom." The acts that followed that evening included Tim Hardin, Arlo Guthrie, and Joan Baez.

As midnight approached, so did the traditional New York summer thunder and lightning. It got really muddy and really cold really fast. Instead of losing it, the crowd came together.

The first death happened on Saturday morning when a young man asleep in his sleeping bag was rolled over by a tractor. The next day, there was a second death from a drug overdose. Before the weekend was over, there would be another death from an overdose. Four miscarriages were reported. The two births that took place started the circle again, perhaps even resurrecting the souls of the recently departed.

The show continued on Saturday afternoon with Country Joe McDonald's "F*ck" cheer that led into the Fish's "I-Feel-Like-I'm-Fixin'-To-Die-Rag," as well as John Sebastian and San Francisco's own Santana Blues Band. They were on the bill because Bill Graham insisted they be included in return for his help with planning the festival. Canned Heat went on at dusk, followed by the Dead, Creedence, Janis backed by the Kozmic Blues Band, and Sly and the Family Stone. The Who did their thing next. When Abbie Hoffman grabbed the mic and harangued the crowd about White Panther leader, John Sinclair, Pete Townsend hit him with his guitar. His next target was a film cameraman, who Townsend also kicked off the stage.

The Who finished at sunrise and turned the stage over to the Airplane. Newcomer Joe Cocker and the Grease Band launched the Sunday performance around 2 p.m. and won the crowd over with his bluesy version of the appropriately themed, "With a Little Help from My Friends," before thunderstorms delayed the show for a few hours. Guitarist Alvin Lee and his British band, Ten Years After, tore it up. Country Joe, this time with the Fish, played next, followed by the Band. Without Dylan. Dylan never showed, although he was living not far away. Neither did the Beatles, or the Stones, although rumors circulated all weekend that one, or all, might. Johnny Winter, CSNY, and Sha Na Na were among the last to perform. Closing it out at 8:30 a.m. on Monday morning was Jimi Hendrix, backed by Gypsy Sun and Rainbows, whose blistering rendition of the "Star Spangled Banner" was more than memorable.

Robin and Annikki never made it. If they had tried, they would have gotten stuck in traffic with thousands of others.

Although I didn't experience it personally, Woodstock made a true believer of me again. Music could change the world and make it new again. It was a beautiful mess.

That same weekend, one of the girls I had known in high school and who also attended UC Davis, got married. Cathy New and I were both part of the group of people who hung out and dated during high school. She married a fellow student she had met at Davis. Her maid of honor was Julia Bloomer, who was one of my first girlfriends in high school. We were growing up, whether we wanted to, or not.

CHAPTER 46

The week after Woodstock, Gary and I had planned to attend "The Wild West: A San Francisco Festival," a three-day event of music and art at various sites in Golden Gate Park, including a concert scheduled at Kezar Stadium. It was promoted as "a celebration of the spirit of art and music in today's wild west – which is San Francisco and the Bay Area." Organized by The San Francisco Music Council, the festival was endorsed by city officials and would be bankrolled by local businessmen, banks, and two benefit concerts. The three concerts would feature bands from, or associated with, the Bay Area, including Janis Joplin, the Grateful Dead, the Jefferson Airplane, and Santana among others. Everything but the concerts would be free.

Wells Fargo Bank promised three stagecoaches to transport people to each of the six venues. Wally Heider offered to send a full studio setup from LA to record the shows. AM and FM radio stations planned to promote the event with free airtime. Because the organizers hoped to appeal to everyone, the music would be more than rock, perhaps including classical, jazz, and soul. The arts would be represented by plays, poetry, puppet shows, and dancers. A massive, city-wide light show was planned by Head Lights. It would be the first such event hosted by San Francisco since the Human Be-in in 1967.

Unfortunately, it never happened. The organizers cancelled the event the day before Woodstock started, citing the growing environment of violence and threats from various, anonymous radicals, plus complaints from the local musicians' union and hassles from the Mayor's office. The true reason was, as usual, about the money as later revealed by Ralph J. Gleason and *Rolling Stone*.

Mismanagement of the event and the money was rampant. Furthermore, Bill Graham, Chet Helms, and the other organizers couldn't agree on whether the event should be free. Graham insisted that people be charged because it cost money to put on big shows. The people of San Francisco were angry and took it out on Graham. Graham got pissed and threatened to close the Fillmore West and get out of the business altogether. It was not peace and love. But, the show did go on. Promoters, musicians, and venues suddenly had open dates for that weekend, so Graham put on shows at the Fillmore and Helms put on shows at the Family Dog with the bands who could make it. Gary and I caught the Sunday show at the Fillmore, which featured Country Joe and the Fish, It's a Beautiful Day, and the Sons of Champlin. Country Joe had just played Woodstock and It's a Beautiful Day had just released their first album and a single entitled, "White Bird."

During the past spring, underground newspapers had sprung up like mushrooms, especially in California. *The Berkeley Barb, Bullsheet, Good Times, Los Angeles Free Press,* and *San Francisco Oracle* all appeared in the Sixties to print stories about counterculture issues. Even small-town Modesto had its own paper. *The Family Tribune* was written and published by a local named Jack Shackleford. Jack was an unrepentant hippie. You could sometimes see him shuffling around town carrying his peace sign staff. He made it his job to bird dog "the man," whether it was the police, government, or corporations. He covered many of the same stories involving drugs and music that were also reported on in *The Modesto Bee.*

On Tuesday, August 19th, around 8:30 p.m., Stanislaus County Sheriff's deputies, backed by the Modesto, Oakdale, and Ceres police departments, raided the Casa Blanca Court, an 11-unt apartment complex located at Sunrise and Coolidge. The complex was a low-rent, cockroach and rat-infested collection of dilapidated hovels. A lot of dealing went down at "The Ghetto," as it was better known. One of the people caught in the dragnet that August was a kid I'd first known in elementary school. His name was Art Wilcox.

Art and I went through elementary, junior high, and high school together. He was an odd duck. He was brilliant and socially awkward. In elementary school, he had written a stage play about the Three Stooges. Because I had befriended Art and helped with the production, I was selected to play Shemp, until I got a butch haircut and Art rewrote it so I could be Curly Joe. Like the real Stooges TV show, the play was filled with pratfalls, slaps, and clever play on words. Art and I were never close after elementary school, but we had that connection of Garrison and the Stooges.

In high school, we were in the same homeroom, since our last names began with a "W," so we saw each other every morning. Art channeled his uniqueness into art and activism. He became an accomplished caricaturist and was involved in many of the liberal causes of the time. He did a number of posters for bands and organized several on– and off-campus demonstrations. Our senior year, he was selected to portray Caesar in the annual Latin Banquet and was also elected senior class president. Although I voted for him, I was surprised he won. We had a few classes together at Modesto Junior College, but we moved in a different crowd, so our paths didn't cross much. Art would later die a tragic death. He had taken acid and jumped from a bridge into the Tuolumne River near the old Mountain River Lodge and drowned.

The MPD were on the case again a couple nights later. Like many municipal police departments in those days, they were working hard to bust hippies – anybody with long hair who liked rock music and might be ingesting illegal substances. Every Thursday night, a promoter put on a rock concert and dance at the California Ballroom. The ballroom was a venue located downtown that had been used for a variety of things, including plays, musicals, wrestling matches, and concerts. That Thursday, the police didn't like the look of the concert and/or the people attending, so they busted it. Anybody who was carrying anything illegal was booked.

The following Saturday night, likely in retaliation most people assumed, the downtown was engulfed in more than one hundred small fires. Near one of the bonfires, someone had spray-painted on the sidewalk: "The revolution has started."

The next week, the Briggsmore showed a film I had been reading and hearing about. It was called *Medium Cool.* It was written and directed by Haskell Wexler, his first as both a writer and director. It took place in Chicago in the summer of 1968 during the Democratic National Convention, which nominated Hubert H. Humphrey for president after the June assassination of Bobby Kennedy. It mixed documentary, cinema verité footage with a dramatic, fictional storyline. Professional actors performed scripted dialogue and interacted with real people and real events. The title came from Marshall McLuhan's work, in which he described TV as a "cool" medium. The "cooler" the medium, "the more someone has to uncover and engage in the media," in order to "fill in the blanks." The title and narrative also alluded to the nation's attitude toward violence. We had become "voyeurs of violence" – repulsed and attracted as we participated via television. Although we confessed our hatred of it, at some level we dug it. We got hooked. We needed it like a junkie needed his fix.

The film echoed what journalists like Daniel Schorr had said – television relishes conflict. That's why the civil rights movement, Vietnam, and protests got coverage. It was the paradox of nonviolence. Nonviolence was not a passive strategy. It was designed to illicit a violent reaction. The struggle for justice would always be a battle. If both sides were nonviolent, there was no story. Wexler's story also questioned the role and responsibilities of television and its newscasts. He examined how professionalism, or emotional neutrality, contributed to anarchy. How not thinking about the effects of his work allows innocent people to become involved in, and perhaps hurt, by momentous events. The film also featured contemporary music from the Mothers of Invention and Love. The music in Wexler's film, which was integral to telling the story, was assembled by guitarist Mike Bloomfield, who was Wexler's cousin.

Wexler was an accomplished cinematographer, having worked on Mike Nichols' *Who's Afraid of Virginia Woolf,* for which he won the last Academy Award for Best Cinematography (Black and White), and *In the Heat of the Night.* I read in a review that Wexler had helped a young Modesto boy named George Lucas get into USC's film school, after they had met at a car race, a hobby both of them shared. I made a mental note to ask my "buddy" George about this the next time I saw him, if there was a next time. I didn't expect to see him around town because he had left Modesto in 1964, after attending MJC for two years, to go to USC's film school.

Medium Cool was a tough film to watch, primarily because much of the footage was shot during the Chicago riots. It bothered me watching the Chicago police kicking and clubbing kids like me. The film was rated "X," supposedly because of the language and some nudity, but every review I read and commentary I heard said it was rated "X" because of its politics. It reinforced what I was already wrestling with, which was that I needed to do something. I needed to get involved. I needed to get out of the stands and onto the field.

CHAPTER 47

We sipped bad coffee in the Denny's on McHenry at Five Points. Curtis Sanders and I had known each other in elementary school. His Fremont Little League team was competitive with my Garrison team. We went through junior high, high school, and part of MJC together. He enlisted before finishing his first year. He had served his time in Vietnam and was home. For now.

"I've been clean and sober for sixty days," he said.

"Good for you," I answered.

"It was rough there for a while. I was one angry dude."

"Being called a baby killer would do that."

"It was that. And more. People wouldn't look at me. My friends didn't want to talk about it. My girlfriend wanted me to forget it. Nobody got it. So I got mad. Then I got silent. I internalized it. I buried what I was feeling in booze and drugs. I grew my hair. I didn't want anybody to know I'd been there."

"I never felt that way. About you, or the others."

"What did you feel?" he asked, eyes narrowed.

"That we shouldn't be there."

"We were making a difference. We were helping those people. They treated us with respect."

"I get that."

"Their government was corrupt. The commies were coming down hard. They needed us."

"My problem was more with why we were there in the first place. How it all started is murky and there's no end in sight."

"Everybody's got an opinion. What's yours?"

"Money. It's about the money. They have resources we want."

"Like what?"

"Like oil."

"So we get it instead of China, or Russia," he said.

"I'm not sure I believe in the domino theory."

"Why not?"

"Vietnam is an independent country. They've been fighting foreign invaders for as long as they've been a country. They're going to fight for their independence, whether it's us, or China."

"It's not that simple."

"You think we can win?" I asked.

"We can. If the politicians let us."

"I don't."

"We can't walk away."

"I don't want the VC to win, either. There are those who believe everyone who's against the war is on their side. We're not."

"I'd like to believe that."

"Why do you think we're there?"

"To stop communism. To give the people democracy."

"What if they don't want it?"

"Why wouldn't they?"

"Look at their history. I'm a history major. I study history. Their history says they're not interested. Not now anyway."

"Academic bullshit. It's not practical. It's not real. It's ivory tower crap. It's naïve."

"It's a fact. It's information. Real, verifiable facts our leaders should know and act on. If they know it, they're ignoring it. If they don't, they should."

"They know what they're doing. We wouldn't be there if they didn't."

"That's a problem for me," I said.

"What's that?"

"My-country-right-or-wrong. I've got an issue with that. This is supposed to be a democracy. In a democracy, you ask questions. In a democracy, you speak out. In a democracy, you question authority. In a democracy, you don't let them get away with it."

"Get away with what?"

"Fooling us. Lying to us. If you're going to start a war, you better have a damn good reason for doing it because there's no turning back. The dead will remain dead."

"There was a good reason. They fired on us in the Gulf of Tonkin."

"We were in their territorial waters."

"Aiding the South Vietnamese."

"Who had attacked the North Vietnamese."

"We were attacked. That's all that matters."

"Look, I don't think we can win. It's Custeristic."

"If you don't like what we're doing, leave. Go somewhere else."

"Another platitude that doesn't do anybody any good."

"Sorry?"

"Love it or leave it. "

"If the shoe fits."

"I love my country. I'm not Benedict Arnold," I said.

"Doesn't sound that way to me. If you're not willing to fight to defend your country, then you're against your country."

"What about the Founding Fathers?"

"What about them?"

"They went to war to fight tyranny. It was a righteous war. They rebelled against a government that was corrupt and oppressive. It's the same thing the Vietnamese are doing. It's the same thing the protestors are doing."

"I don't see it that way."

"We're the bully in this story. I'm not going to take on a bully if he's twice my size. That's crazy. I'll get my butt kicked. But, I will wait for my moment and I will get even. That's Vietnam."

"It'll take them fifty years to get even."

"One thing I do know," I went on.

"What's that?"

"I hate seeing kids we grew up with being killed. I hate what happened to you."

"We did our duty. We did what our country asked us to do. We fought for our fellow soldiers. We fought for freedom there and here."

"You think our freedom is threatened?" I asked.

"I do. We fought so our children and our children's children would be free. We fought for the same things our Founding Fathers did. 'One nation, under God, indivisible, with liberty and justice for all.'"

"I understand duty to country. My dad fought in World War II."

"Army?"

"Marines."

"What does he think of 'Nam."

"He passed back in '62."

"Damn. Sorry, I forgot."

"He thought war was a terrible waste. Always did."

"He knew what service was."

"Yes, he did."

"He knew what being a soldier was all about. What combat was."

"He never talked about it."

"Sounds familiar."

"Vietnam isn't Germany and 1969 isn't 1945."

"China could be the next Germany. Vietnam could be the next Poland. Tyrants need to be stopped."

"How many buddies did you lose?" I asked.

"Too many. They died for something."

"How bad did things get?"

"Bad enough."

"I have no idea what that's like."

"You can't. It's hard to explain what it's like when you're out there. It's kinda like being in a weird zone, a different dimension. You live in the now, the present, because that's all you've got. You don't remember your past and you don't want to think about the future. You don't even know if you have a future. You have no way of telling time.

"Sometimes, it feels like an eternity and other times it feels like you're double-timing it. You become alive and alert to the land, the elements, and your surroundings. You react instinctively, in a fraction of a second. You can sense danger and the adrenalin controls your reactions. There's another presence. Of good and evil. It speaks to your mind to warn you, or to tell you you're a coward. Which is good, because it keeps you safe. And bad because, if you ignore it, you will die."

"I can't imagine."

"That ain't the half of it. When you're in a war zone, you've got to do something to stay sane. So you block the bad stuff. You don't think about the killing. You do what it takes to stay alive. We watched our buddies get shot up, or die. They gave the ultimate sacrifice. But, we never quit. Day after day and night after night, we stayed together. I was determined to keep my buddy and me from being killed. We weren't going to be the last to die in that hell hole."

"Band of brothers."

"I'm proud of my brothers in arms."

"They all make it?"

"Not all."

"Sorry to hear that."

"Look, I'm proud of my service. What we did mattered. Their lives mattered. We need to be respected and honored for that."

"I do. I respect the sacrifices you made."

"You're one of the few."

"I'm sorry you had to make them."

"I was doing my job."

"I don't mistake the warrior for the war," I said. "I never will."

"Good to know."

"How do you feel about people like me that don't necessarily agree with you on everything?"

"I've known you off and on most of my life. I can let you slide. A little. Even though you weren't there. You weren't in my shoes. You didn't see what I saw, do what I did. You stayed safe in your bed, while I was lying in a muddy foxhole. That's tough to forgive."

"What about all the others that don't feel the same way you do?"

"I'm pissed. About the way I was treated when I came home, by my best friends and the nation. I'm angry that I was called a killer and a loser. I never killed any women, or children. I was spit on. People looked away with disgust when I wore my Army uniform. That hurt like hell."

"There's no excuse for how they treated you. It was a mistake. They're kids, too. Like you. They believe in what they're doing. Like you. That's no justification. They should've understood and appreciated what you'd done and been through."

"I would have liked that."

"Things had changed while you were gone."

"Too much. The protestors, assholes burning the flag and their draft cards, riots in the streets, hippies doing all kinds of crazy shit. I didn't recognize this place."

"Home wasn't home."

"I wasn't me. One time, I was driving down McHenry. Minding my own business. Some jackass honks his horn. Like I could go anywhere any faster. He kept honking and honking and honking. Next thing I know, I'm standing beside his car with a tire jack in my hand. He's staring at me scared shitless."

"What happened?"

"I have no idea. I just lost it."

"Anybody talk with you about it?"

"No. When they finally did, I didn't care."

"You think about it?"

"Every moment of every day."

"I guess it never goes away."

"What about you?" he asked.

"What about me?"

"Are you going to go? Are you going to do your duty?"

"I have my student deferment."

"What about when you lose it?"

"I don't know."

"If you're called, you need to go."

"I don't want to get killed in some rice paddy."

"I didn't."

"I don't want to go through what you've gone through. What you're going through."

"It takes time, but you figure it out."

"You know, I don't blame you," I said.

"For what?"

"For being there."

"Who do you blame?"

"The government. The assholes at the top. The ones that have never been to war. The ones that will never send their kids to war."

"That's the easy way out."

"It's what I believe."

"Do you love your country?" he asked.

"I do."

"You need to fight for it."

"I love it enough to criticize it. I love it enough to call it out when it's wrong. Malcolm X said, 'You're not supposed to be so blind with patriotism that you can't face reality. Wrong is wrong, no matter who does it or says it.' I didn't like Malcolm X, or his politics, but I agree with what he said. Wrong is wrong."

"Matter of opinion."

"Even though we grew up in the same town and were influenced by the same things, we're coming at this issue from two very different places. We're likely never going to see eye to eye on it."

"Probably not."

"At least we can agree to disagree and continue to talk about it. Keep our minds open to other possibilities," I said.

"I can dig it."

"Remember this."

"What?"

"Knowledge is power."

"Depends on who you know it about."

Curt's story about the guy honking his horn brought back conversations I'd had with my dad. He'd experienced something similar, along with his buddies in the Marines. It was now called "combat fatigue." After WWI, it was known as "shell shock." During the Civil War, "soldier's heart." Even as far back as the ancient Greeks, they had a phrase for what the horrors of war could do to a normal person. They called it "divine madness." What would we call it?

I did respect those who had volunteered, like Curt, but I was worried about him. He had the addiction beat. For now. But this other thing sounded even scarier. He would have it the rest of his life if he didn't get help. Even if he did, he'd probably never forget what he'd experienced. It wasn't right that our government had created a situation where young men like him had to witness horrors that would haunt them the rest of their lives. I felt bad for those who were drafted, or enlisted. I sympathized with those who felt their one choice was to leave their country.

This war wasn't about patriotism. It wasn't about "the domino theory," "my country right or wrong," or "my country love it or leave it." It wasn't about pacification, or winning their hearts and minds. From what I could tell, it was about power. It was about maintaining our credibility with our enemies and allies. Ultimately, it was about greed. Our government wanted to protect the natural resources we depended on, and controlled, in Southeast Asia, which China and Russia wanted. Our government fooled us, turned us against each other, convinced us it was about stopping the "Red Menace." Our battles were a distraction. Pitting us against one another, making us fear "the other," covered up what they were doing. That was certainly part of it. But, as usual, it was mostly about the money. That wasn't a good enough reason to send Americans to die in the rice paddies of Vietnam.

Maybe I was an isolationist. Or naïve, like Curt said. I understood the need for a standing army, but I hoped we could manage problems peacefully. Like Switzerland. It seemed like there had been righteous wars and not-so-righteous wars. The Revolutionary War, War of 1812, World War I, and World War II were fought for good reasons. We had been attacked. The Mexican-American War, Spanish-American War, Korea, and Vietnam weren't as justifiable. We were the aggressor in those conflicts. We wanted something and we declared war to get it. It seemed like we had been at war for a very long time following the founding of our country. In fact, America had been at war almost every year since the American Revolution.

It bothered me that Vietnam was a war of privilege; a war fought by the poor, by minorities, by the middle class. Many of the kids who served were high school dropouts. They didn't have the same opportunities, or parachutes, the more wealthy and educated had. They weren't going to be applauded or celebrated or awarded for their service. They were going to do their job; do what they signed up for. With patience, loyalty, hope, and courage. They faced death almost every day. Some died for what they believed. They were true heroes. They were admirable young men.

CHAPTER 48

"All the News that Fits" – September Edition

White Panther John Sinclair is busted for possession of two joints. In Iraq, Muammar al-Qaddafi deposes King Idris. Ho Chi Minh dies. John and Yoko and the Plastic Ono Band perform for the first time at the Toronto Rock 'N' Roll Revival 1969. Premier Alexei Kosygin of the Union of Soviet Socialist Republics visits Premier Zhou Enlai of the People's Republic of China. UCLA Student Body President Rosalio Munoz refuses the draft. Musician Tiny Tim is engaged to Miss Vicky. The Board of Regents of the University of California, urged by California Governor Ronald Reagan, fires Angela Davis because of her membership in the Communist Party. *The Brady Bunch* premieres on ABC. Willie Mays of the San Francisco Giants becomes the second player to hit 600 home runs. The Chicago Eight trial begins. College students at Drake University claim that clues to Paul McCartney's death can be found in the lyrics and artwork of the Beatles' albums. New book releases include *My Life and Prophecies* by Jeane Dixon with John Underwood; *The House on the Strand*, Daphne du Maurier; *Think*, William Rodgers; *The Promise*, Chaim Potok; *San Francisco*, Editors of Sunset Magazine; and *The Seven Minutes* by Irving Wallace. *American Hamburger League* and *Salvation* open on stage. New films include *Bob & Carol & Ted & Alice*; *Butch Cassidy and the Sundance Kid* starring Paul Newman and Robert Redford; *Women in Love* featuring Oliver Reed, Glenda Jackson, and Alan Bates; *Fellini Satyricon*; and *Hell's Angels '69*. New music includes *Abbey Road*; The Band's second album entitled simply *The Band*; *New York Tendaberry* by Laura Nyro; *I Got Dem Ol' Kozmic Blues Again Mama!* by Janis Joplin; *Nice* by The Nice; *Through the Past, Darkly (Big Hits Vol. 2)* by the Rolling Stones; and the single "Okie From Muskogee" by Merle Haggard.

Monday, September 1st, it was late on the East Coast. I was watching the Jerry Lewis Muscular Dystrophy Telethon live from New York and carried locally on KCRA Channel 3. I enjoyed Jerry Lewis, not just because I thought he was talented and funny, as did the kooky French, but also because Gary acted so much like him. Jerry had been raising money for MD since 1952 when a staffer, who worked with Lewis and Dean Martin on *The Colgate Comedy Hour*, asked him to help. The show originated from a variety of locations in New York, including the Americana Hotel. The program featured a talk show-style desk and seating area for Lewis and performers, a performance area for a 19-piece jazz band, phone banks, and a large tote board to keep track of donations. Most of the day's hot pop stars and celebrities would attend, answer phones, and perform.

The show opened with Charlie Chaplin's song "Smile" and ended with Jerry singing Rodgers and Hammerstein's "You'll Never Walk Alone." The show would cut away from time to time to the Sacramento phone bank. There was a point in the show, usually after he introduced a young child in a wheelchair, that Jerry would lose it and begin crying. I had to watch the show until that happened. Then I could get on with the fall and the true start of the new year.

The peaches were done for the season, so I was, too. The Modesto school year would start the following week. The city schools traditionally started after Labor Day because, as an area whose economy relied on agriculture, school didn't start until the peach harvest was over because so many teachers and students worked in the fields. Occasionally, if the season ran long, school would be delayed up to a week to make sure everything was harvested. It ran long this year.

UCD wouldn't start for another few weeks, but we needed to find a new apartment. I didn't want to live with Threlfall or Slevin again, but I did want to room with Gover. Now that Gary had been accepted, he would be living with us. We needed a fourth and Gover suggested a Ceres boy named Mark Perra. Mark was a year ahead of us. He was a buddy of Slevin's from Modesto Junior College. He had visited us at Vanguard and seemed like a good fit.

On Tuesday, Gover and I drove up to Davis in Ugly Orange to scout places to live. We'd be in an apartment again because it was familiar and easy. We checked the *Davis Enterprise* classifieds, real estate agencies, and bulletin boards around town and on campus. We didn't work too hard. We found a fairly new complex in East Davis that seemed nice and was priced right. It was located next to the railroad tracks. It was called Ivy Towne. We signed a one-year lease and were assigned a second-floor apartment at the end of the building looking over a parking lot and the tracks. We agreed a little railroad noise was a good trade for not having anybody on one side of us.

On our way home, we heard on the radio that Ho Chi Minh had died. Maybe his death and the new view of our government toward the war might help bring an end to the conflict. It was something to hope for.

That Friday, the top story reported that Lt. William Calley had been charged with premeditated murder for the deaths of 109 Vietnamese civilians at My Lai in March 1968. Calley was leader of 1ˢᵗ Platoon, Company C, 1ˢᵗ Battalion, 20ᵗʰ Infantry Regiment, 11ᵗʰ Infantry Brigade of the 23ʳᵈ Infantry Division (Americal). They had been conducting a search and destroy mission in the coastal lowlands of Quang Ngai Province. Something apparently went wrong with Calley and/or the soldiers under his command because they shot South Vietnamese women, children, and old men as they ran from their huts. The Americans systematically rounded up the survivors, allegedly leading them to a ditch where Calley gave the order to "finish them off." The soldiers stopped the killing when a pilot landed his helicopter between the Americans and the fleeing South Vietnamese. Between 347 and 504 unarmed people were massacred. Allegedly, the women were gang-raped and their bodies mutilated.

At first, the killings were covered up. It all came to light a year later. Now, Calley and his company commander, Captain Ernest Medina, were charged with crimes. This incident made it clear that some insane things were going down over there. Along with much of America, I was wondering how civilized men and disciplined soldiers could justify mass murder like this. Maybe the Vietnamese had been so dehumanized it was easy to kill them.

That next Wednesday, Modesto's city schools were in session. I wasn't quite ready to hear school bells, and I was certain most of the students weren't either. Tim was starting his second year at Modesto Junior College. Willy would be a sophomore at Davis High. Diane was an eighth grader at Roosevelt, and Cheryl was a sixth grader at Garrison.

The following weekend, Gary and I attended an end of summer/back to school concert at Big Bear Park in Waterford. Waterford was a cow pie to the east of Modesto along Yosemite Boulevard. It was primarily an agricultural area, with wheat having been its biggest crop at one point. The park was located between Yosemite, which was also Highway 132, and the Tuolumne River. We knew about the show because Alan Arnopole and his band, Mother Nature's, were performing. The band featured mostly valley boys, some I knew and some I didn't. John Ryerson, who was a year older, was on guitar; Steve Gillette, also in the high school class above me, played bass; Ty Marrs handled piano and guitar; Alan grinned and picked banjo and guitar; and Malcolm Nicholson hammered on the drums. Alan, Ty, and Steve alternated on lead and backup vocals. They were a country, rock, acid-infused jam band. They played a mix of originals, plus covers of Dylan, Chuck Berry, Hank

Williams, and Jimi Hendrix. Eclectic, to say the least.

Alan was another of our high school friends. I had met him in junior high. He was totally into music. By the time we got to high school, he was playing folk music with a trio called The Wild Men. They were Kingston Trio wannabes, complete with matching striped shirts, white Levi's, and Converse tennis shoes. Several of our girl classmates had formed a folk group called The Womenfolk. Any time we got together, there was strumming and singing – a spontaneous hootenanny.

I saw old friends from elementary school, junior high, high school, and JC. Most of them were home from college and killing time until school started. I was surprised to run into Flora Sai, who I had known since grade school. She and I were sort of "girlfriend and boyfriend," if there was such a thing, in fifth grade. Flora was tall – much taller than me at that age, which made dancing at the school functions difficult. She was sweet and I liked her "a lot," as we liked to say in our yearbook inscriptions. We lost touch in junior high and high school and hadn't seen each other in years. It was nice to reconnect. People danced alone and together, or simply grooved to the sounds. It was a truly beautiful day.

I made an appointment with our California National Guard. Their base, training facility, and recruiter were located on Kansas Avenue. The armory was on Rouse near the Sportsmen of Stanislaus. It was a short conversation. I explained what I hoped to accomplish, which was to join the Guard. I didn't admit I was considering enlisting to beat the draft, but the officer I spoke with knew that was my intention. He had heard it many times already. He told me simply that their quota was filled and there were no openings for new recruits. I told him I was disappointed, thanked him, and left. As I walked out the gate of the chain-link fence surrounding the facility, I looked around me at the cannons, the troop transport trucks, the Guardsmen in uniform, and was inwardly thankful they were full.

I was feeling sorry for myself. Driving around town considering my options, Dad's voice kept interrupting my thoughts.

"Life deals the cards. You must accept them. But, once you have them, it's up to you and you alone to decide how to play them. You can fold and walk away. You can bluff and hope it works. Or, you can figure out the best strategy to win with the cards you've got." He was a savvy card player. He always came up with something, no matter how bad the hand.

As I drove, I recalled one of our last conversations. He was lying in his hospital bed.

"Most men lead lives of quiet desperation and go to the grave with the song in them," he said.

"Did you come up with that?"

"Thoreau did. You'll learn more about him as you grow up." He shifted and sat straighter.

"It happened to me. I didn't do everything I wanted to do."

"You have time," I replied, not even able to convince myself that was true.

"I don't want that to happen to you. Ever. Never give up. Do what needs to be done to take care of yourself, your family, your friends, and your community."

My next option to the draft issue was Dr. Robinson, the pediatrician who had treated me when I ruptured my spleen in 1962. I hadn't seen him for many years because I had grown into being seen by adult doctors. He was the sweet man I remember speaking with as I grimaced through the pain wracking my fourteen-year-old body. He fondly told me about the time brother Tim passed out in his office when he removed a bandage from brother Willy's hernia operation.

"He still does that," I said.

"I thought he would have grown out of it by now."

"He's a sensitive kid."

"So, what can I do for you, Michael? It must be an unusual request considering I'm no longer your physician."

"I was hoping you could write me a letter."

"What sort of letter?" he asked.

"One that might save my life."

"Goodness, I've heard doctors compared to God in the past, but I'm not sure I have that power."

"I've heard that having a ruptured spleen might get me out of the draft."

"I thought this might have something to do with your draft status."

"If you can write a letter to the draft board confirming that I don't have a spleen, maybe they'll reclassify me."

"I have many relatives and friends who have served in America's wars, including Vietnam. In spite of that, I think this war is unjust."

"I was hoping you felt that way."

"I cringe each night I see the bodies of all those young men torn to shreds."

"You probably had some as patients."

"I'm sure I did."

"I don't want to be one of them. A statistic. In a war I didn't start."

"It baffles me what our elected leaders were thinking when they got us into this situation."

"So, you'll write the letter?"

"I will. I'm not sure what good it will do, but I will gladly write it."

"Maybe you've got a bit of the Almighty in you after all."

CHAPTER 49

The second weekend in September was going to be radical. Crosby, Stills, Nash & Young were scheduled to play at the two-day Big Sur Folk Festival. The sixth annual event was part of a series of music festivals, which began in 1964 and was hosted by the Esalen Institute. In addition to CSNY, there would be performances by Joan Baez and Joni Mitchell. Woodstock had happened recently, so it was on everybody's mind. Bruce Grimes, a friend I had met at Davis, gave me a call to tell me about the show. He knew music. He had worked for Bill Graham, had done security at the Monterey Pop Festival, and had booked bands in Davis. He was tuned in to all of it. He was planning to go. We might connect once we got there. It was my first chance to see my rock 'n' roll Gods, Stephen Stills and Neil Young. Tickets cost four bucks. All proceeds benefitted Baez's Institute for the Study of Nonviolence.

Gary was up for the road trip, so we'd take his VW, which was more reliable than Ugly Orange. Tim wanted to go, but Laura had made other plans. I asked Mom and Paul if I could take Willy. He would turn sixteen in November. He also worshipped both Stills and Young and was playing their songs in his band. Mom and Paul agreed, especially since we were only going for Saturday. Kelly and I were not talking. After our last encounter, I didn't want anything to do with Luci. It would be dudes alone.

Buffalo Springfield became my top band shortly after "For What It's Worth" was released in December 1966. Their first album, *Buffalo Springfield*, came out in March 1967. Stephen Stills wrote the song after witnessing the Sunset Strip curfew riots in November 1966. Springfield was the house band at the Whisky a Go Go on the Sunset Strip. The residents and businesses on, or near the Strip were tired of all the kids loitering on the streets and in the clubs at night. They talked the city into passing ordinances to stop loitering and to enforce a strict curfew on the Strip after 10 p.m.

The kids said the new laws infringed on their civil rights. So, they did something about it. They passed out leaflets and convinced the rock stations to announce there would be a demonstration on Saturday, November 12th, 1966, outside the Pandora's Box nightclub on the corner of Sunset Boulevard and Crescent Heights. That night, more than 1,000 people showed up. The rally was quiet at first. Then it got violent. Rallies continued through November and December. That's what Stills wrote about, although some people initially thought it was an anti-war song, perhaps because of the title. The title came about when Stills first played the song and introduced it by saying: "I have this song here, for what it's worth, if you want it." When it was released, the record company added a parenthetical subtitle, "Stop, Hey What's That Sound," so people would recognize it.

The rest of the band included Neil Young on guitar and vocals and Bruce Palmer on bass, both of whom were Canadians; Richie Furay on guitar and vocals; and Dewey Martin on drums. I had never heard a band featuring two lead guitars. Most bands were lead guitar, rhythm guitar, bass, and drums, which is what the Beatles and many of the British invasion bands featured. Springfield had two talented lead guitarists and three equally talented vocalists, who did three-part harmony. Their rock music, colored with some country-western, folk, and psychedelica, was unreal. In addition to the first album, they had released *Buffalo Springfield Again* and *Last Time Around*. Jimmy Messina was recruited to help finish the last one. I snapped them all up as soon as they came out.

After their breakup in May 1968, I continued to follow them. Stills did an album with Mike Bloomfield and Al Kooper called *Super Session* before starting Crosby, Stills & Nash. Young released a solo album in January 1969 entitled simply *Neil Young*. He hooked up with a group of musicians and formed Crazy Horse, releasing *Everybody Knows This is Nowhere* in May 1969. Furay formed Poco and released *Pickin' Up the Piece,* also in May 1969. Their new bands were almost as good as the original.

The chance to see my rock heroes in person was a dream come true. They were slated to play both days, but we only planned to attend Saturday's show. It was an appropriate way to say goodbye to summer.

We got up at the crack of dawn on Saturday and drove out Carpenter to Crows Landing to Highway 33 to Santa Nella where we connected with State Route 152, which was a steep, winding, two lane highway through Pacheco Pass. It wasn't fast, but it was direct. We went through Bell Station, which is where Grampa Owl, my dad's dad, was born on February 15th in 1896 to Rosana Woodworth and John James Wright. We stopped for a pee break in San Juan Bautista, home of one of the last California missions. It was also where my great grandfather, Alonzo "Lon" Woodworth, Rosa's father, had lived and where his right arm was buried.

Alonzo was born in 1824 in Rochester, New York. He worked as a scout for the United States, transporting horses and guiding immigrants across the plains to the west. On his last crossing in 1850, he arrived at Sutter's Fort in Sacramento, where he met Julia Malissa Twitchell, the daughter of Joshua Twitchell. After a brief courtship, they married. Alonzo drove for the Overland Stage Lines, from Los Angeles to Northern California and San Juan Bautista, where he and Julia eventually settled. They farmed 160 acres of land, also raising cattle and horses. He was one of the owners of the San Benito Coal Mine. Alonzo sold the farm in 1867 and moved to Dos Palos, California, where he passed away in 1906.

There was a story behind the burial of his right arm. One of the important fiestas in San Juan Bautista was St. John's Day, which was celebrated every year on June 24th. St. John, or San Juan, was the patron saint of the village. The third and last day of the fiesta traditionally finished with a bull-and-bear fight. The *vaqueros* would lasso a grizzly that had come down to the plains to feed. A large enclosure was built in the plaza. The bear would be tied to a pole in the center with a strong *riata*, giving him enough rope to let him roam twenty feet, or so. The bull was tethered the same way by one leg. It was estimated that 50,000 people attended this event. The bear often died from being gored. The bull might get a few scratches. It wasn't particularly sporting, but it was quite a spectator sport.

In 1856, in addition to the usual St. John's Day festivities, the Plaza Hotel had its grand opening. The Dons, Doñas, and their families came from *ranchos* far and near to the gala celebration. After attending mass in the morning at the mission, the fun would begin. The *caballeros*, finely dressed and riding beautiful horses, would show off their horsemanship. There was an old muzzle-loading cannon in the plaza that had been used for Fourth of July celebrations and other events.

On this day, the cannon was placed on the back of a wagon. It was fired all day. For part of the time, Lon Woodworth was in charge of loading and firing. The cannon would heat up from repeated firings. In order to load the cannon and keep it from exploding prematurely, a man would place his thumb over the vent. The man in charge of that task on this day had been indulging freely. When Lon rammed home the charge, the cannon exploded, tearing off his arm. His severed limb was buried on the hill overlooking the village.

Grampa Owl wore the best and rode the best. Silver buckles and silver saddles, snap-brim Stetson and polished boots. He survived two wives and married a third. He had three children and eight grand-children. He was born, raised, and died a cowboy. His name was Alowishus Owen Wright. "Ace" to his friends. Grampa Owl to us kids because we couldn't pronounce his name.

He took us on cattle drives and to the stock yards. We rode horses and chased rats in his barns. He gave us cowboy boots and hats. He hoped that we, unlike his second son, our dad, would want to take up ridin' and ropin'. But, unlike Grampa Owl, Dad didn't have fond memories of being awakened at sunrise, loading the horses and tack, driving for hours, riding on hot asphalt in some small-town rodeo parade, returning home after dark, and having to bed down the cranky stock before bedding down himself. No, Grampa's dream wasn't meant to be. We were city kids and that's the way it would remain.

Grampa Owl was dark-complected and spoke Spanish like a native. He denied it his entire life, but the odds were that he had Mexican blood. His mother, Julia, looked *mestizo*. His siblings – Uncle Pete, Aunt Aurora, and Aunt Rose – all looked Mexican. He wasn't affectionate, being he was a man of his era. He and my dad were different. Dad tried not to be like his old man. He was affectionate. He was available. He was kind. He was generous.

Thoughts of my grandfather and father ebbed as we drove south on Highway 1 and approached Big Sur. It resembled a gypsy caravan. People had camped out for miles. We parked at Julia Pfeiffer Burns State Park north of the Institute and hoofed it to the show, along with hundreds of others carrying sleeping bags and jugs of Red Mountain and smoking dope. It was some convoy.

Once we got on the grounds, we found a place to sit toward the back of an expanse of tree-shaded grass facing the center of the stage. Thousands of others lounged around us, drinking or smoking. There were booths hawking the usual hippie fare – hot rice, yogurt, fresh melon, and broth. The low stage was set behind a swimming pool with the Pacific Ocean providing a backdrop. It was an incredible way to say goodbye to summer.

Joan Baez opened the show with Bob Dylan and the Band's "I Shall Be Released." Because she offered a workshop on music at Esalen entitled, "The New Folk Music," she was the reason this festival was able to attract the acts it did. On Sunday, she closed with the Edwin Hawkins Singers' arrangement of the hymn, "Oh Happy Day." She also did "Song for David," which was dedicated to her husband, Stanford graduate David Harris, who had been arrested in July for refusing induction and was serving his sentence.

The Incredible String Band followed, surrounded by exotic and numerous instruments, singing soft, sweet tunes of the romantic troubadours. Sal Valentino, lately of the Beau Brummels, performed a short set of three songs. Then it was Dorothy Morrison's turn, whose set was stopped briefly when a guy leapt into the Esalen pool, which was just in front of the performers.

Joni Mitchell was dating Graham Nash, which partly explained why she was there. She sang "Woodstock," her original tribute to the festival that she didn't attend, having previously committed to being on "The Dick Cavett Show." She later sang back-up with CSNY on The Youngbloods' song, "Get Together." She was having fun and looking fine. John Sebastian and the Flying Burrito Brothers also performed.

The Burritos had been formed by Gram Parsons and Chris Hillman after they had met while recording *Sweetheart of the Rodeo* with a revamped Byrds lineup, and had both left the band. *Sweetheart* came out in August 1968. It was another album I had to have because of the Byrds' history and the country rock sound. Recorded in Nashville and Los Angeles, the album featured a style Parsons called Cosmic American Music. Whatever he dubbed it, it was rock 'n' roll crossed with the country music of Ernest Tubb and Hank Snow. The *Gilded Palace of Sin* was the Burritos' first album, which had been released in February.

CSNY closed the Saturday show playing nearly every song they knew. Around 7 p.m., Crosby said before they started the final song, "This is the last one we know." They were backed by Dallas Taylor on drums and Greg Reeves on bass. The tranquility was shattered when Stills, who had a bad temper, got into an argument and a fistfight with a heckler. Stills tried to throw the dude in the pool for interrupting the show. Stills was missing a front left tooth, which led me to believe this might not have been his first dust-up. It was a far cry from the peace and love vibe that had carried over from their, Sebastian's, and Baez's performance at Woodstock.

Bruce never made it and, despite being prodded by Gary, I didn't bother to catch Neil Young's attention to remind him of our previous encounter.

As the sun set in the Pacific. we packed our blanket and cooler, walked past miles of sleeping bags and tents under pine and eucalyptus trees, and drove home.

CHAPTER 50

On Monday, the new television season began. I was looking forward to watching the debut of shows like *The Bill Cosby Show*, *Love, American Style*, and *The Smothers Brothers Show*, as well as old favorites like *Bonanza*, *Mission Impossible*, *Rowan & Martin's Laugh-In*, *the Mod Squad*, *the Johnny Cash Show*, *Hogan's Heroes*, and *the Hollywood Palace*.

A few days later, draft-aged men like me got some good news. President Nixon announced that the U.S. would withdraw 35,000 troops from Vietnam. He also ordered the cancellation of all draft calls for November and December, thus reducing the number of draftees by 32,000 in November and 18,000 in December. The decision was part of his strategy to turn the war over to the South Vietnamese, withdraw U.S. troops, and quell anticipated anti-war protests by students returning to college campuses after the summer break. It was a positive sign, even though none of us believed him. We'd see how successful it would be.

Although it was a positive shift in policy, I wasn't off the hook. I needed to go where most of the anti-war work was being done. That was the Draft Resistance Center in Oakland. Nixon's announcement came on Friday. I went on Monday.

After waiting nervously in a cold, somber, pseudo-reception area in my slacks, sport coat, and tie, I was ushered into an office by a young black woman with a righteous Afro. Behind a large, cluttered, wooden desk sat a man, actually a kid because he didn't look much older than me, with wire-rimmed glasses, long, stringy blonde hair, and a wispy, Buffalo Bill Cody goatee. Plastered around the walls were posters for rock concerts and recent demonstrations, newspaper articles, and children's artwork. He stood and we exchanged an awkward, sweaty on my part, brother handshake.

"Name's Rick," he said, gesturing for me to sit. "You going to a funeral?" he asked.

"Sorry?" I said, confused.

"The suit, dude. You're a little over-dressed." I guess I was, considering he wore a tie-dyed T-shirt, Levi's, and sandals.

"I didn't know what to expect," I stammered.

"Family, my brother," he said. "We're all in this together."

"Right on," I said, unconvincingly.

"You know much about what we do?" he went on, thrusting his thumb at the posters behind him.

"You help people like me get out of the draft."

"That's part of it. We also work with the community on issues like school lunches and rent control. We consider ourselves a community center. A place where people can hang, do artwork, play music, stage events. Whatever it is they're into."

"Sounds cool," I said, trying to sound as hip as him.

"If you stand and fight alongside people when they're trying to control their own lives and get what they need, they'll listen to your rap."

"I can dig it." I was trying way too hard to be righteously cool.

"We're past the point where we can collect like-minded people. We have to move people. To do that, you got to spend the time to get to know them. If you're defying the man, like we are, you may want protection. The people are the only protection you got. So, you better be tight with them."

"Makes sense," I replied, impatient to talk about my problems, not the problems of the people in Oakland.

"Summer of '67, several groups got together in San Francisco to plan a massive demonstration. We called it 'Stop the Draft Week.' We pledged to shut down the Oakland Induction Center from the sixteenth of October through the twentieth." I nodded my head and listened politely. "You heard of Dave Harris?"

"Sure. Married to Joan Baez. Class president at Stanford."

"He and some others started an anti-draft group called 'The Resistance.' Got a bunch of guys to burn their draft cards. They were the pacifist side of the movement. Some others wanted to be more militant."

"Militant?"

"They wanted to crack heads the way the pigs were cracking heads."

"Got it."

"That first day, we had three thousand people in the streets. We marched to the Induction Center to hand out anti-war leaflets to the inductees as they entered. We staged a peaceful sit-in in front of the building. Over the next few days, we were up to 10,000 protestors."

"That's a mass of people."

"Truth. That's why Oakland PD busted 123 people on Monday, including Baez and Harris. I guess that's how they hooked up."

"Love is strange."

"On Tuesday, we had 6,000, some wearing hard hats and carrying shields. Around 7 a.m., the pigs showed up in riot gear. They weren't there to arrest us. They were there to bust heads. It wasn't only the protestors that got hit.

TV, newspaper, and radio reporters got beat down. That was the first time the cops used a liquid tear gas called Mace. Nasty shit."

"First I've heard of it."

"The cops cleared the streets, but they got some bad press. Someone got an injunction to keep them from attacking again, so they cooled it for the rest of the week."

I was antsy. I had questions and wasn't sure how much time I had to ask them.

"Any chance you were there?" he asked.

"No, I missed it. Sorry."

"No need to apologize. We do what we can do."

"Anything happen after?"

"The feds refused to prosecute any of our leaders. They were afraid it'd lead to more rioting. So this right-wing DA and Reagan man named Frank Coakley charged seven men with conspiracy to commit misdemeanors, which was a felony. It was a bogus charge, but it carried a max of three years in state prison."

"Damn."

"Damn is right. The trial of what became known as the Oakland 7 started in January of this year."

"Like the Chicago 8."

"Somewhat. Charles Garry was an attorney for both cases."

"I've read he's done a lot for the anti-war movement."

"He has. He's a good attorney. The trial lasted eleven weeks. The turning point came when the prosecutor asked to play excerpts from a 'Stop the Draft Week' rally that had been held at UC Berkeley. The judge said play it all, or play nothing. They screwed themselves. The tape was typical Berkeley wackness. It was obvious there were no conspirators. Just bunches of people pissed off at the government. On March 28th, after three days of deliberations, the jury returned not-guilty verdicts for all defendants. The jury ruled the protest as free speech, not conspiracy."

"That was that?"

"Totally."

"So, what's all that got to do with me?'

"It's history, friend. Context. As Faulkner wrote, 'The past is never dead. It's not even past.'"

"I'm a history major."

"Then you get it." I nodded. I glanced up at the wall clock. He noticed.

"So, what can I do you for?" he asked.

"Help me get out of the draft. The things I've considered aren't panning out."

"What have you done so far?"

"I don't have a spleen."

"Might help you."

"I've asked for a note from my dentist about my bad jaw. Not sure what he wrote, though. He sealed it before I could read it and sent it to my draft board."

"That can screw you sometimes, depending on if he's a hawk, or a dove."

"Spoke to the National Guard."

"Long shot."

"Don't I know it."

"What about CO?" he asked.

"Even longer shot. We quit the church when my dad was alive. He didn't like that the reverend was always asking for money. He was driving a brand-new Caddie and we were driving an old Chevy."

"Dad's gone, huh?"

"Yes, he is. I've got a new dad."

"Good deal."

"It is."

"Don't get me going on the issues with the modern church," he continued. "We never go to church. Except maybe Easter and Christmas Eve."

"'Jack Christians,' as some like to call it."

"We don't even say grace."

"It doesn't have to be religious. It can be on moral grounds, too."

"Really?"

"But, it's no easier making the case."

"That's how out of it I am. I have no idea what it takes."

He pulled some papers out of a manila folder in a drawer. "You have to appear before your draft board and explain your beliefs in writing, or verbally."

"I'd probably write it. I hate public speaking."

"You have to explain how you arrived at your beliefs," he said, scanning the document. "The influence your beliefs have on how you live your life. Your reasons can't be based on 'politics, expediency, or self-interest.' Your lifestyle prior to making the claim must reflect your beliefs. Based on that, they make a decision."

"What if I don't like it?"

"You can appeal."

"What then?"

"If you win and they grant you CO status, you're offered two types of service. If you're opposed to any service, you can do Alternative Service."

"Like what?"

"A job that 'makes a meaningful contribution to the maintenance of the national health, safety, and interest.' That includes jobs in conservation, caring for the very young or very old, education, or health care."

"I could do that."

"If you're okay with serving, but refuse to carry a weapon, you'll serve as a noncombatant."

"What's that mean?"

"Working in construction, or supply. Maybe training. Or, becoming a medic."

"Hammering I can do. Stopping bleeding I can't."

"You're expected to serve the same amount of time as your military service, which is usually 24 months."

"So, two years. That's not bad."

"Where are your mom and stepdad on all this?"

"They're against the war. My stepdad will drive me to Canada."

"It's a good option, but there can be problems."

"That's what I've been told."

"It would take a while to become a citizen, if you wanted to do that. You've got to find a job and a place to live. Some Canadians don't want you there."

"It won't be easy."

"How long your dad been gone?"

"Seven years."

"Condolences, man. I don't get along with my old man because of all this." He gestured to his hair and the posters. "I'd like to be closer."

"We've even talked about me going to Europe and never coming back."

"That's a long way from home."

"I like my home."

"You're lucky. I couldn't get far enough fast enough."

"What's the deal with the lottery?" I asked.

"They throw all the birthdays in a hopper. Pull them out one at a time. The low numbers get called in for a physical. If you're classified 1-A, you go."

"How many numbers they going to call?"

"Depends on how many grunts they need."

"Who decides that?"

"The Army. They're doing most of the fighting in 'Nam. They send Selective Service a monthly quota, then Selective Service tells your draft board who tells you."

"That's not good."

"What's your draft board like?"

"Tough. I live in a conservative community. Farmers and ranchers. The men on the board are old, white, and conservative."

"Rough audience."

"I think they're all hawks."

"Thinking about anything else?"

"Some stupid things I'd never do, like get married and have a kid. Or cut off a finger."

"Smart man."

"Any suggestions? I'm starting to freak."

"Keep the student deferment as long as you can. Bummer is that means you're eligible for the draft until you're 35."

"Damn."

"Good news is, maybe the Vietnamese will start kicking ass and Nixon will stop leading with his dick."

"I read they've reduced the number of draftees."

"They have. If you hold out long enough, maybe it'll all go away. Worst case, you get dumped into a holding category and likely never get called."

"Right now, that sounds like best case."

"I like your optimism." I would have smiled at this if I hadn't been so uncomfortable.

"What else?" I asked.

"You could refuse."

"I don't want to go to jail."

"Don't blame you."

"Thanks."

"A couple cases I know about, the guy had the physical and was ordered to report for duty. He shows up, they ask him to raise his right hand to get sworn in, and he flat out refuses."

"Right there?"

"Right there and then. They send him home and order him to come back for an interview. Want to check how bats he is. Ends up, they fine him a few grand, put him on probation, and order him to do community service."

"I could handle that."

"Speaking of jail," he went on. "Some dudes have been given a devil's choice. They'd been busted for selling, or taking drugs. Could've been grass, acid, or something stronger. Didn't matter. When they faced the judge during their court appearance, they were given two options. They could do the time, or they could do Vietnam. They all chose Vietnam. Basically, the criminal justice system viewed doing Vietnam as a cut above doing time."

"Solomon's choice. There's no winning no matter what you choose."

"Here's some food for thought," he continued.

"What's that?"

"This is a poor man's war. Guys like you, who are educated or maybe got some money or know somebody, can figure out a way to get out. Black men, Latinos, and working-class stiffs don't have the same privileges. They're not the sons of senators. They're not part of the ruling class. They're the ones being drafted and coming home in bags. That's why we're here. Level the playing field. Help everybody who wants help. So, I guess what I'm saying is you need to get more involved. Fight it. Resist. Don't use your privilege. Don't let some poor schmuck go in your place. Maybe something you do now will help him later. And you."

"That's intense."

"I got nothing else, my man."

"Sorry to hear that."

CHAPTER 51

The next day was the fall or Autumnal Equinox. On that day, the center of the visible sun was directly above the equator. The length of the day and the length of the night were approximately the same duration across the planet. The word came from the Latin *Aequus*, which meant "equal," and *Nox*, which meant "night." From here on, the days would be shorter and the nights longer. For me, it was the true end of summer. Autumn was around the corner.

Where did the time go?, I thought to myself. *Who knew.* Thoughts about time passing quickly often came to me with the change of seasons, a birthday, a holiday, seeing someone I hadn't seen in some time, or a song like Judy Collins' *Who Knows Where the Time Goes?*. This question recalled a poem by Dr. Seuss, "How did it get so late so soon? It's night before it's afternoon. December is here before it's June. My goodness how the time has flewn. How did it get so late so soon?"

As I grew older, it felt like time passed more quickly than when I was younger, not that I was that old now. I had heard Mom and Dad and Grampa Owl speak of how it seemed time moved faster the older they got. In a psych course, the professor lectured about studies theorizing that this feeling in older adults had to do with a person's perception of how much time they had left – their future time – the limited number of years they felt they had. Young people only thought in terms of their biological age because their future still lay ahead of them, open-ended. Such perceptions by older people often led to regret. Perhaps because they felt time had been wasted. That they had no vivid memories of certain important events. That they would have been more aware, engaged, and productive if they had only known. That they had no control over any of it. Dad often said we shouldn't lament what we missed, what we didn't do. We should instead celebrate what we experienced, what we did do. I had a hard time doing that because time was hard for me.

For me, and others like me, it was always about time. Slipping away. Being wasted. Running out. Standing still. Flying. Being lost. Filling, making, and killing it. Or, having enough of it. We worried about it being the last time, or the last time around. It was always time to do this, or that. We thought about time zones, time outs, and real time – just in time or the nick of time or putting in time. We told stories about once upon a time and shared proverbs about a stitch in time. We fondly recalled the first time and agonized over the only time. We tried to take things one step at a time. We longed for the time when time was on our side.

Time and again, we talked about prime time, big time, me or my time, good time, nap time, in time, alone time, night-time, hang time, Christmas time, every time, lost time, quiet time, any time, wintertime, sleepy time, strange time, short-time, part-time, all-time, the right and wrong time. We read *Time Magazine* or the *New York Times*, *Of Time and the River*, or *The Time Machine*. We nostalgically looked back to the times of our life and hoped we had the time of our life. We set our clocks to Greenwich Mean Time and Pacific Standard Time. From time to time, we pondered time management, which we'd get around to when we had time, and time travel which inevitably required a time machine. We tried to imagine what having time on our hands, or the end of time, actually looked like. We questioned if there was world enough and time. We sang "The times they are a-changin'," "Time is on my side," "Time has come today," and "By the time I get to Phoenix." We often didn't have time to take our time. What came first, life or time? As one Brainiac pointed out, "if it weren't for time, everything would happen all at once at the same time." And, finally, there came a time when we discovered that Father Time waited for no one.

The older we got, the less there seemed to be of it and the faster it went. Something we thought took place two years ago was actually five. And we insisted on rushing toward then without living in the now, this moment. Only to look back and wonder why we were in such a hurry for the arrival of tomorrow when today would soon enough be gone to yesterday. It had been said that yesterday was the past, tomorrow was the future, but today was a gift and that was why it was called the present. I chuckled as my thoughts were interrupted by a quote from Groucho Marx, "Time flies like an arrow; fruit flies like a banana."

On Wednesday, September 24th, the trial of the Chicago 8 kicked off in the Windy City. Eight anti-war activists were charged with inciting the violent demonstrations at the August 1968 Democratic National Convention. The defendants included David Dellinger of the National Mobilization Committee (NMC); Rennie Davis and Thomas Hayden of the Students for a Democratic Society (SDS); Abbie Hoffman and Jerry Rubin, founders of the Youth International Party ("Yippies"); Bobby Seale of the Black Panthers; and activists Lee Weiner and John Froines. The defendants were charged with conspiracy to cross state lines to incite a riot.

The trial would be presided over by Judge Julius Hoffman. All but Seale were represented by William Kunstler and Leonard Weinglass. Seale retained Charles Garry. Knowing some facts about Kunstler and Garry, and having read about and observed the actions of the roster of defendants, it was shaping up to be a spectacle.

The fall quarter was scheduled to begin Monday, September 29th, with classes commencing the following Monday, October 6th. It was time to pack and say our goodbyes to family and friends, many of whom were returning to their own schools. Including Kelly. But, nothing had changed. She wouldn't take my phone calls. I didn't dare go by without her permission. I was disappointed, but I had convinced myself it was all her fault. I had tried. She wasn't interested. Maybe end of relationship. My pessimistic side was kicking in and I was okay with it.

We returned to Davis that same Wednesday. Gover rode up with me in Ugly Orange. Gary followed in the VW. My truck was packed with suitcases, bedding, things for the walls, odds and ends for the new apartment.

The Ivy Towne apartment had a living room, small dining room, even smaller kitchen, one bathroom, one large bedroom, and one small bedroom. Gary and I were going to room together, Gover and Mark were going to be roomies. We flipped a coin to see who got the bigger room. I won. Gover wasn't too disappointed. He didn't plan on hanging around on weekends. Nancy was finishing up at San Jose State. Gover assumed he'd be there most weekends. Mark didn't plan on hanging around much, either. So, it worked for everyone.

Gary and I covered one wall of our bedroom with a huge American flag I'd found in a thrift shop. We dotted it with a peace sign, posters, and other small reminders. It hung above a childhood desk Gary brought from home. He also brought his parent's old console stereo that we squeezed into the wall-length clothes closet. We liked having our sounds close by. We set up a color TV and Gover's recliner in the living room, alongside the usual apartment furniture. It was college comfortable. We agreed to continue buying a meal ticket at Webster-Emerson, at least for the first quarter, because nobody could cook, or wanted to.

Every day and every night we'd hear the train rumble by. It didn't take long to get to a point where we never heard it. All our guests did.

While settling in those first few days, we met our downstairs neighbors. All three were sophomores and excited about being on their own. Olav Messerschmitt was somehow related to the German airplane manufacturer. Tim Mondavi was part of the well-known Napa winemaking family. Doug Starr was simply "Big Dougie." The nice thing about having a budding winemaker downstairs was we got to taste his vintages and we could get Mondavi wine cheap. The Robert Mondavi Winery was the new kid on the block, having been founded in 1966 by Tim's dad. We had Gallo, which had been making wine in Modesto since 1933.

Once I was back on campus, I avoided Luci. I didn't want to see her. I didn't go to any of the places we had gone. I wasn't interested in being mixed up in her craziness. My head was in the sand and I intended to keep it there.

CHAPTER 52

The chain-link fence glistened in the moonlight. The beige shade cloth rippled in the breeze. The grass inside the cage was dotted with clumps of sleeping fur. The skeletal arms of fake trees stood barren. An insomniac chimp spun in circles on a blue barrel suspended by chains from a metal support strut. The enclosure looked like an outdoor exhibit at a metropolitan zoo. Except for one thing. The animals were all primates. Different sections held different breeds. Chimps, apes, orangutans, and baboons.

The building beyond the cages was bathed in security lights. It looked impregnable. Until it wasn't.

The explosion blew out all the front windows and doors. The primates in the outside cages dashed out of their sleeping perches and flung themselves against the farthest fence, desperate to escape. Primates freed by the explosion disappeared into the night. Their chattering was eerie and frightening.

The next day, the incident dominated the Sacramento and national news. Reporters speculated about why the center was targeted. Who was responsible? I was hoping Mitchell and Maple, the two guys I played softball with who worked there, hadn't been working the night shift.

The National Primate Center had opened in 1962. The research was financed by a federal grant from the Animal Research branch of the Institute of Health. The center had many breeds of both Old and New World monkeys and apes, such as chimpanzees, baboons, as well as the owl and languor species. The basic work of the researchers was to study such human ailments as tuberculosis, placenta cancer, and thalidomide effects. In other words, they were using the monkeys as guinea pigs for experiments they couldn't do on humans. According to some radical groups, the center was also doing research on chemical weapons and biological warfare.

The apartment phone rang. I was alone, watching the evening news coverage of the explosion. It was Luci.

"I need to see you," she said.

"I'm not interested."

"This is serious." I could tell from her shaking voice it was. "Meet me at the Buckhorn." The Buckhorn was a dive bar in Dixon.

"When?"

"Now." She hung up.

The Buckhorn was dark, smelled of beer and cigarettes, and a little desperation.

"I have to leave town," Luci said. She looked exhausted. And scared.

"Why?"

"Have you seen the news?"

"Yes."

"That's all I can tell you."

"The Primate Center."

"I've already made your life and mine more complicated by being here. Even dangerous."

"Bullshit," I said. She gave me that look I had seen a number of times in our relationship that meant she wasn't kidding.

"Where are you going?" I asked.

"I'm catching a plane in 'Frisco at midnight."

I hated people who called San Francisco, "'Frisco." It was so not local, even though she was. Those who really knew San Francisco called it, "The City." She said "Frisco" and it put my teeth on edge. Especially now.

"Then where?" I asked.

"I can't tell you."

"What's next?"

"There's more work to be done." She leaned in and kissed me. "It's been real," she said.

"I can't save you."

"I know." She stood, turned, and walked out the door without looking back.

Wally and I played liar's dice for beers at The Cave Inn. I was losing. Badly. He had also come up early to settle into his new apartment at Wake Forest, which was where Slevin had moved with new roommates, including two of my softball teammates, Jay Barber and Bobby T. Wally was rooming with Uhland and Amlin again, as well as a guy named Chuck Fuller. The Cave Inn was a bar and restaurant downtown that sat kitty-corner to the Antique Bizarre. It had an upstairs bar and seating for diners and a downstairs for the serious drinkers. That's where we were.

"Damn," Wally said. "I didn't think she had it in her."

"Did you know about it?" I asked.

"Not a thing." He said it in a way that wasn't convincing.

"This is nuts," I said.

"Some serious shit going down."

"People could've died."

"They don't care. In fact, they want people dead. Martyrs for the cause. You've studied your history. That's what it's all about. The more collateral damage the better."

"'The radicals in Russia were the first to use dynamite to carry out acts of terror. Revolution by any means. That's how they radicalized people, mostly students. Had them witness murders, or kill someone."

"That's how it all begins. And ends."

"I hope you're done with her."

"Sure," another inconclusive reply.

"Being around her is dangerous."

"I can handle it."

"Until you can't."

"End of story," he said, slamming down the dice cup. He tipped it up and said, "Five sixes."

Talking to Wally and thinking of Luci, I realized this was not a game. It never was. It wasn't textbook revolutionaries, novelized terrorists, or cinematic anarchists. This was real. All too real. Property was being destroyed. Men, women, and children were dying. These people weren't heroic. Heroes were people who did the right thing, even if it meant giving up their dreams, doing for others, sacrificing their lives. The world needed real heroes, not these jokers.

That same day, The Zodiac shot a young couple picnicking at Lake Berryessa. The woman died, but her boyfriend survived. He said the man who shot them was wearing a black executioner's hood and a breastplate with crypto lettering on it.

The new school year brought the re-opening of the Coffee House, the place Luci and I had often met after we first met. It had originally opened in February 1968. Its student founders said, according to *The Aggie*, "there was no place to go in Davis that didn't ring with sterility." The student-run facility had offered warm hospitality and better-than-usual entertainment. It had grown into an independent operation offering food at low prices to students. It had done well enough to warrant reopening for the fall quarter.

On opening night, there was a street dance. That Tuesday there was an all-day open house with free coffee. More street dances were held the rest of the week. A Davis theater group performed "The Séance" inside on Friday,

Saturday, and Sunday. A number of students took study breaks there rather than going back to their dorm, apartment, or frat house. I preferred Sycamore Lane, the library, or Olsen Hall, now that Luci was on the run.

That first Monday of the new quarter was a busy one. The same day, the army dropped murder charges against eight Green Berets accused of killing a Vietnamese national. Colonel Robert B. Rheault, commander of the 5th Special Forces Group in Vietnam, and seven other Green Berets, had been charged with premeditated murder and conspiracy to commit murder when they executed Thai Khac Chuyen for being a double agent and compromising a secret mission. The case against the Special Forces soldiers had been dismissed because the CIA, for reasons of national security, refused to release highly classified information about the operations.

My first thought was that the army was covering its ass and taking care of its own. National security seemed to be used too often these days to cover up things the government didn't want the public to know. How was it justifiable that you could kill a man without a trial, even if he was Vietnamese and it was in a theater of war? It seemed like anything was justifiable when it came to Vietnam.

CHAPTER 53

"All the News that Fits" – October Edition

Daniel Ellsberg, a military analyst employed by think tank Rand Corporation, copies top-secret documents about America's involvement in the Vietnam war. Professional golfer Walter Hagen dies. An earthquake rocks Santa Rosa, California. *Monty Python's Flying Circus* debuts on BBC Television. The Gold Rush Music Festival in Lake Amador, California, features Santana and Ike & Tina Turner. Ice skater and film star Sonja Henie dies. Tom Dempsey of the New Orleans Saints kicks a 55-yard field goal. The Weatherman splinter group of the SDS blows up a police statue in Haymarket Square in Chicago to launch the "Days of Rage." Tammy Wynette and Johnny Cash win the female and male vocalist of the year award at the third Country Music Association Awards. Canada considers banning the hunting of baby harp seals. Jazz musician Miles Davis is shot by an unknown assailant after performing at a Brooklyn nightclub. A one hundred to one shot at the beginning of the season, the New York Mets defeat the Baltimore Orioles to win the World Series. The final single by Diana Ross & The Supremes, "Someday We'll Be Together," is released. Nixon's attack dog, the ever-glib Vice President Spiro Agnew, is quoted as saying, "A spirit of national masochism prevails, encouraged by an effete corps of impudent snobs who characterize themselves as intellectuals." Father of the "Beat Generation" and author Jack Kerouac dies. A believer in "change through rapprochement," Willy Brandt is elected Chancellor of the Federal Republic of West Germany. The Beatles issue a press release denying the rumors that "Paul is dead." The University of Wyoming dismisses 14 black players from the football team for asking to wear black armbands during the upcoming home game against the Brigham Young University Cougars, a few of whose players had used racial epithets the year before. *Life* magazine does a feature on consumer advocate and muckraker Ralph Nader and "Nader's Raiders," a corps of law, medical, and engineering students. The Advanced Research Projects Agency Network (ARPANET) sends its first message between computers at UCLA and Stanford. Activist and Black Panther Bobby Seale is gagged and manacled at the trial of the Chicago 8. A terrorist group called "The Beaver 55" shreds Selective Service records in Indianapolis. New book releases include *Them* by Joyce Carol Oates; *The Selling of the President*, Joe McGinniss; *Present at the Creation: My Years in the State Department*, Dean Acheson; *The Human Zoo*, Desmond Morris; and *Ambassador's Journal* by John K. Galbraith. *The New Music Hall of Israel*; *From the Second City*; *Lend an Ear*; *From Israel with Laughter*; *Oh, What a Wedding!*; and *Jimmy* open on stage. New films include *Paint Your Wagon* starring Lee Marvin and Clint Eastwood, *The Undefeated* featuring John Wayne and Rock Hudson, John Huston's *A Walk with Love and Death*, *The Sterile Cuckoo*, and *Tell Them Willie Boy Is Here* with Robert Redford and Katharine Ross. New music includes *Led Zeppelin II*; *In the Court of the Crimson King* by King Crimson; *Elvis in Person at the International Hotel*; *Rhymes & Reasons* by John Denver; the single "Leaving on a Jet Plane" by Peter, Paul and Mary; and *Free* by Free. To capitalize on the success of *From Elvis in Memphis*, RCA also releases *From Memphis to Vegas/From Vegas to Memphis*, which is the King's first double album and first live album.

My birthday fell on a Sunday this year. I had big plans for the days before my birthday weekend. On my birthday, the number one song in America was "Sugar, Sugar" by the Archies. Puke. "Bad Moon Rising" by CCR was number one in the U.K. Better. In the latest issue of *Rolling Stone*, it was reported that Crosby, Stills, Nash & Young were working on a new album at Wally Heider Recording in San Francisco. I confirmed it with my friend, Bruce, the fellow Aggie who had worked for Bill Graham.

My present to me was to stake out the recording studio to see if I could run into Stills and/or Young on their way in or out of the sessions. It didn't take much to convince Gary to go along. Just the two *amigos* again, like we had done when we had traveled to Mexico in August '67 and Los Angeles over spring break.

Gary and I had driven his VW from Modesto to Mazatlan, Mexico, in the summer of our freshman year at MJC. The parents were concerned. We weren't. We were somewhat worried about stories we'd been told of police planting dope in the cars of tourists, especially hippie Americans, so they could extort money. We were determined to keep an eye on the car and our stuff.

It was a long, surprising, and incredible trip. We encountered wonderful people, plenty of *puente angostos* (narrow bridges), mangy cattle, terrific food, and scary *federales* armed to the teeth. We entered through Nogales and traveled to Hermosillo and on to Guaymas, which is where my grandfather went every year to fish for yellowfin tuna. He and my step-grandmother,

Marybelle, would dissect the catch and bottle it in oil. They always gave me some, which I took back to Davis for us starving students to share.

Grampa Owl loved telling tales about the old *gringo* fooling the locals when they spoke badly about them in Spanish. He'd come back at them with some street Spanish and swear words that made their jaws drop. From then on, they were best *amigos*.

While we were eating dinner at the Guaymas Inn, a hurricane swept in from the Gulf of California. We were told to pull the Volks up next to the restaurant wall so the hurricane wouldn't snatch it up, which we immediately did. We were in the middle of dinner, when the power went out. The owners apologized, saying they needed to get home to their families. They lit some candles and left us to finish our food. The storm blew through without significant damage.

We continued south through Los Mochis and Culiacán to Mazatlan. We rented a room at *Las Gaviotas* – the Seagulls – which sat on the beach of the same name. We were befriended by a kid named Luis who gave us the tour of the town. We ate dinner at El Shrimp Bucket. As the sun went down, we sat on the beach, drank Superior beer, and watched the light show, as the last of the storm blew across the Gulf toward Cabo San Lucas. It had been our first trip out of the States. We returned home feeling like world travelers.

Gary and I drove to the City early on Thursday, thinking that would be the best day to catch Stills or Young. Our reasoning was that it wasn't a Monday when nobody wanted to work and it wasn't a Friday when everybody was trying to leave town. The studio was located on Hyde Street in the Tenderloin. Not the most upscale neighborhood in the City.

Thanks to our Los Angeles journey, we knew the sessions likely wouldn't get going until late, so we looked for a coffee shop near the studio. We found a classic. The Lafayette Coffee Shop was an all-night diner located across the street from Heider's. We found a parking spot on the same side of the street as the Lafayette. We ducked into the diner to see if any of CSNY were there. There were people eating, including some longhairs, but none of the band; at least not musicians we recognized. We ordered coffee to go and returned to the car. We drank coffee, fed the meter, read *Rolling Stone* and the *Chronicle*, bought more coffee to go so we could use the bathroom, and waited. Our patience paid off. Around 8 p.m., Neil Young sauntered down Eddy Street, crossed Hyde, walked toward us, and went inside the Lafayette. We waited long enough for him to find a booth and place his order.

He was sitting in a red Naugahyde booth at the back of the diner. He looked up as we approached.

"Mind?" I said. It took a moment for him to recognize us. Out of context and all. He smiled as he recalled his first words to us on the beach last March. He gestured for us to sit.

"You always travel in pairs?" he asked.

"We've been friends a long time," I said.

"Longer than you and Stephen," Gary added.

"Well, long may you run," he answered. "Long may you run."

"You, too," I replied.

"Been here long?" Gary asked.

"Just got here."

"No, in the City," I corrected.

"A night, or two. Was looking at some property down near La Honda."

"You thinking about moving up here?" Gary asked.

"Might be. I don't dig the LA scene all that much."

"I know a filmmaker who feels the same," I added, dropping hints like I did the last time.

"Where you staying?" Gary asked.

"A motel called the Caravan Motor Lodge. A few blocks from here."

"Sounds dicey," I said.

"It's close," he said and shrugged. "Some heavy stuff has gone down in a short period of time after you two stalked me down in LA."

"Your buddy Charlie really messed up."

"I knew that Manson cat was strange, but I never thought he was that strange. All the people in the canyons who knew him thought he was coming for them next. That was the nail in the coffin for the mellow LA scene. And me. Angelenos started locking their doors and carrying guns."

"Knocked the wind out of the whole peace, love, and brotherhood of man thing," I said.

Gary replied, reciting a poem, because he loved poetry and was now writing some.

"'*Turning and turning in the widening gyre*
The falcon cannot hear the falconer;
Things fall apart; the centre cannot hold;
Mere anarchy is loosed upon the world,
The blood-dimmed tide is loosed, and everywhere
The ceremony of innocence is drowned;
The best lack all conviction, while the worst

Are full of passionate intensity.
Surely some revelation is at hand;
Surely the Second Coming is at hand.
The Second Coming! Hardly are those words out
When a vast image out of Spiritus Mundi
Troubles my sight: somewhere in sands of the desert
A shape with lion body and the head of a man,
A gaze blank and pitiless as the sun,
Is moving its slow thighs, while all about it
Reel shadows of the indignant desert birds.
The darkness drops again; but now I know
That twenty centuries of stony sleep
Were vexed to nightmare by a rocking cradle,
And what rough beast, its hour come round at last,
Slouches towards Bethlehem to be born?"

"Eliot, right?" he said.

"Right," Gary replied.

"Manson slithered into the Hippie Garden of Eden and all its stardust children lost their innocence," I said.

"He was a broken mirror reflection of all the greed and ugliness that's taking place, especially in California. Especially in LA. We had a golden time, and then we lost our way. Everybody seems to wonder what it's like down here."

"A few days later you were all at Woodstock," I pointed out.

"Yin and yang, light and dark," he said.

"You played Chicago after all," I said.

"I did. Our first live gig. We left from there and went directly to New York."

"How'd it go?" Gary asked.

"It was our second live show together. CSN played an acoustic set with those three alone. Then I came out."

"Had to have been a rush," I said.

"It was. It was like 3 a.m. Sunday morning by the time we got on. Man, there were a bunch of eyes out there."

"Half a million according to some reports," Gary said.

"I'm not sure they could hear us. I couldn't hear us. So we played on."

"They were awake?" I asked.

"If they weren't, they were when I cranked Old Black up."

"What was that whole scene like?" Gary asked.

"Bizarre."

"What do you mean?" I asked.

"Peace, love and flowers. That's where I was at when we did Woodstock. We were all one. We were all speaking for ourselves. We were all speaking for our generation."

"Righteous, right?" I interjected.

"It turned into a bullshit gig."

"What I saw looked far out," Gary said.

"That was one of the problems. Suddenly, there's a camera in my face. I told them I didn't want to be filmed."

"Why not?" I asked.

"The camera got in the way. The film got in between. It took away the essence. It was totally distracting. I was trying to get into the music and there's this dickhead with a camera in my face."

"That sure wasn't how it was portrayed."

"You had to be there. Everybody was on their Hollywood trip. It wasn't about the music. It was about the egos and the money. Music is its own thing, not a commodity."

"Anything memorable?" I asked.

"Hotwiring a truck and driving it around with Jimi Hendrix on the hood."

"Hendrix a hood ornament," Gary said and we laughed.

"Hearing him play. That cat makes me look like a hack."

"Bummer about Crosby's girlfriend," I said.

"Knocked him down. Still getting over it. We'd be playing Winterland tonight if that hadn't happened. Instead, we thought we'd do some recording."

"So, you're here," Gary said.

"We are."

"The 'Everybody Knows' album is unreal," I said. "I dig 'Cinnamon Girl' and 'Cowgirl in the Sand.'"

"Those sessions were natural. And real. All done in that burned-out basement in Topanga."

"Sold a bunch of records, too," Gary said.

"I'm proud of that, but prouder of the music."

"Then you left Crazy Horse and joined CSN," I said.

"That was a weird time. I'd be in one studio working with the Horse, then switch over to another studio to record with the band. It was schizo."

"What made you change your mind?" I asked. "To join them, I mean."

"Ahmet Ertegun, head honcho of Atlantic Records."

"You worked with him when you were in Springfield," I replied.

"They needed somebody to beef up the band, especially when they did an electric set. They could sing all the songs on their first LP, but couldn't play them. Stephen wanted to get a keyboard player. He went after Steve Winwood."

"Wow, that would have been cool. All that Spencer Davis and Traffic vibe," Gary said.

"He wasn't interested, so Stephen tried Mark Naftalin, who played with the Paul Butterfield Blues Band. Not into it, either. Talked with Al Kooper, who he'd done Super Session with. No go. He even tried John Sebastian of the Spoonful. That's when Ahmet stepped in and pushed for me."

"A Springfield reunion."

"Similar, I suppose. I made it clear I wasn't a hired gun. An add-on. I belonged to myself. I wanted equal billing. If I was expected to give my soul and spirit, it had to be a four-way street. If not, no deal. What I say, I do."

"So the best sounding law firm in music became CSNY," I said, smiling.

"They're calling us a supergroup. Lame."

"Kind of fits," Gary observed.

"When Stephen came around to talk to me about it, it felt like old times. I was thinking we could do something as good as Springfield was, or could have been."

"Expecting to fly," I said. He glanced over at me, his eyes narrowed.

"I'd gotten a taste of being in a band again and I dug it. I wanted to play with people. CSN was technically superior to the Horse. Plus, I didn't have to be out front. Those three could be. That was freeing."

"How'd they handle you joining?" I asked.

"Stephen was reluctant because of the past. Croz was all for it. Nash was worried it would ruin the good thing they had going. But, I brought something they didn't have."

"What was that?" Gary asked.

"Intensity," he replied, glaring at us with that dark, unsettling gaze. He smiled, disarming us both. "A taste of bitter with the sweet."

"That was your first free gig," I said. "We made it to the second one."

"Yeah, Big Sur. That wasn't bad."

"You sounded good," I said.

"Especially with Joni joining in," Gary added.

"Until Stephen opted to mix it up with some dude who was hassling us about making too much money instead of being poor hippies."

"That was nasty."

"It was a great place to be and listen to music," Gary said.

"Speaking of which, how's the session going?" I asked.

"Take a guess. Four writers, singers, and producers. Croz just lost the love of his life. Nash just broke up with Joni. Stills is mooning over Judy. I'm working on a solo album with Crazy Horse."

"No lady in your life?"

"No time."

"Sounds complicated."

"It is, but I like what I'm doing here. I've at least two songs of my own that will be on the album."

"Titles and stories?" I prompted. He smiled as the words triggered a memory from our previous meeting.

"'Helpless' is a song about nostalgia and the loss of innocence."

"A little like 'I Am a Child?'" I asked.

"A little, I guess. Too bad the mix on that album was such a mess. Don't get me going on the processing they did."

"When do you think you'll wrap up here?" Gary asked.

"End of December."

"That's a lot of studio time," I said.

"Not when it takes ten hours to do one song."

"Damn."

"Stephen gets into it. And they've got money to burn."

"Kids in a candy store," Gary said.

"What's doing with you two?" he asked, tired of talking about himself.

"It's my birthday tomorrow," I said.

"Well, happy birthday to you," he half said, half sang, and handed me a guitar pick he had pulled from his Levi's pocket.

"Thanks."

"Both back in school," Gary replied.

"I'm dealing with the draft," I said.

"That sucks," he said.

"I'm a little weirded out," I added.

"I would be, too. If I weren't Canadian," he said, smiling.

"I'll know how bad it is when they do the lottery," I said.

"I've heard about that. It's coming down soon."

"This December."

"Waging war is absurd," he said.

"It doesn't make any sense," Gary replied.

"Nixon and his tin soldiers need to start waging peace."

"I'm a history major," I said. "There's every indication we'll never win this war."

"Even Walter Cronkite said so," Gary added.

"If Uncle Walter says it, it must be so," he said. "My father is a journalist and broadcaster. A writer, too."

"Really?" Gary said.

"Big fan of the truth."

"Colonial powers have never defeated native revolution," I said. "Not Alexander, not the Carthaginians, not the Romans, not the Ottomans, not the British. The British Empire fell because it was fighting on too many fronts and was trying to control too many colonies. We're almost there."

"You doing anything to avoid going in?" he asked.

"Researching. Talking. Visiting. Checking out what's available to me."

"Any good leads?"

"Well, it looks like there's a few ways to go. Depends on what happens with the lottery. If it's good, I'm good. If it's bad, I'll try to keep my student deferment for another quarter. Maybe by then they'll come to their senses and stop the war."

"Even if they did, it's gonna take some time to stop that train," he said.

"Or, they'll start drafting the younger men and pass over old men like him," Gary replied.

"If that doesn't happen, I may go to Europe," I added.

"Or Canada," Gary chimed in.

"I miss my home sometimes," he said.

"They've been good about taking in draft dodgers," Gary pointed out.

"I hope it doesn't come to that," I said.

"This government madness fires me up," he said.

"I know one thing," I continued.

"What's that?"

"I'm not going to kill people who are defending their homeland," I went on. "I'm not going to kill women and children so our government can get more oil. I'm not going to kill innocents so our government can stop Communism."

"Right on," he said.

"You guys have always been against the war," I continued. "You've always spoken up."

"We have a voice. We have a platform. We use it. To speak for this generation."

"I guess that's what we're doing when we protest or burn our draft cards or refuse to serve," I said. "If enough of us do it, if enough of us raise our voices, if enough of us take to the streets, if enough of us stop 'business as usual,' maybe they'll listen. Maybe they'll get the message."

"Dude take a breath," he said. "Man, Mario Savio's got nothing on you."

"I get worked up," I replied.

"Brother, you've got to do what you've got to. You know what's right. Your gut will tell you."

"My life depends on it." We sat silent for a moment, staring into our empty coffee cups.

"Again, on that note," he said. "Gotta split. We're working on my songs tonight."

"Titles and stories?" I asked once more.

He smiled again. "'Helpless' I told you about. A montage of songs called, 'Country Girl.' One I wrote with Stephen called, 'Everybody I Love You.'"

"The album have a name?" Gary asked.

"'Déjà vu.'"

"We have all been here before," I said.

He grinned and said, "We're also doing a cover of a new song Joni wrote about the New York festival. Called 'Woodstock.'"

"We heard it at Big Sur," I said.

"It was beautiful," Gary said. "She's beautiful."

He stood. "I feel good. I feel like tonight's the night."

"Why's that?" Gary asked.

"It's a full moon. I like recording on full-moon nights."

"With the werewolves," I said.

"My brothers," he said. "See you around."

"Yeah, see you around," Gary and I replied.

"Don't let them bring you down," he said.

"We'll try," I answered.

CHAPTER 54

My family was notorious for celebrating birthweeks, not birthdays. My little sisters would have been thrilled to have birthmonths, but my parents weren't allowing it. Unfortunately, October 5th, which was a Sunday and the actual day of my birth, was also the day before classes began. I planned to start my birthweek celebration the Friday before and continue it at home the weekend after.

Gary and I returned from the City to our apartment late Thursday. The first stop on Friday was L&M Liquors, which was located on Chiles Road, exactly three miles from the Richards Boulevard underpass. It was that distance from campus because a state law banned liquor stores anywhere within three miles of the university. We bought cheap Lucky Lager Beer and even cheaper gin and tonic. It was my birthday, but we were on a student budget. The next stop was the Safeway in University Mall. We bought all the "fixin's" for a "junk food picnic." Lay's BBQ and regular chips, sour cream and Lipton's Onion Dip Mix, corn chips and clam dip, smoked oysters, Braunschweiger, tortilla chips and salsa, sardines, rye bread, salami, and cheddar cheese. All my favorite greasy and salty snacks.

We cleaned the apartment, including the disgusting bathroom. Unfortunately, none of my roommates could shoot straight. We set the food on the coffee table in the living room and on counters in the kitchen; stuck the alcohol in plastic coolers filled with ice on the stair landing outside the front door; put up a card table for poker and the dining room table for pinochle; mounted a dart board on the wall next to the TV. We'd patch it later if anyone missed. We invited Wally and the FYNCers, Steph, Rod, and the boys from the apartment below. Everyone was encouraged to bring girls, so it wouldn't be a room filled with testosterone.

We wanted to get an early start on the festivities, so we fired things up at four. Wally came stag. Amlin and Uhland brought their steadies. Rod and his wife, Marilyn, joined us, as did Steph and his lady, Jo. Tim, Doug, and Oly all came solo, but Tim brought wine, so he was forgiven.

We had alerted the apartment managers about the party. They were fine, but skeptical. Once things got rolling, it got very loud, very fast. I was worried, figuring they would shut us down. They never did.

We drank and got stoned. We played drinking games, some cards until the dancing got going, and, as the evening came to an end around midnight, sang our swan song, "Slimy Madge," to the tune of "O, Tannenbaum." All in all, it was a good way to kick off the unofficial birthday weekend. Nobody had passed out, got in a fight, or hurled.

On Saturday night, we decided to hit some frat parties now that school had just begun, and the frat boys were welcoming new recruits. Most of the houses were located along Russell Boulevard, so it was easy to walk from house to house. Plus, most of the partying was happening on the front lawns. My group of wing men for this journey was small. Gary, Gover, and Wally.

We launched things at Alpha Epsilon Pi, which was one of the largest frats on campus. The kegger was rolling. We filled our plastic cups and guzzled a few before moving on to Chi Pi, which had opened last May. As the new kid on the block, they wanted to impress the students and show up their frat neighbors, which meant they had a huge spread, including steak and lobster. It was hard to tear ourselves away, but we did. On down the street, we stopped at Sigma Alpha Epsilon. Sig Ep had a couple brothers from Modesto. Jim Allred was a year ahead of us. Gover knew him because they were both on the swim team at Davis High. We tracked him down, talked about home, the frat, and the upcoming intramural, flag football season. A loud, clanking noise distracted us. It was horseshoes.

Gary and I formed one team, Gover and Wally another. There were two well-groomed pits. We signed up to play next. When we were up, we thumped our frat opponents, which made them none too happy. But, they were wasted, so it didn't matter. The others didn't do so well. Wally didn't like losing, especially when he was drinking. Things got heated between him and a beefy, short-haired brother. I finally negotiated a peace settlement, the two toasted and shook hands. Because Friday night had been a long one and we'd been partying for most of two days, it was time to go home. I drove because I was the most sober, even though it was my party and I was the birthday boy.

Although Sunday was my actual twenty-first birthday, we all needed a day to recover and get ready for the dreaded Monday and first day of class. We summoned enough energy to go to Giant Burger for breakfast. Their fluffy eggs and greasy hash browns were perfect for soaking up the residual alcohol and helping with the hangover. So was the surprise dip in the apartment pool, which my roomies fooled me into falling for by saying there was someone at the pool who had a surprise for me. It was a shove in the deep end. Although it was invigorating and made me feel like a new man, I got even by chucking a few deck chairs at them. We went back upstairs and watched football, but mostly slept. We did some cleaning, but not enough to make any difference. We popped a beer late in the day for a little "hair of the dog" and to toast my special day. We had an early dinner and my roomies hit the rack. An anti-climax to the big day.

I climbed into Ugly Orange and drove to Central Park. It was a full moon night. I had bought myself a birthday present. A small silver bracelet. I held it up to the moon and it reflected the light. I placed it on my wrist and whispered, "To new beginnings."

Monday came much too early. I had a full load of sixteen units. When possible, I scheduled Monday, Wednesday, and Friday classes so I could have Tuesday and Thursday to study. And, as early as possible, so I could study the rest of those days. That made for long days. My eight o'clock, actually 8:10 because we didn't start on the hour, was "English *Bible* as Literature;" my ten o'clock was "Special Study for Advanced Undergraduates, History" with my advisor Daniel Brower; my one o'clock was "Old English & Early Medieval Literature;" and I finished at three o'clock with "Survey of Russian Literature: 19th Century," taught by Rod. I scheduled my history special study later in the morning so I wouldn't nod out. It was a small class of ten, so I couldn't sit in the back and be inconspicuous.

Miss Van Norden taught the *Bible* as lit class. It covered the Old Testament poetry and prophecy, as well as the Gospels and certain Epistles. The history special study class gave us time with Professor Brower to discuss what our thesis might be. The medieval lit class surveyed the major types, traditions, and conventions of literature in England from the time of Beowulf to the late medieval romances. The class emphasized the heroic strain, courtly love, and the development of Arthurian literature. It was in the medieval lit class that I was first introduced to T.H. White's *Once and Future King*, another chronicle of King Arthur, which became an immediate favorite.

I was excited about my last class, primarily because Rod was teaching it and Steph was taking it. I convinced Gary to sign up, promising him he would enjoy it. He was an English major, so it didn't take much arm-twisting. It was an introduction to the dominant literary trends, the major literary figures, and landmarks of Russian prose and poetry from the period of Sentimentalism to the beginnings of Modernism. The final would be a class project, something meaningful you could do alone, or with a classmate. Gary and I decided we would do the reader's theater project I had mentioned to Rod the previous February. Gary and I had both done that type of presentation at MJC. The subject would be Leo Tolstoy.

I had long been interested in Arthurian legend, likely because I was a history major and an Anglophile. I had revisited some of my favorites, as a result of studying Campbell in Argüelles' textiles class last April. In addition to White's book, I had read Edmund Spenser's *The Faerie Queen*, Sir Thomas Malory's *Le Morte d'Arthur*, and Mark Twain's *A Connecticut Yankee in King Arthur's Court*, and the movie, *Camelot*, starring Richard Harris, Vanessa Redgrave, and Franco Nero, based on the musical stage play by Alan Jay Lerner and Frederick Loewe, which was adapted from the White book. John Steinbeck had been working on a retelling of Sir Thomas Malory's *Le Morte d'Arthur*, reportedly to be called *The Acts of King Arthur and His Noble Knights*, but it had never been published. He, too, was a lover of Arthurian legends, having read them as a child.

By Monday night, we were rested and ready to continue the birthweek celebration. We hit the upstairs bar at Larry Blake's for happy hour. I proudly showed my driver's license. The bartender recognized the significance by comping me a gin and tonic, the signature drink of the bar. Blake's upstairs was classy compared to the Rathskeller downstairs, which catered mostly to the beer drinking crowd. Upstairs, the waiters wore black pants, white shirt, black bowtie, and black jacket. Downstairs, the waiters sometimes wore togas. The upstairs was carpeted, the downstairs carpeted with peanut shells. We preferred the downstairs.

At Blake's, we were simply greasing the wheels for the main event. The Kat Patch in Dixon. The Kat Patch was one of two strip clubs in the nearby farming town. It was located just off the highway between the Dixon Livestock Auction and the Casa Blanca Motel. Both clubs catered to the cowboys and the college kids. They smelled of cigarettes, beer, body odor, and perfume. The beer was cheap and fresh and the ladies were mostly co-eds making money to pay tuition. Gary had fallen in love with one. A dark-haired girl named Joanne. Gary was so infatuated, he had stolen her tip tray, tucked it into his pants, and now used it as a receptacle for his car keys and change. It still had her name handwritten on a small piece of paper taped to the top of the tray.

The birthday crew included Gover, Gary, Wally, Gant, and me. Steve was already toasted when he arrived in his VW. We piled into the bug and Wally's Opel and motored west on 80 for Dixon. The place was quiet, which wasn't unusual for a Monday night. Joanne was working, so we didn't see much of Gary. We ordered a round, dumped change into the jukebox, and snagged a table front and center. The performers were as tired as we were. It must have been a busy weekend. They gave it their best shot and we showed our appreciation with a few tips. After Wally announced that it was my birthday, the girls sang me a sloppy version of "Happy Birthday." I got a can of Bud on the house, a half-hearted lap dance, and slaps on the back from the farmers and truckers.

As the evening wore on and we wore down, Stevie was winding up. He and Wally could make a tough team when they were whacked. And they were. That's when one of the cowboys got tired of their act. Stevie bumped into him when he was ordering another beer. "Tex" took exception. He slid off his stool and shoved Gant. Gant was trying to focus on the guy when Wally stepped in front of Gant. A few words were exchanged and things were escalating when the bar owner stepped in between. He flashed a small handgun and suggested the boys make up, or take it outside. Wally smiled that crooked smile, toasted the dude, dragged Gant back to our table, and suggested we call it a night. We did. It took some convincing, but we were able to drag our love-struck roomie away from his co-ed. The birthday week was off and running.

October started with a bang, not a whimper. Not thanks to my birthday celebrations, but thanks to the Weathermen in Chicago. On October 6th, the Weathermen blew up a statue erected in memory of the policemen who had died during the 1886 Haymarket Riot.

The Haymarket affair took place during a peaceful rally supporting a worker's right to an eight-hour day and in reaction to the killing of several workers by police the day before. As police moved in to disperse the crowd, someone threw dynamite at the officers. The bomb blast and gunfire that followed led to the death of seven police officers and four civilians, with dozens more wounded. Eight anarchists were convicted of conspiracy. Four were hanged.

The Weathermen's blast shattered more than 100 windows and scattered pieces of the statue onto the Kennedy Expressway below. It set the tone for the "Days of Rage" to follow. The goal of this act was to "Bring the war home!" and create enough chaos to awaken the American public and force them to focus on Vietnam. The Weathermen were tired of the ongoing, predictable demonstrations that had led to nothing. They planned to shake things up. To use violence to illuminate violence. The Weathermen expected it to be the largest protest of the decade. They anticipated thousands. Hundreds showed up. But, they were dedicated and effective.

The "Days of Rage" started innocently enough on Wednesday, October 8th. Approximately 800 kids gathered in Lincoln Park, sitting around bonfires, rapping, and making music. The park had symbolic significance because that was where, a year earlier, demonstrators and police had squared off during the Democratic National Convention. Radicals from across the country had come to Chicago once more to protest the war, the draft, and the trial of the Chicago 8.

These demonstrators came prepared, unlike their predecessors at the convention. Some wore football helmets, others wore motorcycle helmets. Some wore gas masks, others goggles. They were armed with lead pipes and chains. They dared the police to bust them. The police waited. Speeches were made. The crowd listened and waited for the signal. It came at 11 p.m. The demonstrators moved out, picked up bricks, and began smashing car windows. It touched off four days of violence.

Their next target was the affluent Gold Coast neighborhood. Police used teargas and squad cars to stop the mob. During a half-hour of rioting, 28 policemen were injured, six Weathermen were shot, and 68 rioters were arrested. The demonstrators followed the anarchy with an uncharacteristic few days of peaceful rallies. On October 10th, the Weathermen marched through The Loop, Chicago's financial district. The protestors broke through police lines and smashed the windows of cars and stores. Within minutes, the police arrested more than half the crowd. When the smoke cleared, 75 police had been injured, several demonstrators hurt, and 287 arrested. A city attorney lay crippled, paralyzed for life. Some of the leaders were arrested and jailed, others went into hiding.

The SDS and Weathermen had served notice to the man, the pigs, and the public that the anti-war movement was stepping up the cut.

The same Tuesday night the "Days of Rage" started, we attended a concert on the quad sponsored by KDVS to start the school year. The bands included Modesto's own Mother Nature's, along with Brotherhood, Rush, J. Silverheels, Spice, Homewood, and Doby Strange. The master of ceremonies was one of the station's jocks. A guy named Bruce Riordan. He had been on the air from the day I first came to Davis. Arnopole and Mother Nature's got invited to play thanks to a frat brother of one of the band members.

The rest of the school week was uneventful. It was time to buckle down for the new quarter. It didn't take long to get into my school routine. I was more disciplined than Gary or Gover. They figured they had all the time in the world. I knew better. The twelve-week quarter would be over in a heartbeat.

The return of school meant the return of intramural sports. The I.M. Department was one of the best in the country. It was run by Gary Colberg, a true sports nerd. There were more sports and more divisions for men and women than most schools. For FYNC, fall meant flag football. Our quarterback was Doug Uhland, who was also one of the strong arms in our softball team's outfield. Rich Amlin and the beefy players played up front, giving Uhland time. Barber and I were split out as wide receivers. We also played defensive backs – him because he was tall, me because I was quick. My teammates nicknamed me "the Modesto Flash." Like the Mud Bowl, we had plays drawn up on 3x5 cards, so we wouldn't waste any time in the huddle. Each position was assigned a number so you knew who you were and what you had to do on each play. One specially designed play featured me lining up at center. After hiking the ball, I'd run a fly pattern. Because most centers were slow and usually blocked, this strategy nearly always resulted in a long gain, especially if we hadn't played the team before. Once we ran it, we couldn't run it again. We played in the open, off-campus division, which was just below the frat league in competitive talent. When we were on, we were tough to beat.

CHAPTER 55

Back in the saddle on campus, it was time to address my draft status. Like nearly all college campuses, Davis offered draft assistance.

One of the resources was the Davis chapter of The Resistance, which the Oakland guy had told me about. I attended their first meeting of the year. The guest speaker was Loren Basham, a San Francisco draft counselor. He told the crowd of nearly 100 people that draft resistors were flocking to San Francisco because judges there were likely to order probation before prison, which was also what the Oakland counselor had mentioned. According to Basham, that was because the courts were logjammed and able to handle about 200 cases per year. Poor scheduling and long delays were compounding the problem he added. He went on to say that most of those indicted in San Francisco were receiving probation, ranging from two to three years. Much of what was happening in the Bay Area courts was thanks to a phalanx of attorneys, who were providing services *pro bono* to those opposing military conscription.

Leaving the meeting and walking into the crisp autumn night, I realized it was an option, although not a good one.

Between classes that week, I visited the Draft Counseling Center. It was located on the second floor of South Hall. The counselors were ministers and priests from the Davis area, who donated their time to help students confused about what to do about the draft. The advisor I had an appointment with was a minister for the Methodist church. After I had given him a summary of what I had looked into, who I had seen, who I had talked with, and what they had advised, he leaned forward and clasped his hands together on his desk.

"We're not here to encourage resistance. We're here to make sure that if you choose to refuse the draft, that it's the best alternative for you."

"I get that," I replied.

"This center was set up because a large number of students said they were interested in ways to avoid the draft without breaking the law."

"Like me."

"With close to twenty students per day being classified 1-A, a number of them find that they don't have the information to make an informed decision on the draft. Sometimes, they discover too late that they made the wrong one."

"That's me, all right."

"With all that you've told me, I think you've done your research. You're more prepared than most. You know your options and have a good idea about what you might do."

"But I don't know what to do. I was hoping you had the answer."

"We don't give answers, only advice."

"That doesn't help me."

"I would suggest that you keep researching. Keep talking with people. We've been told that there may be a student-led organization coming soon that will be a part of the Center. They may be in a better position to give you some recommendations based on your specific situation."

"Any idea when?"

"Before the end of the year."

"That doesn't leave me much time. I was planning to graduate this June. I'll probably lose my 2-S."

"If anything changes and you have more questions, we'll be here."

"But no answers."

"I'm afraid not."

That weekend, the three of us went home to celebrate my birthday. Mom bought a blueberry cheesecake and Paul barbecued chicken marinated in Woody's BBQ sauce, the way Dad used to. It was good, but it wasn't the same. My present from the family was *Abbey Road*, which I hadn't bought yet. I was touched. Diane and Cheryl gave me home-made birthday cards. My roomies gave me cards, which ranged from heartwarming to profane. We had a few beers, Willy played some songs, Gary sang and played flute. It was a wonderful celebration. But, my mind was elsewhere. I needed to see Kelly and get things back on track.

Things had not gone well during the summer and we hadn't spoken, although I had tried. I had sort of given up on her, even though I thought of her all the time. I had blown it. I needed her, which is why I found myself parking Ugly Orange outside her apartment in Berkeley. I was hoping she would answer instead of a roommate. She did. Before she could say anything, I handed her a bouquet of daffodils.

"It's a symbol of rebirth and new beginnings." Shock, surprise, and mild anger washed over her face.

"I did not know that."

"Can we get back to where we were?" I asked.

"We can never do that."

"Why?"

"We're different people now," she replied.

"I'm not."

"You are. You're a junior in college. You're 21. You're not the same person who misled me."

"I apologize for that."

"I trusted you."

"I trusted you."

"Trust is a hard thing to earn," she said.

"And get back."

"We both needed time alone."

"Are you?"

"What?"

"Alone?"

"I am," she replied. I smiled. "It's not funny," she said.

"It's not, but it gives me some hope."

"Because nobody wants me."

"I do."

"Can I trust you?"

"Cross my heart," I said, crossing my heart.

"You really hurt me. More than you know. I had a miserable summer. An even worse fall."

"So did I."

"I missed all those things we did together. I missed your friends," she continued.

"Our friends."

"I don't ever want to feel that way again. Ever."

"I was punishing you. You didn't deserve that."

"It's punishment if the person doing the punishing means something to the person being punished."

"Do I?"

"What?"

"Mean something."

"Depends."

"On what?"

"This." She kissed me. I kissed her back. I wrapped her in my arms. We stood there, kissing, for a long time. She pulled away. I frowned, again with the worst-case scenario thoughts swirling inside my head.

"You pass," she said and smiled. "There's still something there." I smiled.

"If you ever – "

"I'll never. I promise." She took my hand, led me inside, and closed the door.

The first time Kelly and I had made love was during the summer of our senior year in high school, during a freak storm.

The sky was dark that day. There was a flash of lightning, a peal of thunder, and heavy drops of rain. Buffalo Springfield's "In the Hour of Not Quite Rain" pulsed quietly through the speakers above us. Kelly and I sat cross-legged and barefoot, facing each other in the center of the family room on the blankets and pillows I had spread out. The family was visiting Disneyland. We had the place to ourselves. We could take our time. To explore.

This was the first time for both of us. I didn't know what she knew, or what her friends had told her. Dad and I had suffered through "the talk" and my friends had shared their experiences, or fabrications, depending on who it was. None of it had prepared me for this moment. I had so much to learn. I suspect she did, too.

I was fascinated by, and believed in, the concepts of courtly love and chivalry. A true romantic at heart. A troubadour in another life. I wanted to love someone completely and be loved completely. To respect and honor and be respected and honored. To live as equals. I dreamed of being Lancelot and finding my Guinevere, of Rick finding his Ilsa, of Dante his Beatrice, of Romeo his Juliet. I aspired to act nobly and do whatever my beloved desired in order to earn her love. Unlike courtly love, mine was not spiritual or platonic, nor was I pursuing a woman already committed to someone else. It may have been an unattainable goal, but it was mine. It wouldn't stop me from dreaming.

The Beatles' "Norwegian Wood" filled the room. We played a game of Wahoo, a marble board game akin to Parcheesi my family loved, to settle the nerves and cope with the awkwardness. When one of us got a bad roll, or made a mistake in the game, we'd razz the other and give them a small poke, or shove. It was the same way we flirted on the playground in elementary school. It was always simply about the touching.

"Open the door, please," she said. "I love the smell of rain." I went to the door, opened it, stared out at the sky above the park, and inhaled the wet air.

"It's ominous," I said as I sat.

"It's exciting."

"It's a nice break from the heat."

"You love the heat."

"I do. I'm a lizard."

"I like it, too."

"It's relaxing. It's nice to not have to wear all those clothes all the time."

She smiled. I thought there was something in her smile, in the way she moved and looked at me, that made me think she was thinking the same way I was.

We finished the game. She had won. I changed the record to Tim Hardin's "Reason to Believe." With the game over, there were no more distractions; no more reasons to delay. We were scared, but too curious and excited to stop. I slid the game off to the side and moved closer to her. I smiled. She touched my face with her hands and kissed me. I closed my eyes and kissed her.

Running through my mind was the Everly Brothers song, "Never knew what I missed 'til I kissed ya." I had kissed other girls before. I had touched other girls before. I had never gone beyond that. We kissed shyly, waiting and wondering. She slipped her tongue between my lips. We kissed more passionately. Her warm breath blew across my cheeks. The lightning shook the sky, but it felt unreal. The only reality was her body clinging to mine; her lips on mine.

She pulled away. She took my face in her hands again, and stared into my eyes; an unspoken confirmation that this is what we both wanted to do at this moment. I smiled. She leaned back and unbuttoned her blouse. I unbuttoned my shirt. Neither of us hurried. We savored each moment; each movement.

She unclasped her bra and let it drop in her lap. She covered her breasts with her arms. I put my arms around her. Her skin was soft and warm. She put her hands on my hips. I could feel her rigid nipples against my chest. Her heart beating fast and rhythmic. We kissed. More urgent this time. She lay back on a pillow and wriggled out of her shorts and panties. She tossed them at me, then covered herself in my "blankie," a light blue blanket I had had from the time I was a baby. I removed my cutoffs and boxers, flinging them at her. She batted them aside. I gently pulled the blanket off so I could see all of her. Her face, her breasts, her stomach, her thatch of hair, her thighs, her legs. I grabbed her little toe.

"This little piggy – " I started, but didn't finish. She pulled me to her.

The rain splashed on the window. The thunder rumbled in the distance. The storm was passing. She lay face-down, naked, beside me. I gazed at her. I felt so damned good. Joyous. Contented. At peace. I ran my finger down her spine. She shivered, laughed, and turned to look at me, heavy-lidded. My hand moved across her bottom and inside her thighs.

"That didn't take long," she said.

"It's your fault."

The sun moved across the floor. John Mayall's "Broken Wings" played above us. We lay in each other's arms, wrapped in the blanket.

"We need to get dressed," I said.

"Was I that bad?" I bit her shoulder and kissed her.

"You said you needed to be home by six."

"I'd rather stay here."

"I'd rather stay here forever."

"But, . . . "

"But, the world keeps spinning," I said.

Here we were again. This time, in her bed in her apartment, which smelled of gardenias. The sounds of Berkeley hummed outside. This time, neither of us had to be anywhere, or be anybody. The Chinese wind chime tinkled outside her window. The sun streamed through a stained-glass window and arced in a kaleidoscope across our blanketed bodies. We laid facing each other, inhaling the other's breath. Trying again to stop the hands of time.

"Would you go with me?" I asked, toying with her little toe.

"To Canada?"

"Yes."

"I don't want to lose you."

"Then come with me."

"You don't know for sure."

"I'm just preparing for all the things that could happen."

"Let's wait and see."

"Okay. Let's wait and see." She kissed me and I let it all float away.

CHAPTER 56

I returned to Modesto Saturday evening. In time for the rest of the birthweek celebrations. Gary and Gover came over. We played pinochle, drank some beers, and listened to music. We ate hot dogs and potato salad. We went to the Uptown Arena to listen to some local bands, including Eisage and the Rookery. We connected with friends, who were living in town. We finished the night with breakfast at the Greyhound bus depot across the street.

Sunday morning, I drove around town. I wanted to see some of my favorite places – to see if they had changed, like Kelly said I had. She was right. I had changed. So had Modesto. I now saw my hometown with different eyes; the eyes of a twenty-one-year-old.

Things were not the same. Buildings had been renovated, or torn down and replaced. The town was bigger. People dressed differently. The downtown core was dying. The Strand and the State were decaying. The bus depots were looking tired. The car dealerships had moved to the edge of town. The private residences in the heart of the city were falling apart, or had been razed. Many of the businesses that had been the town's core had relocated out McHenry Avenue, or along Yosemite Boulevard. Growing up, everything was downtown. You could park in one spot, get most of your shopping done, have lunch, and see a movie in one afternoon. Now you had to drive to a number of places to do the same. I didn't like it.

That Sunday, the craziness around the rumors that Paul was dead got amped up when a radio station played "Revolution No. 9" backward to prove that the lyric was "Turn me on, dead man." I wasn't buying it.

Two days later, the Zodiac sent another letter to the *Chronicle*, writing he had killed cabdriver Paul Stine on October 11th. As proof, he included a bloody piece of Stine's shirt. He added that the police had stopped and questioned him, but let him go. He threatened to target a school bus and school children, which led to panic throughout the Bay Area.

On Monday, we won our first I.M. football game. We beat the M.U. Floggers 7 – 0. Over the next several weeks, we beat the Zephyrs 7 – 0 then lost to the Cleveland Wrecking Co. 12 – 6, beat the IUD's 18 – 6 and the Vet Sophs 19 – 0, before losing to Conspirators 13 – 7.

Gary and I waited in the rain on the west steps of the State Capitol. There were thousands of others standing beside us as the sun set on October 15th. John Burton, Democratic assemblyman from San Francisco, read reports written by French generals fighting the Vietnamese 15 years before. Their optimistic dispatches sounded like pronouncements being made currently by American officials. Alan Cranston, the junior U.S. Senator from California, urged us to continue our anti-war protests. He called on President Nixon to prepare, publicize, and follow a timetable to withdraw American troops from Vietnam. Cranston said he was convinced Nixon wanted peace, but some of his key advisors wanted to resume escalation of the war "in pursuit of something called victory."

The senator continued, "We must make it plain that these men do not speak for us or for America or for mankind." Organizers who spoke after Cranston announced that a similar protest would be held on November 14th and 15th, as well as a third in December if necessary, to keep the pressure on the government to end the nation's involvement in Vietnam. A sense of muted optimism filled the crowd as we dispersed. It was the end of a wet day of protest around the country.

Absently scanning the crowd, I caught a fleeting glimpse of someone who looked like Luci. I looked again, but whoever it was had disappeared.

On the drive back to Davis, we listened to the news coverage of the Moratorium to End the War in Vietnam. It was estimated that two million people had peacefully participated in America alone, while millions of others participated around the world, which was the largest protest against the war so far. In towns and cities throughout the U.S., students, working men and women, school children, the young and the old, took part in "M-Day" on street corners, in meeting halls, in churches, in street rallies, and along parade routes.

One of the biggest demonstrations occurred when 100,000 people converged on the Boston Common, where Democratic Senator George McGovern of South Dakota spoke. There were counter-demonstrators who flew American flags, drove their cars with headlights on, and heckled the protestors. Millions of others sat it out, preferring to watch the fourth game of the World Series. On the evening news, Walter Cronkite called it "historic in its scope." He added, "Never before had so many demonstrated their hope for peace." In contrast, Governor Reagan said of those taking part in the demonstration, "I don't care how sincere they are in their motives, they are lending aid to the enemy and that enemy is killing young Americans." Sam Brown, a coordinator for the Vietnam Moratorium Committee, countered by saying, "This has been the most gratifying day in our years working against the war. It is the kind of day that gives you hope for change because the American people showed a willingness to get involved in the war issue."

On October 17th, the Rolling Stones set down in Los Angeles to begin their U.S. tour. Their first in the States going back to 1966. They were going on the road to support *Let It Bleed*, their new album that was scheduled to release in December. It would be the first time without Brian Jones and with Mick Taylor. They planned to play large venues, like Madison Square Garden, and they were traveling with more sophisticated sound and lighting. They had enjoyed their Hyde Park concert so much, there was talk they might do something similar in the States. The bottom line was that due to drug busts and tax complications, they needed to make some money. They could count on doing well in the good old U.S. of A.

The week following the Moratorium, I read an article in *The California Aggie* that didn't fill me with much hope. Members of the Davis Resistance, the anti-draft organization, had been sentenced to jail time for violating the Selective Service Act. In other words, for resisting the draft. One was already serving an 18-month sentence at Lompoc Federal Prison in southern California, while another was appealing a two-year sentence. Both had been sentenced during the past summer. A half-dozen more were expected to be sentenced in the next several months. In spite of the sentencing, the Davis chapter remained committed to the nationwide movement.

The article went on to quote a member of the Davis Resistance, who said that opposition to the draft had created a "tremendous backlog – and an increased inefficiency – in court cases." As a result, he believed, "the courts are not prosecuting everyone." This echoed what I had heard at the draft resistance meeting earlier in the month. The article also said that, in addition to refusing induction, some draft resistors were creating disturbances in prison and raiding draft board offices to destroy selective service records. They were continuing the fight, but it didn't sound like they were winning.

As usual, when I was bummed, I turned to music. I'd visit Steph in the Browsing Room to hear the latest classical, jazz, and electronic albums. October had been a good month for new album releases. Among the new records were Led Zeppelin's second album and first albums by John Denver and Area Code 615, which was a collection of seasoned session musicians based in Nashville, who picked the area code as their name. They had backed Dylan on *Nashville Skyline*. The end of September had delivered *Abbey Road*; the Rolling Stones *Through the Past, Darkly (Big Hits Vol. 2)*; and The Band's second album.

Then there were *The Masked Marauders*.

In the October 18th issue of the *Stone*, there appeared a review by T.M. Christian of an album by a super session of musicians, including Dylan, Jagger, Harrison, Lennon, and McCartney. It sounded too good to be true. The cuts from the album were getting airplay in San Francisco and Los Angeles, including Jagger doing "I Can't Get No Nookie" and Dylan's "Duke of Earl." In November, after competing for the rights with several other labels, Warner's Reprise released the album under their Deity label. The album spent twelve weeks on the Billboard album chart and peaked at 114.

Turned out, The Masked Marauders were a hoax dreamed up by *Rolling Stone* editor, Greil Marcus, who wrote the review. His pseudonym, T.M. Christian, was taken from the novel of the same name written by Terry Southern, who had written *Candy*. Marcus was doing a spoof of the whole "super group" phenomenon that was infecting rock music. The response was so surprising, the pranksters at the magazine hired a Berkeley band, named the Cleanliness and Godliness Skiffle Band, to imitate the singers and record the album. In a *Rolling Stone* and Ralph Gleason *Chronicle* article, the perpetrators came clean, finding it incredible that anyone had believed the ruse.

Our annual homecoming kicked off on Monday and ended the following Saturday. The theme this year focused on welcoming students back instead of making it an alumni reunion. A P.J. Fashion Show was held on Wednesday, featuring song girls and cheer leaders wearing the latest nighttime fashions. The Pajamarino dance followed the show. The Frosh-Soph tug-of-war took place on the main Intramural Field, where a cavernous mud hole had been created to claim vanquished and victor alike. The week included a parade and bonfire. The celebration ended Saturday with a 1 p.m. game at Toomey Field against San Francisco State. The Homecoming Dance was that night at Freeborn Hall, where the homecoming queen was crowned, with music by Cold Blood and Country Weather.

CHAPTER 57

As October wound down, the madness did not. Would it ever stop? At the end of October, during the Chicago 8 trial, U.S. Federal Judge Julius Hoffman ordered Black Panther Party activist Bobby Seale to be gagged and bound to his chair during his trial, after he repeatedly shouted accusations and insults at the judge and prosecution, disrupting the court proceedings. When Hoffman severed Seale from the trial of the other defendants, it became the Chicago Seven.

Another chapter in the story of People's Park was written when Dan Siegel, student body president at Berkeley, was removed from that office by Chancellor Heyns. It had been recommended that Siegel be placed on probation due to his suggestion during the rally last May that people should "go down and take over the park." When the crowd did what Siegel advised, there followed two weeks of martial law in Berkeley and days of street warfare. Dave Hubin, student body president at Davis, would be speaking at a rally in Berkeley on Friday, which was Halloween, to raise money for Siegel's defense fund. Siegel was scheduled for trial on November 3rd, to determine if he acted criminally when he made his speech.

October 31st was not only Halloween, or All Hallows Eve, it was also the beginning of *Dia de Los Muertos* (Day of the Dead), which was a three-day holiday focusing on gatherings of family and friends to pray for, and remember, friends and family members who had died, and to help support their spiritual journey. The Anglo version was also a three-day observance called Allhallowtide, which was the time in the liturgical year when people remembered the dead, including saints (hallows), martyrs, and the faithful departed.

Traditions connected with the Day of the Dead included building private altars called *ofrendas*, honoring the deceased using *calaveras*, or skulls, Aztec marigolds, and the favorite foods and beverages of the departed, as well as visiting graves with these as gifts. On October 31st, the children would make a children's altar to invite the *angelitos* (spirits of dead children) to come back for a visit. November 1st was All Saints Day, and the adult spirits would come to visit. November 2nd was All Souls Day, when families would go to the cemetery to decorate the graves and tombs of their relatives. The three-day fiesta was filled with marigolds, the flowers of the dead; *muertos* (the bread of the dead); sugar skulls; cardboard skeletons; tissue paper decorations; fruit and nuts; incense; and other traditional foods and decorations.

I had first learned about *Dia de Los Muertos* when I had visited San Juan Bautista to attend the annual Christmas play offered by *El Teatro Campesino*, a theatrical troupe founded in 1965 by Luis Valdez, as the cultural arm of the United Farm Workers. The original actors were all farmworkers, and *El Teatro Campesino* enacted events inspired by the lives and work of their audience.

Early performances were on flatbed trucks in the middle of the fields in Delano, California, during the California grape strike. The theater troupe had a small gift shop with *ofrendas*, *calaveras*, and small wood carvings depicting Day of the Dead symbols.

Friday was the almost perfect night for ghosts and goblins of all ages to celebrate Halloween. Gary and I drove home right after our last class ended. Gover wasn't joining us because he was headed to San Jose to see Nancy.

Mom had decorated the house, as she did every year, with cobwebs, witches, ghosts, and black cats. Draculas and Frankensteins hung, dangled, and flew in the living room and family room. Paul and the girls had carved pumpkins and placed them on the front porch. The annual Horror Movie Marathon with Bob Wilkins on Channel 3 would begin at 8 p.m. Except for this one night, his program of classic horror films on *Seven Arts Theater*, followed the station's 11 p.m. newscast each Saturday night.

When I was young enough to "Trick or Treat," Mom would dress the five of us in costumes she bought at Sears, or we would dress ourselves in homemade outfits. I remember being a tiger one year and a cowboy another. We'd wear our costumes to school on Halloween and march in a parade on the school grounds. That night, we'd go out together to see how much candy we could score. As the oldest, it was partly my job to keep an eye on the younger kids.

Each year, our neighborhood crawled with children. The weather was cool and sometimes smoky from fireplace chimneys, which was excellent for setting the mood for a spooky experience. There was the smell of sweet maple in the night air, as the leaves on the trees turned. Mom loved handing out candy and trying to scare the little ones. When I was too old to go, I would spend time with my high school friends. Sometimes, our activities were less innocent. Bill Magruder, who I had gone climbing and caving with, became known as the "Mad Bomber." That's because he and Robert Zeff had devised an impressive bomb made of black powder stuffed tightly into CO_2 cartridges. They'd pack the cartridge with the black powder, stick a fuse in the tip, crimp the cartridge closed, light the fuse, and get out of the way.

Our targets on Halloween included brick bathrooms at neighboring parks, like Pike Park in our neighborhood and Graceada Park near downtown, or metal garbage cans. We picked those two park bathrooms because the sound was incredibly amplified when the bomb exploded. After we'd blown up a few things, we'd caravan around town in Zeff's pickup truck, or in another friend's Model A, and toss eggs and water balloons at unsuspecting trick or treaters. We were assholes, but it was fun. More than once, the Modesto Police Department nearly busted us, but we knew a few back roads that saved our bacon.

One time, as we scattered to avoid the cops, two of our cars nearly collided, as we simultaneously approached one of the escape routes from opposite directions. It was a house that sat in the center of a "Y," where Sycamore split in two, with the top of the "Y" facing south. The right arm of the "Y" was one way and curved around the house and back onto Griswold. The left arm of the "Y" was one way starting at Griswold and circled the house back to Sycamore. If you did it right, you could turn left onto Sycamore, while heading east on Griswold, and continue around the house, instead of going straight, and end up back on Griswold, where you could go straight, or turn left or right. Ideally, your pursuer would continue straight on Sycamore toward Roseburg and you'd have eluded them. On this specific night, one of our group was about to enter the "Y" from the Griswold side, prepared to swing around the house, when someone else in our group approached from the Sycamore side, intending to take the right fork of the "Y." They almost crashed head-on at the tail end of the "Y."

Most of the friends we wreaked havoc with hadn't come home from school this year, and the locals were out of town for this Halloween, so Gary and I stuck close to 1500 Del Vista. We had beers, put on some music, and hatched a plan for the night. I had a ¼" reel-to-reel tape deck that had a built-in amplifier. You could plug in a microphone and use it like a public address system. The sound came out the internal speakers, unless you connected external speakers to the deck. I dressed up like a ghost in a white sheet with eyeholes cut into it and my old Fedora hat. I would sit in an easy chair on the front porch. Positioned behind me were speakers running to the tape deck.

As children approached, Gary would speak to them in a low, ominous voice. After they got over the shock of hearing a disembodied voice, and the lure of candy made them brave enough to move toward the front door, I would jump to my feet, yelling and screaming. They about died from fright. I about died from laughing. We did it a few times because I was afraid we'd scare somebody to death. We retired Mr. Ghost for the night and spent the next few hours handing out sweets. When the flood of kids became a trickle, we shut everything down, turned off the front porch light, left a basket of candy on the porch for the stragglers and the teenagers too old to be looking for treats, popped more Burgie beers, and sat with Mom, Paul, and the girls to watch the old horror movies.

On Saturday, I rode along with Gary to his home in La Grange, so he could get his laundry done and spend some time with his mom and dad. La Grange was a gold rush town located in the foothills near Don Pedro Reservoir. Gary's mom and dad had moved there when his dad got a job as the ditch tender for the Old Don Pedro Dam. It was owned and operated by Modesto Irrigation District, which supplied water to farms throughout Stanislaus County and electricity to most of Modesto. Gary's parents had left Modesto before he finished high school. He spent his senior year commuting back and forth with his mom, who worked for a local insurance company. His two sisters were both married with children of their own and had moved out of the Modesto house years before.

After we had unloaded his suitcase and dirty clothes, said our hellos to his parents and his dog, Zeke, we walked back down the road to the banks of the Tuolumne River, which eventually wound its way down to where I had stood on New Year's Day. I again stared at the river. Mesmerized. Gary hit rocks into the river with an old wooden bat. Zeke tried to catch them. I looked upstream at where the water came from. I looked downstream to where the water was going.

"It's all connected," I said.

"What's that?" Gary said.

"The past flows into the present and feeds the future. When you look upriver, then look at where you're standing, then look downriver. It's like the past, present, and future right before your eyes. You learn from yesterday, live for today, and hope for tomorrow."

"What brought all this heaviness on?" Gary asked, hitting a Texas Leaguer into the air, which Zeke caught.

"Some stuff I've been thinking about. Worrying about."

"The draft?"

"That and some other things."

"Anything to do with crazy Luci?"

"I don't know if she's crazy, but I do know she's going at it the wrong way. War isn't the answer. Violence isn't either. Only love can conquer hate. Only peace can end war. Martin Luther King, Jr. said, 'Darkness cannot drive out darkness; only light can do that.'"

"Noble ideals. How does that translate into the real world?"

"I don't know. Maybe instead of blowing up bridges, we build bridges."

"What does that mean?"

"Haven't worked that out exactly. But, it has to do with being more involved, doing something, to change things. Some way. Somehow."

Gary smacked a long one into the river. We had to corral Zeke to keep him from plunging into the river after it.

CHAPTER 58

"All the News that Fits" – November Edition

Rumors are swirling that the Beatles are squabbling and Apple Records is about to fold. "The Beaver 55" strikes again, infiltrating Dow Chemical's Midland, Michigan, offices to scramble magnetic tapes containing biological and chemical research, including napalm. Anti-war activists ransack six Selective Service offices in Boston, splashing ink and chemicals on draft records. *Sesame Street* debuts on PBS. On his way to a concert by the Rolling Stones, The Doors' Jim Morrison is arrested for drunkenness by the FBI after his plane lands in Phoenix. Incumbent President Ferdinand Marcos wins an unprecedented second full term as president of the Philippines. On the warpath again, Vice President Spiro T. Agnew accuses network TV news departments of bias and distortion, stating, "Perhaps the place to start looking for a credibility gap is not in the offices of the Government in Washington but in the studios of the networks in New York!" The rumors of Paul McCartney's death are buried following a cover story in *Life* magazine. The Jackson Five's "I Want You Back" is their first single to enter the top 100 and the first produced by Berry Gordy's Motown label. Strategic Arms Limitation Talks (SALT) begin in Helsinki between the United States and the Soviet Union on arms control. Businessman, investor, and ambassador Joseph P. Kennedy, patriarch of the Massachusetts Kennedy clan, dies at the age of 81. Apollo 12 Mission commander Charles "Pete" Conrad and lunar module pilot Alan L. Bean walk on the moon during the second moon landing. Henry Cabot Lodge resigns as head of the American delegation at the Paris peace negotiations, complaining that while the United States was prepared to negotiate, "the other side has flatly refused to reciprocate in any kind of meaningful way." President Nixon renounces chemical warfare weapons and orders the destruction of all germ warfare stockpiles. John Lennon returned his Order of the British Empire medal to Buckingham Palace, in protest against Britain's involvement in the Nigeria-Biafra fight, against its support of the U.S. in Vietnam, and against "Cold Turkey" slipping down the charts. Cream performs its final concert at Royal Albert Hall in London. The Beatles' single featuring, "Come Together" and "Something," reaches number one on the *Billboard* Hot 100 chart. New book releases include *Puppet on a String* by Alistair MacLean; *The French Lieutenant's Woman*, John Fowles; *The Collapse of the Third Republic: An Inquiry into the Fall of France in 1940*, William L. Shirer; and *Fire from Heaven* by Mary Renault. *Rondelay* and *Stomp* open on stage. New films include *Downhill Racer* with Robert Redford; *Goodbye, Mr. Chips* starring Peter O'Toole; Elia Kazan's *The Arrangement* featuring Michael Douglas and Faye Dunaway; and *Muhammed Ali, The Greatest*. New music includes *Mother Earth Presents Tracy Nelson*, *Melanie* by Melanie, Jefferson Airplane's *Volunteers*, *The Allman Brothers Band*, *Ballad of Easy Rider* by The Byrds, David Bowie's debut album *David Bowie*, *To Our Children's Children's Children* by The Moody Blues, *Willy and the Poor Boys* by Creedence Clearwater Revival, the Grateful Dead's *Live/Dead*, and Joe Cocker's first album, *Joe Cocker!*.

When we got back to business as usual at school, I was feeling like I might have a handle on the situation. Things seemed good. I was thinking that if I let it be, it might come together after all. Maybe I could figure out what to do about Luci and Kelly, what to do about the draft, and what to do about the role I would play in all this. I knew what was right and I knew what I had to do. Trust my instincts. Trust my sense of what was right. As my father had said many times, if I used my own good judgment, things would work out.

Of course, I was totally going against my usual mindset, which was to expect the worst and hope for the best.

The euphoria was short-lived. Unfortunately, the real world kept intruding and threatening my decision.

On the first Sunday in November, the SDS held a regional conference in Davis at Freeborn Hall. It was organized by the regional council of the Northern California SDS. The agenda was progressive, which was no surprise. The SDS wanted to build strong personal and political relations with university workers "to facilitate struggles against the university as an exploitative employer as well as a perpetrator of racism and anti-working-class attitudes." They also discussed whether moratoriums were the best anti-war strategy.

They were advocating a more aggressive approach, likely driven by the more radical Weathermen faction. There was also talk of countering moves by government agencies, big business, and union leadership to pit the predominantly white and skilled union construction workers against the semi-skilled, non-union black workers. SDSers were also supporting national actions against racism. Throughout the day, there were skits performed by the Radical Arts Troupes of Sacramento-Davis, UC Berkeley, and San Francisco City College.

I attended because I wanted to see if their positions had changed from the meeting Luci had arranged. They had. They were now as radical as they were political. Just like Luci. I was also curious if she would make an appearance, even though she had gone underground. The fact that I might have seen her in Sacramento at the march made me think it was possible.

It was. And she did. She was wearing a wig, glasses, and make-up, but there was no mistaking her. The monarch butterfly tattoo on the back of her neck gave her away. I saw her standing to the left of the elevated stage. She saw me about the same time. As I moved toward her, the session ended and people got up to stretch their legs, pee, or get something to eat or drink. The bodies obscured my view. By the time I reached the stage, she was gone. A rose lay on the floor where she was standing. The symbolism wasn't lost on me. When a Roman hung a rose, it meant anything said beneath it was confidential. In the Middle Ages, when a rose was affixed to the ceiling of a meeting place, everyone was sworn to secrecy.

The next afternoon, I was caught up in our last I.M. football game, which would determine if we went to the playoffs. FYNC was slated to play Blackacre A.C. on the Orchard 1 field. It promised to be a messy game. It had been raining all weekend and hadn't let up. I wasn't sure if the field conditions were going to work for, or against, us. We were both off-campus teams and had done well in our respective divisions. It would be a slog.

Due to the muddy conditions, it became a defensive battle. Uhland kept this passes short for most of the first half, trying to gauge their strengths and weaknesses. They did the same when they had the ball. I returned to the huddle telling Uhland I could beat my guy long. I did, until their deep back and defensive end double-teamed me. Toward the end of the first half, Uhland connected with Barber, who was head and shoulders taller than his defender, for the first score of the game. On a power sweep to the right we scored the extra point. The score was seven zip. At halftime, we took a breather and discussed strategy. Play defense and hold them was the best we could do, considering we were wet, cold, and miserable.

In the second half, we switched goals. We were heading south, they were heading north toward Russell. As the game wore on, my defender got more physical. I tried to juke him, but he stuck like glue. I'd spin, turning my back on him, and trying to roll to one side. If I didn't trip over my feet, he knocked me down. I bitched to the ref, but he shrugged his shoulders. I couldn't see half the time because I was wearing my plastic tortoise shell glasses strapped to my head with an adjustable elastic band. The raindrops splattered them, while my hot breath fogged them. When we forced Blackacre to punt on one series, their kicker boomed it and pinned us close to our goal line. On the first play, they stunted and sent a defensive back up the middle, who got Uhland's flag before he could release the ball. It was a safety. Two points for them. The score was now seven to two. Time was running out.

We went back and forth as the clock ran down. Three and out sometimes, a first down or two, then stopped and forced to punt. They had the ball as the minutes ticked off. They were on our twenty. I was playing defensive back on our left side, their right side. Barber was on our right side. Reed "Gramps" Rosenberg was playing linebacker. Everyone else was on the line. The quarterback handed off to the right end, who had gone in motion. I went with him in man coverage. He handed off to the left end on a double reverse. We all bit. He pulled up and hit the halfback on a hook over the middle. Touchdown. We held them on the extra point attempt. The ref blew the whistle. Game over. Final score: 8 to 7 Blackacre. Our season was finished. Bummed, we piled into our cars and headed to the Skeller for a beer. The playoffs started the following week. The field was whittled down to four teams, then two. The Sig Ep Purple Machine beat the Old Sh*ts 7 – 6 under the lights of Toomey Field to claim the campus championship.

The night of our loss, our President gave his latest speech on the government's evolving Vietnam policy. It would become known as the "Nixon Doctrine." He had first introduced the concept in July during a press conference in Guam. The policy would eventually be called "Vietnamization." Basically, Nixon was trying to move America away from being the "policeman of the world." He stated that "the United States would assist in the defense and developments of allies and friends," but would not "undertake all the defense of the free nations of the world." In other words, each of our allies were responsible for their own security. The U.S. would act as a "nuclear umbrella," as needed.

For Vietnam, that meant South Vietnam was responsible for defending themselves against North Vietnam. We would honor our treaty commitments and would continue providing military and economic support, but we would not provide more troops. In Nixon's own words, it was up to "the nation directly threatened to assume the primary responsibility of providing the manpower for its defense." It sounded like Nixon was trying to get us out of Southeast Asia. Finally. Until he said, "Let us be united for peace. Let us also be united against defeat. Because let us understand: North Vietnam cannot defeat or humiliate the United States. Only Americans can do that."

The President introduced a new term that had the news media buzzing. In closing, he said, "And so tonight – to you, the great silent majority of my fellow Americans – I ask for your support." It was obvious he was referring to all those in middle America who didn't demonstrate against the war and who weren't part of the counterculture; i.e., hippies. Our President was pitting them against us, the vocal minority. It was typical Nixon. He gaveth with one hand and taketh away with the other. He was de-escalating the Vietnam conflict, while escalating the cultural one. He wasn't the first to use this term. The phrase had been used in the nineteenth century as a euphemism for people who had died. Warren G. Harding used it during his 1920 presidential campaign. John F. Kennedy used it in his book, *Profiles In Courage*. In 1967, labor leader and AFL-CIO president George Meany used the phrase to describe labor unionists who supported the Vietnam War. Nixon really was a plagiarist at heart.

Nixon's rise to power had been beautifully explained in *The Peter Principle: Why Things Always Go Wrong* by Dr. Laurence J. Peter and Raymond Hull, which had been published earlier in the year. The book explained that a competent employee was often promoted and given more responsibility until they reached a point where they were no longer competent – having plateaued at incompetence. The Peter Principle stated, "In a hierarchy every employee tends to rise to his level of incompetence." Thus had Nixon.

CHAPTER 59

The following Friday, the Rolling Stones kicked off their American tour in a gym at Colorado State University in Fort Collins. The Stones had asked that the show be kept quiet in case it didn't go well. Two banks of folding chairs and bleacher seats were set on the hardwood floor. Stage, lights, and sound system were shipped in and set up. Blues great B.B. King opened. Tour manager Sam Cutler introduced the Stones as "the greatest rock 'n' roll band in the world." It was a title he first used at their concert in Hyde Park last July. He would use it for the rest of the tour.

Jagger jumped out from behind the amps dressed in black. Pants and T-shirt with the omega sign on his chest and a red-white-and-blue Uncle Sam hat. Girls screamed, fainted, and got carried out by security. Guys whistled and yelled for their favorite songs. The band did some old material and some off the new album – "Jumpin' Jack Flash," "Stray Cat Blues," "Under My Thumb," and "I'm Free." When the opening to "Satisfaction" ripped out of the amps, the crowd rushed the stage. The Stones were ready for America and America was ready for the Stones.

The next night, they played the Forum in Los Angeles. Pandemonium *redux.* The same reaction to the same set. "Has it really been three years?" Jagger shouted at the crowd. "It doesn't seem that long." It had taken a while to get everything delivered from Colorado and set up, so the show started late. The opening acts came out around midnight. The Stones hit the stage at almost two in the morning. There wasn't the usual police presence in front of the stage because the Stones didn't want them there. The band played a blistering set to a rabid crowd. Then it was "good night" Los Angeles and they were gone. B.B. King didn't play rhythm and the Stones didn't do encores. The band later apologized for the late start in an ad in the *Los Angeles Times.*

Rolling Stone, the magazine, had been hyping Rolling Stones, the band, for some time. The band's third concert at the Oakland Coliseum coincided with the second anniversary of the magazine's founding. Launched in San Francisco in 1967 by Jann Wenner and Ralph Gleason, the first issue had a cover date of November 9th, and featured a cover story about the Monterey Pop Festival. In that inaugural issue, Wenner described the publication as "sort of a magazine and sort of a newspaper." He explained that the title came from the phrase, "A rolling stone gathers no moss," which inspired a

Muddy Waters' song that inspired the name of the British band. Plus, "Like a Rolling Stone" was Dylan's first rock record. The goal of the magazine was to cover the "hippie counterculture," while avoiding the radical politics of underground publications like *The Berkeley Barb*. It was about the music, as well as "about things that music embraces."

Prior to the Oakland show, the Stones held a press conference at the Edgewater Inn, which is where they crashed before the show. A reporter with long hair asked, "Why haven't the Stones made any statements concerning the U.S. youth movements, marches, and the pitched battles with the police?" Keith Richards answered, "We take it for granted that people know we're with you." Mick added, "We admire your involvement but we're primarily, um, musicians, and last night, for instance, the crowd in Los Angeles needed to . . . weren't ready to . . . relax. They wanted to be cool and intelligent and it took time to get into the frame of mind where it's just fun . . . We want them to just get up and dance."

Promoter Bill Graham produced the two Oakland shows. Two cameras in front of the stage fed a huge TV screen. During the first show, when the crowd rushed the stage and trampled the cameras, Graham jumped on the stage and pushed them back. Cutler yelled at Graham to get off the stage. Graham told Cutler to get off his stage. Graham swung at Cutler and Cutler swung back. Their fight was a small indication of the rancor that had been brewing from before the tour when the Stones denied Graham's request to handle the whole tour. They offered him the tour, but with a low percentage and no name recognition. He declined, so they gave him the Oakland and San Diego shows.

Graham also wasn't happy with the financial arrangements and some of the clauses in the contract. When the Stones got to their dressing room before the show, they found a huge poster of Graham flipping the bird. The Stones answered with cream cheese and a partially deflated rubber. During that same show, the Stones blew out the brand-new amps Ampeg had supplied. Jagger and Richards played a few acoustic tunes while the damage was repaired. In the second show, the Grateful Dead made their amps available. For that show, Ike and Tina opened, followed by Terry Reid, and B.B. King. The second show ended at four in the morning. It was on to San Diego and Phoenix.

The following Sunday, several representatives of numerous Native American tribes gathered at Pier 39 in San Francisco. They read a proclamation claiming Alcatraz by right of discovery. They were able to do this based on the 1851

Treaty of Fort Laramie, which stated that surplus federal property could be reclaimed as Native land. They offered to buy Alcatraz Island for $24 in beads and cloth. They boarded a boat and sailed around the island. Several passengers dove overboard, hoping to swim to the island. One made it. The notorious bay currents swept the others away, until they were rescued. That night, a few fishermen ferried 14 activists to the island, where they spent the night. It was the opening salvo.

Alcatraz had once been used as a place of banishment for Indians who had been ostracized from their tribes. It also served as a refuge for natives trying to escape missions established by Spanish Franciscans. The U.S. Army built a fort on the island in 1850 to house Confederate soldiers during the Civil War. During the Indian wars of the late nineteenth and early twentieth centuries, natives were imprisoned there. During the Great Depression, the Department of Justice built a maximum-security penitentiary, which housed such notorious criminals as Al Capone, George "Machine Gun" Kelly, and Robert Stroud, the "Birdman of Alcatraz."

Due to its decaying condition, Attorney General Robert F. Kennedy closed the prison in 1963. It had remained vacant. In the spring of 1969, businessman Lamar Hunt, co-founder of the American Football League and owner of the Kansas City Chiefs, proposed turning it into a shopping center and museum celebrating the American space program. Public opposition forced the board of supervisors to reject the proposal. In November, Richard Oakes, who was teaching at San Francisco State and had created the first Native American Studies department there, appeared on the scene.

CHAPTER 60

I hated Mondays. I always had. It was inevitably a comedown after the weekend. I was often depressed, which made Monday morning classes painful. This Monday was going to be particularly memorable. I had returned to the apartment after my morning classes. My roomies were gone. I had the place to myself for once. I was checking the refrigerator for any edible leftovers when the apartment doorbell rang. I opened the door. The men in dark suits, sunglasses, and shiny shoes were back.

"Mr. Wright?" one asked.

"Who's asking?" I answered, knowing full well, but wanting confirmation.

"FBI." They both flashed their credentials. They held them out almost long enough for me to read them.

"I'm Mikey Wright," I said.

"May we come in." It wasn't a question.

"It's a free country," I said, wondering why I was being so cavalier about having the FBI still interested in me. They came in. I gestured toward the couch for them to sit.

"We'll stand. This shouldn't take long." The other agent must have been there for backup because he wasn't talking.

"Do you know what these are?" the lead agent asked, as he pulled a set of keys inside an evidence bag from a small leather briefcase he was carrying.

"Keys," I replied, again baffled by my bravado. The lead agent wasn't amused.

"This is serious business, Mr. Wright," he said.

"I've never seen them before."

"They were found in the bed of your truck."

"Of all the trucks in this town, in this area, why did you happen to look in the bed of my truck?"

"We received a tip."

"From who?"

"Anonymous."

"What do they open?" I asked.

"You recall an explosion at the Primate Center here in Davis a few months back?"

"I do."

"These unlock the doors to that facility."

"You think I had something to do with that?"

"We do now."

"I wasn't anywhere near that place. I was out of town."

"Do you have people who can verify that?"

"I do."

"We'll need names and contact information." The second agent handed me a pen and notepad.

"No problem," I replied.

"Do you have any idea who might have been involved with that incident?" the lead agent asked. I did, but I wasn't sure I wanted to squeal on Luci. She was nuts and getting nuttier. As I stood there, I realized it was probably her who had planted the keys and called the feds. I didn't want to be a narc, but I had no idea what she would do next. And what that would mean for me. I owed her nothing.

"I do. A woman named Luci Dolgushkin." The second agent pointed at the pad and pen, encouraging me to write down her particulars.

"Do you know for a fact that she was involved?" I did, but they didn't need to know how much I knew.

"We had classes together. We dated for a while. It didn't end well. She would sometimes talk crazy."

"About?"

"About the war and the government."

"Did you ever witness her doing anything illegal."

"Only if smoking dope is illegal."

"It is." These two had no sense of humor.

"Why would she do that?" I asked myself, as much as I asked them.

"Maybe she figures it's a good way to get you back on their side. If you aren't already. It happens all the time. It's a strategy terrorist organizations use. If one of their people is wavering, they figure out a way to blackmail, or incriminate them, so there's no turning back. If you look guilty, you might as well be guilty."

"I'm not guilty. I'm not involved. With her, or any of it."

"When was the last time you saw her?"

"The first of the month. At an SDS rally."

"You were there?"

"I was."

"You know they're a radical organization?"

"I do."

"That doesn't bother you?"

"It does now."

"So, you're really still involved with some of it?"

"I was one of many people at that meeting."

"Is there anything else you would like to add?"

"Not really."

"If you change your mind, here's my card," he said, handing me his business card. "Call any time."

"I'm getting quite a collection of these," I said, marveling again at being so flip.

"You wouldn't be collecting them if you didn't fraternize with the wrong people."

"And kept your nose clean," the silent agent had finally spoken.

"Noted," I said, handing the pen and paper back to the silent agent.

"Thank you for your time, Mr. Wright. We'll be in touch."

"I hope not."

That Wednesday, an author I admired was victimized for telling the truth. I had been introduced to Alexander Solzhenitsyn in my Russian literature class. I had read *One Day in the Life of Ivan Denisovich*. It was a brutally honest depiction of life in a Soviet work camp in the 1950s. He was formally expelled from the Writers' Union of the Russian Republic for exposing the horrors of the *Gulag* forced labor camp in his writing. Knowing the history of Russia and the Soviet Union as I did, I knew this would not be the end of his troubles.

That same day, the Stones played the Moody Coliseum in University Park, Texas, with Chuck Berry opening.

Another major headline hit the news that Wednesday. Journalist Seymour Hersh filed a story about the charges made by the U.S. Army against 1st Lt. William L. Calley at My Lai. Hersh wrote, "The Army says he [Calley] deliberately murdered at least 109 Vietnamese civilians during a search-and-destroy mission in March 1968, in a Viet Cong stronghold known as 'Pinkville.'" Charges had been brought by the Army against Calley in September. More details would be made public in the next few days. It was disturbing.

Born and raised in Chicago, Hersh held many positions on his way to a career in journalism. Copyboy; police reporter for the City News Bureau; correspondent for United Press International (UPI) in South Dakota; Associated Press (AP) correspondent in Chicago and Washington, where he met I. F. Stone, who would be an inspiration for Hersh's reporting style. Following a disagreement with his editors at AP over the editing of a story on biological and chemical weapons, Hersh left the AP and sold the unedited story to *The New Republic* and wrote a book about the issue. He left journalism to become press secretary for Senator Eugene McCarthy during his presidential campaign. Following a disagreement over campaign tactics, he returned to journalism and worked as a freelancer covering Vietnam. It was while doing that reporting that he was told about My Lai by Geoffrey Cowan, a lawyer who had also worked on the McCarthy campaign and was writing about Vietnam War for *the Village Voice*.

As horrific as this news was, it was about to be overshadowed.

CHAPTER 61

The second Moratorium to End the War in Vietnam was scheduled to begin the next day. It started on Thursday when anti-war campaigners staged a "March Against Death" in Washington, D.C. An estimated 45,000 participants, each carrying a placard with the name of a dead U.S. soldier, or destroyed Vietnamese village, marched silently from Arlington National Cemetery through the city. As they passed the White House in single file, each protester called out the name of the soldier, or village, on their placard. The march began at 6 p.m. on Thursday and continued until 7.30 a.m. on Saturday. It ended at the Capitol, where the placards were placed inside coffins. Additional marches were organized by the New Mobilization Committee to End the War in Vietnam, also known as "New Mobe," and scheduled for Washington, D.C., San Francisco, and other major cities throughout the country and around the world.

The goals of the "New Mobe" were more radical than the other anti-war organizations. According to news reports, the purpose of the November demonstrations was the "immediate and total withdrawal of American troops from Vietnam and self-determination for Vietnam and black America." It was also a move to "stop the repression, free all political prisoners, end ABM and all forms of militarism, end racism and poverty, and promote free speech for GIs." It was an ambitious agenda.

We planned to join the demonstration to be staged in San Francisco. Gary, Tim, and me. For two reasons. One, we wanted to show our opposition to the war. And, two, CSNY was playing the second of four shows at the Winterland Ballroom that Friday. The show had been re-scheduled when the October show was cancelled after the death of David Crosby's girlfriend in September.

On September 30th, Crosby, Stills & Nash's debut album had gone gold. On that same day, girlfriend Christine Hinton borrowed Crosby's VW bus to take her two cats to the vet near their home in Novato. En route, one of the cats jumped into Christine's lap, startling her, and causing her to lose control of the car, which drifted into the oncoming lane and collided head-on with a school bus, killing her and seriously injuring a female friend. Crosby spread Christine's ashes in the ocean from onboard his sailing vessel, the *Mayan*. It was on this voyage that "Wooden Ships" was written.

The rescheduled CSNY show featured Cold Blood, Joy of Cooking, and Lamb with lights by Little Princess. We didn't get back to Brad's until almost 2 a.m. We would be lucky to get any sleep.

The San Francisco march was scheduled to start at 8 a.m. simultaneously at three locations: the Embarcadero, Pier 29, and Sansome and Chestnut. It would move up Market Street to the Polo Fields in Golden Gate Park. A major rally was scheduled for 2 p.m. Participants could join the march at various points along the route. Scheduled speakers included former Senator Wayne Morse of Oregon, Dr. Ralph Abernathy of the Southern Christian Leadership Conference, Chicago 8 defendant Rennie Davis, David Hilliard of the Black Panther Party, and Dolores Huerta of the United Farm Workers (UFW). Scheduled entertainers included Buffy Sainte-Marie, Arlo Guthrie, and Phil Ochs.

It was a cold, drizzly day. We had crashed for the night on the living room floor of Brad Bassi, a high school classmate and fellow Mud Bowler, who was attending San Francisco State. He was going to the demonstration with his fellow "Gators." Driving back to Davis after the CSNY show and back again to the City for the march didn't make sense, so we accepted Brad's invitation.

We got to downtown San Francisco around 6 a.m. to make sure we could find a place to park. We found a spot on Francisco. We walked to the Embarcadero then to Chestnut. We had arranged to meet Kelly and her Berkeley sorority sisters there. Gary was predictably excited about that. The crowd was massive by the time we joined up. People were funneling in from all the side streets. There were signs being carried by individual protestors, labor groups, civil rights groups, teacher unions, student organizations, and plain bodies in the street like Gary, Tim, Kelly and her friends, and me. People who wanted an end to war. We followed Sansome to Pine to Montgomery to Post. We followed Post to Presidio to Geary, turned left on 30th Avenue, and into Golden Gate Park to the Polo Fields.

Demonstrators followed the directions of the police, who attempted to keep the traffic moving in spite of the human congestion. The marchers mostly did what the police asked and the Moratorium captains kept the crowd moving in an orderly manner to the Park. There were a few incidents, but nothing major.

There was a huge stage with massive speakers and music equipment set up. It felt like a rock concert. Several marchers had brought, been given, or picked up red, yellow and blue plastic coffee can lids. They were spinning them through the air like Frisbees. The seagulls, who were searching for food, had to dodge the flying objects. People were arriving when the program began. One of the speakers said there was a line stretching all the way back to downtown. I wasn't sure if it was true but, if it was, that meant a ton of people had shown up. I had never been in a place with so many people.

As we came into the park, I noticed some Hells Angels near the stage. I didn't know if they were there to get off on the music, or for security. The Grateful Dead and the other San Francisco bands had been using the Angels to help with crowd control at their Haight concerts. The Angels had been part of the San Francisco music scene since the first outdoor festival. The Fantasy Fair and Magic Mountain Music Festival was held on June 10th and 11th 1967, in the amphitheater on Mount Tamalpais in Marin County. It had been postponed a week by bad weather. The concert was put on by radio station KFRC to benefit the Hunters Point Child Care Center. Tickets cost two bucks. The festival featured 30 bands on two stages, including the Airplane, the Dead, The Doors, the Byrds, and Tim Buckley. There were vendor booths, performers, and family-friendly things to do. It reminded me of the Renaissance Pleasure Faire, which had its first run in 1963 in Los Angeles and expanded north to Marin County in 1966. It was a colorful mix of hippies and straights.

The Angels had heard about the show and wanted to attend. The organizers got approval from the California Highway Patrol for the Angels to take their bikes up the mountain. When the one road to the performance area got clogged by the "Trans-Love" shuttle buses and cars, the Angels motored the performers in on their hogs. Gary, Tim, Laura, and I were there. With Scott McKenzie's song in mind, I debated wearing flowers in my hair and decided it was too self-consciously hip. I remembered seeing Paul Kantner of the Airplane riding behind an Angel with his guitar slung across his back. The Angels seemed peaceful that day. The Monterey International Pop Festival was scheduled for the following weekend. It would later be called the first rock music festival in history. But, Magic Mountain was actually the first.

The Angels had also spent time with Ken Kesey and his Merry Pranksters, dropping acid at Kesey's acid tests in La Honda, on the peninsula south of San Francisco. Kesey said they were cool, so they were. The Angels had been born one hundred years too late. They could have been Old West gunfighters. The hippies looked on the Angels like fellow counterculture rebels. It was a brotherhood of outcasts. Except the Angels were working class and tough, the kids were white collar and college-educated. The Angels weren't into the counterculture myth. People had forgotten that during one of the anti-war marches in Berkeley. When the protestors entered Angels' territory, the Angels did not hesitate to dive into the crowd and bust some hippie heads. They were much more law and order than peace and love. The one thing both groups seemed to share was a hatred for the *status quo*.

The Moratorium program alternated between speakers and music. Marchers covered in slogans and carrying placards and flags listened and cheered as rhetoric and tunes washed over everyone. Abernathy said that "this great demonstration must continue, month after month. You and I must move Richard Nixon out of Washington." Speakers representing SDS, the UFW, and various groups followed Abernathy, condemning our involvement in Southeast Asia and generally whipping the crowd into a frenzy. It was chilly, so a few spectators started fires stoked by signs, placards, and draft cards. I wrapped my arms around Kelly. She snuggled closer.

The moment arrived that I'd been hoping for. A couple longhairs wearing light-colored, furry coats stepped on stage, strapped on their guitars, and moved to the microphones. It was Crosby, Stills & Nash, without their friend, Young. I had a feeling they would be there, mainly because they were in town and they were totally against the war. They launched into "For What It's Worth" and brought us all to our feet. We never sat again.

I noticed that David Crosby hadn't sung back-up on the song. Graham Nash must have read my mind because he told us that David was hoarse from two nights of performing at Winterland, which got a huge applause, and wanted to save his voice for the final two performances, which also got a monstrous response. Stills tuned for a moment and said, "Politics is bullshit. Richard Nixon is bullshit. Spiro Agnew is bullshit. Our music isn't bullshit."

It was totally mind-blowing. Until it wasn't.

I went in search of a portable bathroom, which I didn't expect to find – or at least one that didn't have an endless line. Gary said I'd have to pee into an empty jug of wine. I grimaced. Kelly offered to escort me. I smiled, embarrassed, said it wasn't necessary, and left. I guessed if there were portable Johns, they'd be near the stage, so I went that way. As I got closer, the crowd near the stage rippled back and away, in slow motion. I moved around the wave and nearer to the stage. This time, the wave was accompanied by a few yells. The spectators parted and I could see the eye of the storm.

The Angels had corralled some longhairs, who were tripping on something. It looked like the Angels were holding onto them to keep them from hurting themselves, or anybody else, and just trying to calm them down. It was different than the last time I'd seen the Angels mixing it up with the hipsters. I was hoping they wouldn't do that again – use violence to maintain the status quo.

I saw a familiar face. Motown stood near his biker brothers. He turned to look at the dust-up, then across the scuffle at me. He smiled a crooked smile and turned back to the music.

I moved on. I didn't find a bathroom, but I did find a stand of trees that provided some cover. Judging from the smell, I wasn't the only one that had used this spot. As I buttoned up the fly on my Levi's, I looked up to see if anyone had seen me. Nobody had. But, I was surprised to see someone. It was Luci. She had dumped the wig and glasses and gone back to the short hairdo and militant clothes. She was walking with some people I assumed were fellow SDSers. I guessed that because one of them had spoken to the crowd earlier and had identified himself as a member. As they walked toward backstage, I thought about the contrast between them and the Angels at that moment. Unlike the bikers, Luci and her cohorts were using violence to change things. A fleeting thought crossed my mind. *Were they here to blow something up? It would be a great opportunity and give them some press.*

Someone else must have had the same idea because I saw two suits emerge from the crowd and block Luci's way. It was the same agents who had visited my apartment. They showed their credentials and said a few words. The talkative one grabbed Luci by the arm. The silent one blocked her colleagues, likely telling them that they were at risk of being arrested for being accessories and that he was also armed. They backed off. The silent agent backed up and joined his colleague. I watched Luci being escorted through the crowd. She looked back at her comrades, then scanned the crowd, as if looking for someone. She stopped looking when she saw me. She smiled a small smile and turned away.

CSN, with C forcing his voice to go where it shouldn't go, continued with an incredible *acapella* version of a new song, "Find the Cost of Freedom," and ended with a cover of John Sebastian's "How Have You Been." As I worked my way back to Gary, Tim, Kelly, and her friends, I thought about what I had witnessed. I had seen both sides now. Neither held the answer. At that moment, CSN finished with a rousing power chord. To add a *coda* to the day, Crosby held up his guitar and croaked, "'This machine kills Fascists.' Woody Guthrie had a sticker that said that stuck to his guitar." The crowd went nuts. We were all connected at that moment. And I understood. The answer was music. The power of music. Music would energize us, unite us, transform us, and lead us into a new world.

My mind was bouncing all over the place. I remembered a quote from Plato: "Music is a moral law. It gives a soul to the universe, wings to the mind, flight to the imagination, a charm to sadness, and life to everything. It is the essence of order, and leads to all that is good, just and beautiful, of which it is the invisible, but nevertheless dazzling, passionate, and eternal form." My mind kept reeling. It played back a song from CSN's first album, "Teach Your Children." Maybe that was the solution. At least, it might be part of the solution. The draft hadn't gone away. It was still a problem, but at least I may have found a goal, a purpose, to pursue when all this was finally resolved. Something that meant something. Something that could make a difference.

As the program came to an end, it rained. It was a sign. The event had been baptized and blessed. We left, picking up garbage as we went. Most everyone else did the same. It was shocking how much litter a crowd could generate in such a short period of time. As we exited, it was no surprise, at least to me, when we saw CSN without Y moving through the crowd, still wearing those fur jackets they'd worn for the inside cover photo of their album. My guess was they wanted to feel what it was like to be a part of the crowd. They looked pumped, although they should have been exhausted. It had been a long day and they had a Winterland show that night. We followed in their wake. On our way home.

The rest of the demonstrations across the country were even more impressive. An estimated 500,000 marched in Washington, D.C. It opened with a march down Pennsylvania Avenue to the Washington Monument. Pete Seeger, Peter, Paul and Mary, and the touring cast of *Hair* performed. Seeger led the crowd in singing John Lennon's new song, "Give Peace A Chance." The rally was mostly peaceful. One group of about 6,000 broke loose and marched on the Justice Department. It was allegedly led by members of the Yippies. Nearly 100 protestors were arrested after they threw rocks and bottles and burned American flags. Several cities in Europe witnessed rallies, including Frankfurt, West Berlin, and London, with the largest taking place in Paris.

About the march on Washington, President Nixon said, "Now, I understand that there has been, and continues to be, opposition to the war in Vietnam on the campuses and also in the nation. As far as this kind of activity is concerned, we expect it; however under no circumstances will I be affected whatever by it."

Despite what Nixon said or believed, it felt like we were heard. It felt like peaceful protest might turn things around. It felt like nonviolence might change things. Little did we know.

That night, the Stones played two shows at Assembly Hall in Champaign, Illinois, with B.B. King opening. The following night, they did two shows at the International Amphitheatre in Chicago with Chuck Berry. During the Chicago show, Abbie Hoffman, who had been trying to reach the Stones for days, convinced an usher, who recognized him, to seat him down front. Hoffman sent a note to Jagger saying he wanted to see him. Right before show time, they met in the dressing room. The two men complimented each other. Wild-haired and vested Hoffman told Mick, "Your thing is sex, mine's violence." He asked Jagger if he knew he was playing at the same site where the Democratic Convention was held last year. Jagger knew. Hoffman took a hit off a joint being passed around, then hit Jagger up for some money. "Could you lend us some money for our trial? It's expensive making the revolution." Mick replied, "We've got our own trials," slipped on his shoes, and left Hoffman hanging. As he left, Hoffman said, "Bunch of cultural nationalists." It wasn't clear if he was joking, or not.

CHAPTER 62

The following Tuesday, *The Aggie* published an article entitled "Draft Help is for You - - - ." It was an interview with Wayne Harrison, a student counselor with Draft Help, which had recently finished its first year of operation. The article explained that draft help was "a joint project of the Associated Students of UC Davis (ASUCD) and the Dean of Students Office." Its job was to provide information and counseling services on the draft and a student's military obligation. It was located in South Hall and was open each day from 2 p.m. until 5 p.m. Harrison explained that student problems with the draft fell into two categories. "The first, and most common, is procedural, involving such things as obtaining and retaining a 2-S student deferment, or confusion at the local board level over an individual's status." Harrison pointed out that these problems required a lot of work specific to each case and that most of them were handled by Andy Hendry, assistant dean of men. Harrison went on to say that the second problem area involved "a student's religious or philosophical conflicts with the idea of conscription and of military service." This latter area was the specialty of Draft Help. Much of that work involved providing information on qualifying as a conscientious objector, and the definition of the Selective Service's classification for men opposed to war. Harrison said that the individual considering this option needed to make an important decision. Draft Help was there simply to "help the individual make this decision, and then guide that person through the proper C.O. channels."

The other services included providing information for those considering resisting the draft or emigrating. When asked about the legality of their services, Harrison answered that it became an issue "when a draft counselor takes on the role of advocating one position or another. Draft Help is designed to help students make up their own minds, and not impose someone else's view upon them." Harrison was concerned that not enough students with actual issues about the draft were using their services. He urged men to visit Draft Help as soon as they were bothered by any aspect of participating in Selective Service, or the military. "We won't make an individual commit himself, but we may be able to help him straighten out his feelings."

At the end of the article, Harrison was asked about President Nixon's proposed lottery system. He said, "it may have the effect of lulling men into a false sense of security" and that they "may feel the pressure is off when in fact it isn't." Even with a student deferment and the approval for grad students to finish the academic year, men would still be subject to the draft when the deferment expired and their studies ended. For grad students, that was extended to age 35.

I had first heard about the draft lottery scheme in May. I wasn't too worried because I had my 2-S. Although I'd been actively trying to figure out a solution, I'd been lulled, like everyone else. Now I was definitely concerned. A lottery meant my number could be one, or 365. It was a crapshoot. One that my life now depended on. The pressure was back on.

A few days later, the Indian invasion of Alcatraz ramped up. Mohawk Indian Richard Oakes led nearly eighty Native Americans on a second, this time successful, attempt to occupy Alcatraz Island, reclaiming the abandoned prison facility in the name of "red power."

Representatives of more than 20 tribes from around the country had gathered in San Francisco. They called themselves, "Indians of All Tribes." Oakes had recruited Native Americans from the Bay Area and indigenous students from UCLA. Not long after landfall on Alcatraz, they elected a council to establish and organize the daily activities of a community. The occupiers graffitied the walls claiming, "Indians Welcome" and "Indian America Land." They set up house in the former prison. A teepee was erected on the grounds.

They initiated formal negotiations with the government of the United States. Oakes sent a message to the San Francisco Department of the Interior that read, "We invite the United States to acknowledge the justice of our claim. The choice now lies with the leaders of the American government – to use violence upon us as before to remove us from our Great Spirit's land, or to institute a real change in its dealing with the American Indian. We do not fear your threat to charge us with crimes on our land. We and all other oppressed peoples would welcome spectacle of proof before the world of your title by genocide. Nevertheless, we seek peace."

The government reacted a few days later by ordering a Coast Guard blockade designed to force the squatters off the island by preventing delivery of necessary supplies and to keep supporters from reaching the island. Some government officials recommended ignoring the occupiers in hopes the occupation would fall apart in due time. A few locals showed their support by circling the island and the Coast Guard cutters in small pleasure craft with signs saying, "We Support You" and "Alcatraz International Territory."

The media covered the occupation and the demonstrations held around the country to support the Indians' claims. Each day, more San Franciscans and tourists flocked to Fisherman's Wharf to view the siege.

On Thanksgiving, the occupiers would enjoy a dinner that had been prepared by a San Francisco restaurant and delivered by yacht from Sausalito. There were nearly 400 Native Americans on the island at the time. It would be the highest number of the occupation.

The Sunday before Thanksgiving, the Stones played *The Ed Sullivan Show*. Their set included "Gimme Shelter," "Love in Vain," and "Honky Tonk Women." Jagger sang live, while the rest of the band played along to prerecorded tracks. This was their sixth appearance on the Sullivan show. It was somewhat different from their last appearance in 1967 when Sullivan asked them to change the lyrics of "Let's Spend the Night Together" to "let's spend some time together." The Stones complied. It was reported that Sullivan's exact words were, "Either the song goes, or you go."

The next day, which was the beginning of an historically slow news week because most reporters were occupied with thoughts of turkey and football, Lt. William L. Calley was charged with premeditated murder in the death of 109 Vietnamese civilians at My Lai and was ordered to stand trial in military court.

The announcement was made in Washington by Army Secretary Stanley Resor and Army Chief of Staff William C. Westmoreland. Lt. Gen. William R. Peers was appointed to "explore the nature and scope" of the original My Lai investigation that took place in April 1968. The army re-opened the case because the initial probe ruled there had been no massacre and, thus, no further actions were needed.

That night, CBS aired Mike Wallace's interview with one of the soldiers who participated in the killing. The interview had taken place a few weeks after Calley had been charged with murder. Private First Class (PFC) Paul Meadlo lived in Goshen, Indiana, following his discharge from the military when he lost part of his foot after stepping on a landmine the morning following the massacre.

"Why did I do it?" Meadlo told Wallace. "Because I felt like I was ordered to do it, and it seemed like that, at the time I felt like I was doing the right thing, because, like I said, I lost buddies." Meadlo's mother told Wallace that she "raised [her son] to be a good boy, did everything I could. They came along and took him to the service [and] made him a murderer." Meadlo's father said, "if it had been me out there I would have swung my rifle around and shot Calley instead, right between the God damned eyes." "How do you shoot babies?" Meadlo was asked during the CBS interview. "I don't know. It's just one of them things," he replied.

It was tough watching the interview. Meadlo was merely a year older than me. From the heartland. A guy who probably gave Vietnamese kids candy because they had nothing. Who killed innocent people in cold blood because those were his orders. A kid like me. I couldn't imagine being in that situation. It made me angry that smug, white assholes in Washington were making decisions that did things like this to our soldiers, knowing full well they would never be in a situation like Meadlo. They would never have to carry out the orders to kill civilians. It made the war, all of it, seem even more insane.

That Monday, the Stones played Olympia Stadium in Detroit with opening acts B.B. King and Terry Reid. The next night, it was the Spectrum in Philly with the same two acts. On Wednesday, the Stones moved on to the Civic Center in Baltimore with King and Reid.

That same day, President Nixon signed the draft-lottery bill. It had been passed by the Senate earlier in the month. The bill mandated a single year of draft eligibility. Previously, draft-eligible men were subject to seven years of draft uncertainty before no longer being available to be drafted. Men would be drafted via a lottery system. The lottery would randomly pick birthdates of nineteen-year-olds, instead of continuing the previous policy of drafting the oldest men first. Secretary of Defense Melvin Laird said the government hoped to implement the lottery in time to select the next group of draftees in January, if not before.

Men who were eligible for the draft under the previous system would be drafted as nineteen-year-olds, regardless of their age. Men not drafted during the 12 months that followed would be assigned a lower priority; would be re-classified 1-H, which was a holding category; and would be called up only in the case of an emergency. Nineteen-year-olds would continue to be eligible for student deferments. When their deferments ended, they would also be re-classified 1-H and be subject to the draft. It seemed the government generally announced bad news right before a holiday so the media couldn't cover it. In a heartbeat, everything had changed.

Gover, Wally, Gary, and I were playing dominoes at the small, round table in our apartment's tiny dining room. Gary and I were a team. Again. A pyramid of Golden Crown was being erected. Again.

"Sure, I'm a Marxist," Gary said. "Of the Groucho type." Wally had been grilling us about the Moratorium march in San Francisco.

"You sure they were FBI?" Wally asked me.

"I could tell by their outfits that they weren't cowboys," I replied. Right on cue, Merle sang, "The Bottle Let Me Down."

"To Merle," Gover said in toast, hoping to ease the tension.

"It was the same two men who confronted me right there," I said, pointing at the front door.

"Just doing their job," Wally said.

"I hadn't done anything," I said.

"Hanging with the wrong people, maybe," he replied.

"So were you," I said, struck that he used nearly the same cautionary words as the FBI agent.

"I knew what I was doing."

"She got to you, too."

"That's what she thought."

"Meaning?"

"I let her."

"Let her what?"

Wally slammed down the double-five on my blank-five. "Let her think I was in," he said.

"It looked more than that."

"Looks can be deceiving," he answered, smiling his crooked smile.

"So, she was full of shit? Making me think you were involved?"

"Something like that."

"Okay, dude, quit dicking around. What's the deal? 'Cause I was flipping out then and I'm still not sure what's going on. All I know is that they got her. And she's gone for good."

"Thank you," he said.

"Thank who?"

"Me."

"Why?"

"Shake the hand that pulled the trigger," he answered, extending his right hand.

"You helped the Feds?" I asked.

"A little free-lance undercover work for my uncle."

"Holy shit. You were stringing her along the whole time?"

"Roger that."

"I figured you were pissed about your dead friend and wanted someone to pay."

"I was pissed about what happened to him. I still am. I didn't blame the government. He was doing his duty. His passing gave me a good excuse to do what needed to be done."

"Did you know?" I asked Gary and Gover.

"No clue," Gover replied.

"Not guilty," Gary replied.

"Man, oh man," I said. "Good job."

"Fooled you."

"Yes, it did. Puts my mind at rest, though."

"You really didn't think I fell for that horse-puckey?"

"I didn't know."

"Then you really don't know me, cowgirl."

"I guess not," I said. "Give me the boneyard. I got no play." I drew the rest of the dominoes.

CHAPTER 63

I was ready to go home. To familiar surroundings. To the comfort of family and friends. I didn't want to think about school, Luci, Vietnam, or the draft. I wanted to celebrate Thanksgiving. To do nothing but eat turkey, watch football, drink beer, and chill out. The one thing I was most looking forward to over turkey day was the Mud Bowl.

The Mud Bowl was a football game we had started playing on Thanksgiving Day, 1964, which was our junior year. There was often a debate about the exact date we first played together, but that was part of the experience. Two groups of high school friends combined separate games of football into one. One bunch had played at Roosevelt Junior High. The other at Pike Park. After graduating from high school, we agreed to get together and play one game. We did that because we enjoyed football and it was a way to see classmates who had been away at college. There was no place any of us would rather be on Thanksgiving day than at the Mud Bowl. The combined game was moved to a tiny park near Dry Creek called Kewin Park because it was a central location. Paul Seideman and I were responsible for calling everyone to make sure they showed up.

In our senior year, we had all played together once before the merge on a weekend in fall. There were about twenty of us. It was a competitive game until Larry Simmons, a classmate who I had known in elementary school and played Little League with, and me collided. He buried his teeth in my forehead. I went to the emergency room and got stitched up. I talked Mom into letting me return to the game, which continued to rage on. I wore a bright white bandage and had blood caked in my hair. I hadn't cleaned up partly because I wanted to impress the senior girls, who sometimes came out to watch. One in particular was the daughter of one of our teachers. I made the impression I wanted. As soon as I walked onto the field, I was surrounded by girls and teammates, all curious how I was doing. It was cool being the center of attention. Larry never made it back to the game.

The Mud Bowl was also the one time of the year we "Boys of Autumn" could revert to being kids again – to refuse to grow up. Peter Pan had nothing on us. We could ignore reality for one day and dream of being a football hero. It was the last bastion of male chauvinism. Women weren't allowed to play.

Each guy wore the same "uniform" each year; a combination of college sweatshirt, gym pants, tennis shoes, and hat stenciled with the name of some professional sports team, vacation spot, or business. Except for one guy. Jeff Highiet, AKA "Putz," usually wore a T-shirt featuring the image of a naked woman bent over and prepared to hike a football to a man with his hands cupped between her legs. The caption read, "Play Naked." Jeff was a Downey High grad. His dad owned the junk yard. He had grown up and attended synagogue with my high school classmates. I first met him at the Mud Bowl. Jeff was a needler. He liked giving people a hard time. He used the long needle with delicious precision. It worked. If you listened.

It was raining Thanksgiving morning. Hard. Gary and I arrived together. The others showed up singly, or with buddies, carrying brown bags holding refreshments. It was good seeing everyone. A few had changed, sporting longer hair, beards, or moustaches. A few looked the same. Many had traveled long distances to get there. These included high school classmates like Don de Camp, whose nickname was "The Dancing Bear," who had come home from DePauw University in Indiana. Peter "Goat" Koetting had motored up from Cal Poly, San Luis Obispo. Terry Shaw, who was known as "Vanston," had come from Chico State, and Mark Peterson, who was "Lanston," had traveled from San Jose State. Paul Seideman, AKA "Si," from Cal Berkeley.

Brad Bassi, who we called "Bo're," came from San Francisco State. Dave Henry, better known as "Henniputz," also from Berkeley. Steve Couture, or "Big Cou," traveled from Colorado College in Colorado Springs. Barney Eredia, or "Hands," was living in Modesto, was married, had a son, and was managing a restaurant. Gary, who was also known as "Orlando," after his favorite baseball player, and me, better known as "Pinky," thanks to my childhood friend, Roy, had come from Davis. Don's younger brother Scott, or "Scur" as he was better known, was also at Cal Poly, San Luis Obispo. He brought his high school friends, including Kevin Clark, who was "Hoden" to us and attending the University of Oregon; Dave Swain, who answered to "Kipling" and was at Cal; Greg Sutton, or "Stein, a step-brother to Don and Scott, was at the University of Washington; Roy "Roy Boy" Ridgway was at MJC; Dave Wherry, who we called "Well," attended San Diego State. Highiet had invited some Downey classmates, including John "Fast Johnnie" Machado, who was also at Berkeley, and Shelly "Hollywood" Thompson, studying at UC Santa Barbara. My brother Tim "T Honey," who was at MJC, joined us, as did Cou's younger brother Chris, or "Little Cou," also at UC Davis, and Laura's brother, Vito, AKA "Pancho," who was also an MJC Pirate.

Down on the field of play, we moved slowly that early November morning, either from lack of sleep or too much partying. We wrapped body parts with athletic tape. A few others pulled on an assortment of ankle, knee, and wrist braces. We were young, but we had done some damage over the years in one or another organized sport. We took our bodies and our health for granted. We were bulletproof, after all. A few parents, friends, and girlfriends braved the weather and huddled under umbrellas. Shaw and Don snapped photos with their new SLR cameras – a Pentax and a Minolta. On the sidelines and the field, we went through pre-game rituals – tossing the ball to warm up our arms, punting the ball, stretching, or running a few patterns.

Arrayed under a tree were several small, plastic trophies that would be voted on and awarded after the game, including best overall player (MVP), the best defensive, and best offensive player. The trophies resembled something you received in elementary school for reading the most books, or winning the hoppy taw championship. Si, who I had first met at Roosevelt Junior High, had bought the trophies. Hanging from a tree was a rubber chicken someone had purchased to award to the best "cheap shot" play of the day.

During warm-ups, there was talk of adding a few wrinkles. Barney said he could get some flags if we wanted to avoid being hurt, not that anyone would ever pull somebody's flag anyway. It was much easier to grab the flag and hold on, which was no different than tackle. We had played tackle before switching to two-handed touch. We had learned that trick playing flag football at Roosevelt each time we played La Loma and Mark Twain, the other two junior high schools in town. Shaw suggested keeping statistics during the game to better decide who should get the post-game trophies. He also mentioned that he had a friend, who also played a football game in the mud, who held a banquet the night before at a local restaurant. That way girlfriends, wives, and significant others could join in. At the banquet, this group would bring photos and other memorabilia to share and reminisce about.

Even though it was morbid, and we were way too young, Si suggested doing a Last Man's Club. He had seen an old movie about World War I flying aces, who kept a bottle of champagne for the last flyer alive to pop and toast the deceased. Most of the players were fine with adding this new ritual to the ongoing tradition, or illusion, as a handful of the parents and girlfriends contended. Highiet suggested making it a bottle of Thunderbird, brewed in a lab by Gallo right in our own back yard. Koetting suggested doing T-shirts, or a memento, to remember the yearly event, to make it "memorial," he said, and realized he meant "memorable." We all laughed and called him "Yogi." If any, or all of this happened, the Mud Bowl would become, and remain, quite a "memorial" event.

Shaw and Kevin marked off boundaries and end zones with bath towels, sweatshirts, or whatever was in the trunk or back seat, of someone's car. They argued as they went. The squabbling sounded like a schoolyard light years ago. The game was schoolyard rules. Two players, generally the ones who quarterbacked, which were Brad and Kevin, picked teams. It was six-on-six, everybody eligible. Live ball on kickoffs and punts, dead ball on plays from scrimmage. One running play for each set of downs. There were two markers for first downs. You could also get a first down with three completions. There were no formal plays. Shaw had drawn up some plays on 3x5 cards. Unlike our FYNC team, nobody paid attention to these schemes.

On offense, everyone went out, usually long, and tried to get open. On defense, it was man-to-man. Zone was much too complicated. Rushers had to count "one alligator, two alligator" before rushing. There were no penalties, unless it was too obvious to ignore, like a defensive back hitting a receiver before the ball got there, or a lineman crushing the QB after the ball was thrown. Even those were let slide because the other team would simply get revenge the next time we changed possession. The kickoff was around 10 a.m. There was a timer, usually a school test clock, to indicate the end of the first half and the end of the game, which was 1:00 or 1:30, or until we got tired, or too wasted on beer, wine, or something else. If it was raining hard, the game was sloppy. If it wasn't, someone might open a sprinkler valve to muddy it up. There was nothing better on a dreary morning in November.

"I think you came the farthest," I said to Don.

"It is a long way to come," he replied.

"He enjoys coming," Brad added.

"He's overcome," Si continued.

"That's a real short-coming," finished Highiet. It was juvenile, but clever.

"Bird at the parents?" I asked Si.

"And icing any body parts," he answered.

"We've been lucky. No serious injuries," Brad said.

"Not yet," Scott replied.

"So far," Kevin added.

"Then poker at my house," Don said. On his last word, Lanston belly-flopped into the biggest puddle of mud. He barrel-rolled to his feet, hooting like a hyena.

"Right on schedule," Shaw said.

"Predictable," I added.

"He's got all year to get dry," Brad said.

"Think we'll ever grow up?" I asked Si.

"Not if we don't have to."

"We'll be our parents soon enough," Barney said.

"You already are," Gary said.

"You're right, I am," Barney replied.

"They're supposed to live forever," Peter said.

"Only in the movies," I said.

"The pillars of our community," Highiet said.

"Some of us," Don answered.

"Scary thought," said Henniputz. "Us. Adults. Impossible."

"Man, in high school, the possibilities seemed endless," Machado mused.

"One day I'm worried about getting to second base," Roy Boy said. "Turn around and I'm worried about paying taxes. One day I'm facing an open road. Suddenly, it's over my shoulder."

"There's no looking back," Gary said.

"We're spoiled," Brad said.

"Our expectations set us up," I said. "All those things our parents and teachers convinced us we could do."

"Human beings are walking expectations waiting to be unfulfilled," Si said. "Expectations equal premeditated disappointment," Henniputz added.

"Jesus. I thought I was a pessimist," I replied.

"Somebody's been taking psychology," Highiet said.

"Cultural anthro," Si answered.

"Lots of money in that field," Swain commented.

"I miss this town. I miss you guys," I said. That prompted sarcastic "aws" from everyone.

"I thought you liked being away from home," Gary said. "I thought you liked Davis."

"I do. I like both places."

"Typical," he said.

"What?"

"When you're there, you want to be here. When you're here, you want to be there. Like some kind of Christmas Gypsy."

"The what?"

"Christmas Gypsy. Wants summer when it's winter, winter when it's summer."

We were interrupted when Shaw shouted, "It's ten. Let's go." Shaw flipped a coin. Scott called heads in the air. Tails.

After consulting briefly with Si, Brad said, "We'll receive."

The two teams walked to opposite ends of the field. Scott booted a towering kick. Barney caught it, dashed to his right, and was downed near the twenty-yard line, or what was supposed to be the twenty. As he was lying there, Highiet piled on. The first cheap shot. The game was on.

Tim and I were on opposite sides. He liked rushing. I liked going out for passes. He'd check me at the line a few times to throw me off. I'd stay in and block, tackling him instead of blocking because he was stronger. And younger.

The game started slowly and badly for us old farts. We couldn't seem to move the ball. The new kids marched up and down the field at will, scoring two rapid touchdowns, largely thanks to Kevin and Scott connecting, which they did many times while playing varsity ball in high school.

I took a breather and joined Gary, Si, and Henniputz on the sidelines. I downed a slug of Schlitz beer. For early a.m., it tasted good. Gary toasted me with his Meister Brau.

"How's Beserkeley?" I asked Si.

"Still a DMZ," he answered.

"The fence remains," Henniputz added. "There are security guards watching around the clock."

"Regents voted to turn the site into a soccer field and parking lot," Si said.

"Bet that went over well," Gary said.

"At least the National Guard is gone," Dave said. "We've got our town and campus back."

"Chancellor Heyns put a small ad in *The Daily Californian* asking people to submit design ideas for the park," Si explained.

"Such a hypocrite," Henniputz said.

"Ray-gun's pissed. Made him look like a pussy," Si added.

"One of Berkeley's city council members called it, and I quote, 'a Hippie Disneyland freak show,'" Henniputz went on.

"There's talk of the city leasing the land from the University," Si said.

"Is it over?" I asked.

"It's just begun," Si answered.

"The calm before the storm," Henniputz finished.

In our next offensive series, Brad hit Si on a long one to bring the over-the-hill gang to within one touchdown. The timer went off. Halftime. The players left the field of battle for drinks, cigarettes, and bullshit. A few tried to walk off stiff or pulled muscles. More family and friends had shown up.

Shaw and Don took more photos. Peter and I took some – me with my new Nikon. A few players jogged to the park's cold, concrete bathrooms, hoping there wasn't a wino asleep inside.

Shaw re-set the timer and the second half began. Scott and Kevin led the young studs onto the field. Brad tried to rally us. For such young men, we were winded. Of course, the indulgences might have had something to do with that. Nearly all of us were infected with the Irish and/or herbal flu.

It was four and out. We punted. Peter shanked one off the side of his foot. "Duck" and quacking noises greeted his effort. Wherry blew on a duck call to make the point abundantly clear. He used it again when his teammate, Hollywood, threw a wobbler. He was immediately replaced by Kevin. With a short field, the kids scored on a trick hook and ladder play.

On the first play of our possession, Tim juked me, rushed Brad, and sent him tumbling ass over teakettle. Second down, no completes. Brad rolled right and hit Don in the chest with a bullet. The ball exploded off his sternum like a cannon shot. Third down, Brad tossed a floater to Gary who caught it, rumbling and stumbling down the field and into the end zone.

An hour later, it was over. The final score was six touchdowns to five in our favor. We had made a miraculous comeback, thanks largely to Brad moving the ball around to multiple receivers and a stunning lack of second half defense by our opponents. Trophies were handed out by the winners of last year's awards, which was also part of the custom. Scott awarded Brad the MVP trophy, Si gave Scott his best "O" award, T handed best "D" to Shaw, and Highiet threw the "Cheap Shot Chicken" at Don. Wet, cold, and shivering, we gathered for the group photo that ended every game. We limped to our cars and home with shouts of, "See you tonight" and "See you next year."

During the year, there had been ups and downs, good times and bad, frustrations and disappointments. Just like life. There would be more. But, on this day, we were all together again. These old friends were boys once more. Just playing a game in the mud.

CHAPTER 64

I arrived at 1532 soaked, muddy, and pleasantly distracted. It had been good seeing everyone. Mom took one look at me at the back door, smiled, and shook her head.

"Strip," was all she said. Or needed to say.

I undressed to my boxers, tiptoed into the bathroom, stripped, showered, dressed in warmer clothes, and joined Paul in the family room to watch the NFL. CBS carried the NHL, NBC broadcast the fledgling AFL. KXTV Channel 10, our local CBS station, was broadcasting the San Francisco 49ers, who played to a 24 – 24 tie with the Dallas Cowboys. On KCRA Channel 3, the NBC station, the San Diego Chargers defeated the Houston Oilers 21 – 17. The AFL was celebrating its tenth anniversary. This would be the last year the National Football League and American Football League would be separate. In the final AFL–NFL World Championship Game prior to the merger of the two leagues, the Kansas City Chiefs defeated the Oakland Raiders 17 – 7.

The first Super Bowl, Super Bowl I, was played on January 15th, 1967, following the 1966 regular season. The game was created as a part of the merger agreement between the NFL and its then-rival AFL. Roman numerals were used to identify each game. Under the agreement, the champion of each league would play in an AFL–NFL World Championship Game, until the merger took place in 1970. Once the merger was in effect, each league would become a conference – the NFL would be the NFC and the AFL the AFC. The conference champions would play to determine the NFL's league, or Super Bowl, champion.

To cap the 1969 season, the Kansas City Chiefs defeated the Minnesota Vikings in Super Bowl IV 23 – 7. The Chiefs were coached by Hank Stram and featured players like Len Dawson, Mike Garrett, E.J. Holub, Bobby Bell, Curly Culp, and Jan Stenerud. The Vikings were coached by Bud Grant and featured Joe Kapp, Mick Tingelhoff, and the Purple People Eaters – Alan Page, Carl Eller, Jim Marshall, and Gary Larsen. The upstart AFL had proven it could play with the big boys. In 1970, the 10 AFL teams, along with three teams from the pre-1970 NFL, became the 13-team AFC. The remaining NFL teams formed the 13-team NFC.

Thanksgiving dinner with my family was deliciously chaotic. As Dad had, for as long as I could remember, Paul ground the stuffing mix early in the morning with an old hand-cranked meat grinder. He stuffed the bird, stitched it together, slathered it with butter, and popped it into the oven. Mom cooked and mashed the potatoes with help from the girls. She made a green bean casserole. She opened a can of cranberry sauce and jars of olives and pickles. She warmed up the Sunbeam brown 'n serve rolls. For desert, there was store-bought pumpkin and mincemeat pies with ice cream. Dad usually asked for a slice of cheddar cheese on his pie, exactly like his Uncle Hank. It was nice sitting with the family and catching up. Mom loved having all her children around. Tim would leave early to have a second dinner with Laura and her family. The rest of us would roll into the family room, stretch out, listen to music, or watch TV. Comfortably cozy with a fire blazing, most of us would nod out for a while. It was a perfect afternoon.

"You okay?" Paul asked, after I had sneezed.

"Just fried."

"You sick?"

"I hope not."

"Any developments?"

"Continuing to gather information."

"Anything look promising?

"A few."

"Sorry for all the questions, Michael, but we're worried."

"I know that."

"Look, I know I'm not your father, but that doesn't mean I don't care about you."

"I know that, too."

"You know, I never thought I'd have kids. It looked like I was destined to be a confirmed bachelor. Until your mom and me found each other. Best thing that ever happened to me."

"She's one of a kind."

"I never thought I'd have sons."

"Now you have three."

"I never thought I'd have to send any of them off to war. That scares me."

"You were a Marine, like Dad, right?"

"I was."

"In the Pacific, too."

"I saw young men die. I don't want that to happen to you."

"Me, either."

"I lost a younger brother."

"That had to have been tough."

"I couldn't save him."

"I don't ever want to face that."

"He was a great kid. Followed me everywhere. He was my shadow."

"Sounds familiar."

"We did everything together. Dressed alike. Looked alike. Did all the same things. It was the two of us. We counted on each other. Relied on each other. Took care of each other. There are times when I wish he were here to help me remember something."

"There'll come a day when I need to do the same thing."

"It's a special bond. Nobody else will ever experience life the same way as two brothers. Cherish it." He stopped, stared out the back windows, eyes glistening, and cleared his throat.

"Your Mom and me will support whatever decision you make. If that means driving to Canada, that's what we'll do. Whatever it takes."

"Thanks."

"We'll never be as close as you and your dad were. But, that doesn't mean I won't do everything I can to protect you. To protect your mom. To protect this family. That's my job now."

"That means more than you'll ever know."

"You need anything. Anything at all. Just call."

"I will."

To keep the good times rolling that night, we gathered at Don's house for what had become another rite. The annual poker game. Depending on how many players were upright and not hospitalized, there would be one or two tables. Tonight, we had seven players and one table.

We played regular games like five-card draw and seven-card stud. We played crazy games like pass the shit, Indian poker, acey deucey, and guts. There were bettors and bluffers, aggressive and conservative players. I was conservative. I never bet much until I had a hand. I'd never win a big pot because everyone knew I never bet unless I had a sure thing, so they'd fold. I wasn't a player. Si and Scott were players. Brad was there to visit and have a few. Shaw was given a hard time because he brought a jar of pennies to bet. When it was empty, he was done. Nobody wanted his pennies, but that's what he had.

I eased slowly into a chair, feeling sore muscles I hadn't used in some time. Around the table sat Brad, Si, Shaw, Peter, Don, Scott, Swain, and me.

The smokers were smoking small, Crooks rum-soaked cigars.

"Acey deucey," Scott named the game.

Acey deucey was not my favorite game. Each player anted into the pot. The ante was a quarter. Two cards were dealt face-up to the player left of the dealer. The player could pass, or bet any amount, including the entire pot, gambling that the third card dealt would fall between the first two cards. If the third card hit in-between, the bettor took the amount he bet out of the pot. If the third card didn't fall between, the bettor added what he bet to the pot. If the third card matched either of the other two cards, the bettor had to throw double what he bet into the pot. If the two cards dealt face-up to start the hand were the same value, the bettor would predict if the next card would be higher, or lower, and would bet. The game ended when a player bet the pot and won.

"Ante asshole," Don said to Shaw. It was said every time we played and on almost every hand, whether or not the player had already anted.

"Deal me a winner," Shaw said.

"Too bad John didn't make it this year," Brad said.

"I stopped by his house," Si said.

"He okay?" Don asked.

"He's messed up," Si answered. "Vietnam scrambled his brains."

"Having your copter shot down and spending days wounded in the jungle will do that," Shaw said. "I think he got involved in drugs and came back with symptoms of schizophrenia."

"Middy was a good guy," Peter said.

"Some of our classmates didn't make it back," I said.

"The ones that did weren't the same," Brad added.

"Shit, or get off the pot," Scott said to Peter as he contemplated his bet.

"I saw Curt this summer," I said to Brad and Si. They had both gone to Fremont Elementary School with him.

"How's he doing?" Si asked.

"Angry," I answered.

"Can't blame him," Brad said.

"He feels like all his friends turned on him."

"Sorry to hear that," Si said.

"When he came home, the demonstrators called him and his fellow soldiers baby killers."

"Assholes," Scott said.

"He was drinking a lot. Doing drugs. Trying to numb the pain, I guess. He's clean now."

"Who here is next?" Si asked.

"To bet?" Swain asked.

"To go," Si answered. "We're all eligible."

"I don't want to think about it," I said.

"Me, neither," everyone else chimed in. We all had it on our minds. We were all dealing with it in our own way. The lottery was looming. The numbers would be drawn on Monday. We were all a few days from a random event that would change our lives. The luck of the draw took on a whole new meaning that night for those of us at the table.

The poker ended with a game of guts. Each player anted. Each was dealt two cards face down. Starting with the player to the dealer's left and continuing around the table, ending with the dealer, each player in turn said "in" or "out," and pushed their cards toward the pot if they were in, tossed their cards in the discard pile if they were out. Players who said "out" couldn't win the pot, but didn't have to put in extra money. If nobody said "in," each player matched the pot and new cards were dealt. If more than one player said "in," all those who were "in" showed their cards. The player with the best cards won the pot. The losers had to match the pot. Scott won the last hand. We called it a night.

CHAPTER 65

I awoke late Friday morning. I was nursing unused muscles, a mild hangover, and my poker losses. After I ate the breakfast Mom had prepared and had my caffeine, I read *The Modesto Bee* until Gary showed up. He had skipped the poker so he could get home for turkey. His mom had asked him to buy a Christmas tree for their home, so he had driven his dad's truck down from La Grange. We went to the same lot both our families had gone to for years. It was managed by the Boy Scouts, who had traveled high into the Sierra Nevada mountains to find their trees. As we wandered the rows of trees, the smell of fresh pine needles helped chase the fog.

"What now?" Gary asked.

"Depends on the lottery, I guess. Maybe I'll get lucky."

"If what you told me about your poker playing last night holds true, you're in deep shit."

"It wasn't one of my best nights."

"Not happy I've still got to think about it, too," he said. "Really not happy I see two of you from time to time."

"And you're not even drunk." Gary mimed a drum rimshot to punctuate my bad joke.

"Don't bitch," I continued. "It may save your bacon. Besides, you can always close one eye."

"Kiss my ass."

"It looks – "

"No, it looks like your face." It never got old.

"You going to keep checking things out?"

"Have to."

"I get it. Keep me posted. We're all in the same boat."

"And sinking fast."

"Keep bailing."

"I'm going to swing by and see a few people while I'm home. I could use a good listener or two, and maybe some advice."

"I hope you get what you want."

"Or need."

"That, too."

"There is one thing I know," I added.

"What's that?"

"I'm incredibly thankful."

"Guess that's part of what this holiday is all about."

As I moved through the trees, touching their soft boughs, I realized there was much I could be thankful for. School was rolling along. I felt good and was in decent shape, except for some post-Bowl aches and pains. The family was doing well. I was relatively happy. And I still had Kelly. *For now,* I thought, as the negativity crept in, as it inevitably did. I was trusting nothing had changed between us. I wouldn't know until I saw her, which would be Saturday night. We had agreed to meet at Putt-Putt Golf, another of our old haunts.

Thursday and Friday nights, the Stones invaded the Big Apple. They were slated to play a total of three shows at Madison Square Garden. They stayed at the Plaza. They were in the big city now and they liked it.

Before the first show, they held a press conference at the Rainbow Room high atop Rockefeller Center. Reporters' questions included, "Do you see yourselves as youth leaders?" "What do you think of the Vietnam War?" "What do you think of America? Do you think it's getting better?" There was always a smart ass who would ask, "Are you satisfied?" accompanied by knowing chuckles. "Sexually, yes," Mick answered, "financially, unsatisfied." With Woodstock fresh on the minds of New Yorkers, the reporters wanted to know if the Stones were going to do a free concert, like they vaguely alluded to in Los Angeles and later in Oakland, after they'd gotten hammered for the cost of the show tickets. The Stones apparently were up for it.

"The free concert will be in San Francisco, but there is no exact location yet," Jagger answered.

"When?"

"December 6th."

"Why are you giving that concert in San Francisco?" the reporter followed up.

"Because there's a scene there and the climate's nice," Jagger said, grinning that Cheshire cat grin.

Inside the Garden that night, frenzied fans tried to get backstage, concocting all manner of wild tales. Security was pushed to its limits. Celebrities dotted the audience, including Janis Joplin. Jimi Hendrix was in the dressing room playing Mick Taylor's guitar, upside down because he was a leftie and it was strung for rightie Taylor. Sam Cutler cruised on-stage and announced,

"Are you ready, New York? Ready for the biggest band to visit New York in a long time?" The crowd roared, "Yes!" Cutler continued, "They've done the West Coast, they've done all sorts of other places in America, now they're in New York! Be cool. Have a fantastic time. Now . . . Let's really hear it . . . Let's welcome the Greatest Rock 'n' Roll Band in the World. The Rolling Stones! The Rolling Stones!"

The crowd blew up. The Stones ran on stage. "Jumpin' Jack Flash" blasted from the amps. They were loud. They were nasty. They burned the place down. The entire building shook. Outside the Garden, inside a Hertz truck, Glyn Johns, the Stones' recording engineer and producer, was manning a recording console shipped in from Wally Heider's in LA. The shows had been so good, he wanted to get the band down on tape.

Jagger asked for the house lights to come up and said, "We're gonna do one more and then we gotta go." Richards and Taylor tumbled into "Street Fighting Man." The final drum roll machine-gunned to an end, the band raced off stage, and into their waiting limos. It was on to Boston for two more shows. They left the crowd wanting more, as they always did.

It was an overcast and windy Friday afternoon when I met Coach Leach at Pike Park. We sat on the newly constructed wooden bleachers. He was looking older than I remembered. Funny how that happens when you haven't seen someone for a while.

"Did you serve?" I asked him.

"I was an 'in-betweener.' Too young for Korea and too old for Vietnam. Plus, I was married, had children, and was teaching."

"Fortunate."

"I suppose."

"Would you have served?"

"It's a different war."

"It's a different world."

"I don't know. It's stunning the difference in perspective between a thirty-five-year-old family man and a twenty-one-year-old college kid."

"I think you would have been out there marching with the rest of us."

"You're probably right."

"The draft lottery is this Monday."

"What's the plan?"

"Depends on what number I draw."

"What are your alternatives?"

"Realistically?"

"Always."

"Resist and go to jail, leave the country and lose my home, serve and maybe come home in a body bag, or wait it out."

"Not very good."

"Do you enjoy teaching?"

"I do. Why?"

"I've been trying to figure out the one thing I can do to change things. To make a difference. To turn things around. It's not fighting in the streets. It's not running for office. It's not volunteering. It's not making bunches of money. It's not non-violence. I've seen those things and I don't like some, or all, of what I've seen."

"They don't speak to you."

"Not at all."

"What does?"

"What you do. Teaching."

"Touching lives. Inspiring minds. Helping students blossom. Seeing that light go on in their eyes. Watching them make their way in the world. Some better than others, which is bittersweet. Perhaps rescuing those who have lost their way. It can be stressful, frustrating, and heartbreaking."

"But, it's all worth it."

"It is. You really can change the world. One student at a time."

"I'd like to be as good as you."

"You'll be the best teacher you can be."

"I hope so."

"Remember, our deeds are our only possessions. We are what we do. In everything, actions speak louder than words." We sat in silence, watching a father toss a football to his young son.

CHAPTER 66

I had one more stop that Saturday before meeting Kelly.

Mr. Gordon sat behind his desk. I sat in the chair facing him. Another teacher counseling a student. A scene I had experienced countless times. An experience I, unlike so many of my peers, enjoyed. I relished having these conversations with mentors – with men of judgment and experience I respected.

"Shaping lives," he said. "Helping people find their way. Setting them on their path. That's the satisfaction I get from this profession."

"Any regrets?"

"About?"

"Choosing a different profession? Doing something different?"

"Regrets are a waste of time."

"I've done some things I wish I hadn't."

"It can't be that bad. You're much too young."

"It can be."

"Learn from them and don't repeat them. It's better to look ahead and prepare, than look back and regret."

"I've got some big decisions to make. And right away. Choices that will determine where I go from here. Choices that will affect the rest of my life."

"You've got a good head on your shoulders. You always have. Trust your gut. It's never steered me wrong."

"I'm being pulled in a thousand directions."

"History is shaped by numberless acts of courage and belief," he said, paraphrasing something Robert Kennedy had said during his speech in Cape Town in 1966. "That includes the courage to say no to war. To stand up for your belief in peace. Passive resistance is true heroism because it takes real courage to resist violence."

"It sounds more heroic than I feel."

"If you can't stand for something, you can't stand for anything. You have to decide what you stand for. All of it is important, or none of it is."

"I think I know what that is. At least, it's becoming clearer. I hope."

"Be practical. Be realistic. Be honest. The moral high ground is a coveted piece of property. It can be painfully expensive."

"It's not going to be easy."

"It never is."

"I hope I can figure it out. Make the right choice."

"You'll know."

"It's scary."

"I understand."

"I've got some work to do. Some things to think about."

"'Every man is guilty of the good he did not do.' Voltaire said that. Remember it."

Kelly looked wonderful. I couldn't believe I had ever messed with our relationship, had ever taken her for granted. Why do we men sacrifice what we have for what we think we want – threaten what we've got for something we want to get? Is it ego, fear, immaturity, selfishness, immaturity, self-destruction? I didn't know what it was, but I was glad it was gone.

"How was your Thanksgiving?" I asked.

"It was good to be with the family and see my friends."

"Sorry I didn't make it by."

"It's okay."

"Really?"

"Really. I'm not jealous of the Mud Bowl."

"It's a busy time."

"You don't look any worse for the wear."

"A few aches and pains."

"How's your mom and Paul?"

"Same old, same old."

"The rest of the family?"

"Growing up." I reached out and took her hand. She didn't pull it back.

"It was good seeing you at the march in San Francisco," I said.

"That was a real eye-opener."

"I hope the government was paying attention."

"They were, but they're not going to change anything."

"I think Berkeley's getting to you."

"It is opening my mind. A bit. It's unavoidable."

"Don't change too much."

"Just enough. To keep everyone off-balance," she answered.

"Even me?"

"Especially you." She removed her hand and placed her palms flat on the table.

"And my father," she continued. "He and I have been having disagreements."

"About me?"

"If only. No, about Vietnam. He supports Nixon."

"Thank God my parents support me. Whatever I decide."

"And what is that?"

"Come Monday night, things will be narrowed down some."

"The lottery."

"Yep, the lottery. My number will be drawn and my fate set."

"To a degree. You have more control than that."

"It doesn't feel like it."

"It's your call. Always has been. Always will be. It's your choice," she said.

"I can't just choose things by letting them happen."

"No, you can't. You're more of a control freak than that. Besides, why would you let someone else decide for you?"

"I wouldn't."

"Would you mind some observations?"

"I would love some."

"I'm about to get real Berkeley on you."

"I can handle it."

"With everything that's going on, we forget that we're part of something greater than ourselves. Call it what you will. A collective unconscious, the Universe, a greater cause."

"Wow, Berkeley has gotten to you."

"Just listen."

"Okay."

"Sometimes we do things, make decisions, that don't reflect that perspective. We focus instead on the here-and-now instead of the then. We make short-term decisions that benefit us with no concern about the consequences."

"I'm not so sure about that, but go on."

"Other times, we refuse to do 'the right thing.' Refuse to act for the greater good because it's too damned hard."

"I think you've been living inside my head."

"The challenge is stepping outside ourselves. Being less selfish. Looking closely at the choices we've made and the things we've done that increase, or diminish, that greater good."

"We are what we do," I said, echoing what Professor Gordon had said hours earlier.

"Don't get me wrong," she continued. "I'm not saying you have to sacrifice yourself to make this a better world."

"What then?"

"All kinds of things. Plant a tree. Pick up litter. Donate food. Teach somebody to read. Anything that will make someone smile. That will make the world a better place."

"I like that idea."

"Any good you do will be good for the community, good for you, and good for the greater good. For example, ending a bad relationship helps you and helps the other person."

"Do you mean us?" I asked.

She just smiled and shook her head. "Depends," she went on.

"On what? I'm experiencing a real sense of déjà vu all over again."

"One thing at a time."

"Okay."

"When you're certain the choice you make and the thing you do is made and done to serve the greater good, then you can be sure that what you're choosing and what you're doing will benefit everyone, as well as you."

I was blown away. Kelly sounded so worldly. She was leaving me in the dust.

"It doesn't have to be out there, in the world somewhere," she said. "It can be right here in your own hometown. And you know what that means?"

"What?" I croaked, stunned.

"The Universe, the greater power, or whatever it is, will back you. Even if it doesn't feel like it, or look like it. When you know you're serving the world, you can make a world of difference."

"Amen."

"I'm being serious."

"So am I. That was incredibly inspiring."

"I hope it helps."

As I stared into her eyes, which were animated by the message she'd shared, I felt somewhat optimistic about it all. Guarded, but still optimistic. I could tell she deeply believed in what she had said. I thought it might hold a possible key to the future. We'd know better after Monday. What I did know now was, I loved this lady.

Rolling along the river in Ugly Orange on my way back to Davis, my mind was ping-ponging. Thoughts of Kelly, the draft, school, my family, my friends, my future bounced around my head, never quite settling on one subject. I recalled reading Hermann Hesse's *Siddhartha*, while working in the peaches last summer. Siddhartha had spent time with the enlightened one, Gotama the Buddha. During one of their encounters, Siddhartha explained to the Buddha that he, Siddhartha, must discover who and what he was on his own. He wanted to know himself, learn from himself, and understand himself. Neither Gotama, nor any other guide, could teach enlightenment because wisdom had to be learned through experience – it could not be communicated through words.

Siddhartha said he could no longer rely on teachers and teachings. Gotama warned him, "Beware of too much wisdom." It struck me that I had been racing around gathering information and seeking advice hoping I would get enough information to find the answer to all the issues I was facing when, in fact, it was up to me; the answer was within me. Always had been. And needed to be.

On Sunday, the Rolling Stones played the final date of their U.S. tour, headlining the First Annual International Palm Beach Music & Art Festival at the International Speedway in West Palm Beach, Florida, which had opened on Friday night with Country Joe and the Fish. The Stones got there late because they sat on the tarmac at La Guardia. All air traffic in and out of New York had been stopped because Nixon was in town for lunch. In the meantime, thousands of kids waited in the mud and cold of sunny Florida. They listened to the other bands, which included Janis Joplin, The Byrds, Spirit, Jefferson Airplane, Grand Funk Railroad, King Crimson, Terry Reid, and Steppenwolf. The Stones took the stage around 4:00 a.m. It was so cold you could see their breath and the guitars kept going out of tune. They played until the sun came up. If it weren't for the alleged free concert they'd promised, they'd be going home. Keith said it best as the new day dawned: "A rock 'n' roller doesn't exist unless he's on the stage."

That same Sunday night in Davis, in honor of the Rolling Stones being on tour and the imminent release of *Let It Bleed*, one of the frats hosted a showing of Jean-Luc Godard's film, *Sympathy for the Devil*, at 194 Chem. Godard had filmed the Stones while they recorded tracks at Olympic Studios in London. The songs would become the band's seventh album, *Beggar's Banquet*, which had been released in the U.K. in December 1968.

The movie, which was also known as *One Plus One*, had opened in the U.S. last April. Film sequences alternated between an inside look at the recording process and statements about art, power, and revolution. It was a powerful, disturbing film. Shots of the Stones in the studio were intercut with documentary footage and staged scenes that resembled reportage from a combat zone. The Stones, dazzling and devilish, were the ultimate subject for a film that Godard stated was aimed to "subvert, ruin and destroy all civilised values." The Stones were portrayed as revolutionaries, anarchists, cultural terrorists. They were still the bad boys of rock, which was a tough reputation to live up to, let alone sustain. The movie was not my "cup of tea." Rumors continued spinning around that the band was considering a free concert when they hit the Bay Area. We'd see. The boys loved their money as much as they loved their image, perhaps more.

CHAPTER 67

"All the News that Fits" – December Edition

British band Blind Faith is believed to be splitting up. The Cook County grand jury indicts 64 Weathermen on 37 counts related to the "Days of Rage." Fred Hampton, chairman of the Illinois chapter of the Black Panther Party, and fellow Panther Mark Clark are shot to death in Chicago. Members of the Weather Underground destroy numerous police vehicles in a retaliatory bombing spree. LAPD's newly formed Special Weapons and Tactics (S.W.A.T.) unit engages in a four hour gun battle with Black Panthers inside their Southern California headquarters. Charles M. Manson and five of his followers are indicted on murder charges in the deaths of actress Sharon Tate and six others. Ed Sullivan introduces The Jackson Five to America. President Nixon's task force on women's rights releases "A Matter of Simple Justice," a report which declares that the federal government "should be as seriously concerned about sex discrimination as with race discrimination" and instructs Congress to develop legislation to eliminate all existing forms of sex discrimination. Entertainer Tiny Tim marries Miss Vicki on *The Tonight Show Starring Johnny Carson*. Bernadette Devlin is convicted of incitement to riot in the Battle of the Bogside, Northern Ireland. The 91st Congress adjourns. The Weathermen group changes tactics, going underground and renaming itself the Weather Underground Organization (WHO). Centerfielder Curt Flood of the St. Louis Cardinals challenges baseball's reserve clause, which prevents players from moving to another team unless they are traded. The United States death toll in Vietnam reaches 48,736, with 11,780 having died in 1969, which is down from a peak in 1968 of 16,899. New book releases include *Halloween Party* by Agatha Christie. *Way It Is, Buck White, The Moondreamers, La Strada, Coco, The Whistling Wizard, The Sultan of Tuffet, Dandelion, Sambo,* and *Group Soup* open on stage. New films include *Hello Dolly!* featuring Barbra Streisand; *On Her Majesty's Secret Service* starring George Lazenby and Diana Rigg; *The Magic Christian* with Peter Sellers and Ringo Starr; *Z* directed by Costa-Gavras; Alfred Hitchcock's adaptation of Leon Uris' *Topaz; They Shoot Horses, Don't They?* starring Jane Fonda and directed by Sydney Pollack; *Anne of the Thousand Days* with Richard Burton and Geneviève Bujold; and William Faulkner's *The Reivers* featuring Steve McQueen with a musical score by newcomer, John Williams. New music includes *Let It Bleed* by the Rolling Stones, the newly disbanded Beatles' seventh Christmas record, *Happy Christmas 1969*, *Diana Ross Presents The Jackson Five*, *Grand Funk Railroad*, *Okie from Muskogee* by Merle Haggard, and *Blue Cheer*.

The clock was ticking. The holidays were coming. The year was ending. School was going well. Kelly and I were solid. Luci was out of my life. But, I still hadn't worked out my draft issue. The shit was hitting the fan. Right when it appeared to be getting good, it went bad.

On that Monday, the first day of December, CBS interrupted *Mayberry R.F.D.* at 6 p.m. PST to broadcast live the first lottery since World War II. Gary, Gover, and I sat in the living room of our apartment and watched as the blue plastic lottery capsules were drawn from a large glass container. It was like a bingo game, except that on this night lives and futures were at stake. Lucky number one went to those born on September 14th. Number two was April 24th. My little brother Tim's popped out at number 17. Mine was 24. Gary was 59. Gover was 236. Tim and I were screwed. Gary wasn't out of the woods. Gover popped a beer to celebrate, Gary to commiserate. I went for a long bike ride.

When I got back, Gary said Mom had called. I dialed the home number. Mom answered and Paul got on the extension.

"I am so sorry," Mom said. I could tell she had been crying.

"Me, too."

"You okay son?" Paul asked.

"It hasn't sunk in yet."

"We're here if you want to talk about anything," he went on.

"Have you spoken with Tim?" I asked.

"Yes."

"How's he taking it?"

"Not well, either."

"I can't believe both my boys are going to be drafted and have to go to that awful place."

"It's not a done deal, Mom," I said, not believing it myself.

"You're such an optimist," she said.

"A guarded optimist," I replied.

"Better than the alternative," Paul commented.

"I'll never give up hope," I said. From some distant place, my mind summoned the lines from an Emily Dickinson poem, "Hope is the thing with feathers that perches in the soul – and sings the tunes without the words – and never stops at all."

Earlier that same day, U.S. Attorney Cecil Poole arrived at Alcatraz to negotiate with Richard Oakes and the occupying Native Americans. The government had blinked first.

An article in *The Aggie* the next day printed the entire list of numbers and cautioned against overreacting, which I was. They had been deluged with students and questions, mostly about CO status and the reserves. The answers were complex. The advisors suggested students get competent counseling from the Draft Center and not to give up their student deferment, even if they had a high number. The article stated that it was predicted by some experts that numbers 001 through 122 were certain to be called, 123 through 244 were medium risk, and 245 to 366 were "safe." The article went on to say these artificial divisions were misleading. Individual draft boards could go deep into the lottery draw, even into the "safe" numbers, depending on how many eligible men between the ages of 19 and 26 were under their jurisdiction. That gave Gover some heartburn.

The local draft board ultimately held all the power. They would decide the fate of each draft-eligible man, based on the quota of bodies set by the military each month. Because the Army needed the most men in Vietnam, they would tell the Selective Service how many recruits they needed monthly. The Selective Service would send that to the local draft board. That number factored in volunteers, as well as the percentage of draftees who would wash out. The cut line for how many numbers would be called was based on that calculation.

Men with a number at the cut line and below would be required to report for a physical, mental, and moral evaluation at a Military Entrance Processing Station to determine their fitness for duty. Modesto men would be processed in Fresno. Even if you were temporarily exempt, whether it was being a student, being married, or something else, you received a letter from the draft board with your date to be examined. Once you got the results of the evaluation, you had ten days to file a claim for exemption, postponement, or deferment. The members of the board would review each case and make a decision. The board might choose to interview you and those who knew you to better understand your situation. If you didn't agree with their decision, you could appeal to a Selective Service District Appeal Board. Receiving the notice to report for an induction physical was a bummer of a letter to get because it brought the reality back into focus. I knew mine was coming.

On Wednesday, the shit really hit the fan. The U.S. escalated bombing runs into bordering Cambodia. The justification was that the North Vietnamese were moving men and *materiel* along trails in Cambodia before re-entering Vietnam to hit American targets. Code named "Operation Breakfast," the first carpet bombings across the border had taken place on March 18th. The government had kept it secret from the public and the Congress, fearing an escalation of protests. The *New York Times* had broken the story last May, but nobody seemed to notice.

The one bright light in all this was, as always, the music. It was alive and well and keeping me afloat. Rick Nelson, one of my early favorites, had reinvented himself as a country rock singer with his backing band, The Stone Canyon Band, releasing the single, "She Belongs to Me." Joni Mitchell had stopped performing so she could concentrate on writing songs. CSNY had completed their second album and were on tour promoting it. Neil Young was working on his third album and had worked with San Francisco recording engineer Wally Heider to install a 16-track recording studio in the Topanga Canyon house Gary and I had visited in March. The title was *After the Gold Rush*, as he had told us, and was named after the song he had shared with us on the beach in what felt like eons ago. On Friday, December 5th, the Stones released *Let It Bleed*.

That same night, CSNY performed at Cal Expo in Sacramento, which had just opened in 1968. I had bought the tickets thinking I needed a distraction from the lottery. The show was held inside the building that housed the county exhibits during the state fair's run each summer. The opening acts included Bicycle and Taj Mahal, a black blues singer. Gary and I drove to Modesto, picked up Willy and Don MacRitchie, then retraced our route to the capital city.

The band didn't disappoint. They opened with an acoustic set, playing "Suite: Judy Blue Eyes" and the Beatles' "Blackbird." Stills, Young, and Crosby and Nash each did solo sets. When they went electric, they blew the roof off the place. They played a mix of songs from the first and second album, from Buffalo Springfield, from Neil Young's solo album, as well as a few Byrds and Hollies tunes. I had never seen Buffalo Springfield. I could only imagine what that band sounded like live, as I listened to Stills and Young play their old tunes.

They told stories about those days, talked about how they met, and this collaboration began, and tossed in some politics for spice. They taunted Reagan, whose sandbox they were in, as well as Nixon and Hoover, whose radar they were on. People were passing joints down our aisle. I was shooting

Willy and Don the evil eye. I wasn't about to let them get stoned on my watch. Everyone was in good voice, including Stills, who most times shredded his vocal chords. Throughout the show, the band talked about a gig in the Bay Area that was happening the next day. They had been invited to play with the Stones at their free concert. A location had finally been announced. It was Altamont. After their second encore, they invited us all to join them at the free event and said goodnight.

The concert ended about midnight. Gary and I drove Willy and Nip home. They wanted to go to Altamont, but I had to play the big brother. Again. I didn't want to take a chance that anything would happen to them. I assumed there'd be drugs and other loconess going down that I wasn't sure I was ready for, let alone them. Gary and I nabbed a few hours of sleep. We got up early. I never liked being late. For anything. Sleepy-eyed Mom made us breakfast. She acted like it was our last meal.

"It's just a concert," we explained.

"You need to eat," she answered.

We packed some snacks, beers, low lawn chairs, a camera, blankets, and jackets. Even though it was sunny California, it was still December. Mom kissed us both, which embarrassed Gary, and told us to be careful. We pointed the bug toward the Altamont Speedway.

The Rolling Stones free concert was on and it was taking place up the hill in Livermore, California.

CHAPTER 68

The Stones' concert was pure chaos. Something the Stones attracted and were accustomed to. Before it was over, the show had moved four times. The people involved at various times included the Airplane; the Dead; the Dead's manager, Rock Scully; Woodstock's production manager, Chip Monck; the Stones' tour manager and concert producer, Sam Cutler; Woodstock's impresario, Michael Lang; and attorney Melvin Belli. When the dust settled, the Stones' free concert was scheduled to take place on Saturday, December 6th at the Altamont Speedway near Livermore.

The history of the Stones' San Francisco free concert was as convoluted as it was crazy.

The concert had been discussed the year before when Cutler invited Rock Scully, manager of the Grateful Dead, to London to discuss doing a free show with the Dead. The Dead wanted the Stones to feel the vibe they had been feeling in San Francisco. The Stones pushed for it because they had been accused of charging too much for concert tickets by journalists like Ralph J. Gleason and promoters like Bill Graham. The idea had taken root. Mick Jagger was up for doing San Francisco because that's where things were happening. Plus, they wanted to make up for not being at Woodstock. And outdo it. They were also determined to let their fans know how much they appreciated them laying down their hard-earned money, or so they said.

The Stones planned to film the concert and release the finished movie to make up for any losses incurred by the free concert. The Stones had conceived of the idea after Granada Television basically covered all the expenses of the Hyde Park concert by securing exclusive rights to air the show on British TV. The seed of an idea had taken root.

Based on a recommendation by the Dead and the Stones' experience with London's version of the Hells Angels at the Hyde Park event, Sam Cutler initiated negotiations with the San Francisco Angels to provide security for the event.

The original choice for a venue had been San Jose State because a large concert had just been held there. But, the city wasn't interested in hosting another big show. The Polo Grounds at Golden Gate Park was a second choice because that's where all the free concerts by the San Francisco psychedelic bands had happened. It would be billed as the "Concert in the Park." But, Golden Gate Park was suddenly not available. The San Francisco 49ers, who played at Kezar Stadium in the park, had a game that weekend against the Chicago Bears, so that site wasn't practical. Plus, San Francisco and its law and order mayor, Joe Alioto, wouldn't issue permits, partly because the city and the cops had an ongoing battle with the hippies, homeless, and runaways in nearby Haight-Ashbury. The city had ordered a temporary cessation of all events in the park. As it had been said, the devil was in the details and the Stones and their people weren't as sympathetic to the details as they were to the devil.

Nobody had taken care of things like insurance, rent, medical, bathrooms, security, and so on. When things fell apart, the Stones called San Francisco attorney Melvin Belli. The flamboyant, self-styled "King of Torts" had represented Jack Ruby, the man who killed Lee Harvey Oswald in the basement of the Dallas Police Department. Someone in the Stones' entourage thought Belli might be able to grease the wheels with the city fathers. Things were spiraling out of control, which was nothing new to the Stones. The concert was on, but they had no place to play.

On Friday, November 28th, the day after Thanksgiving, the *Los Angeles Free Press* had been the first to break the story that the show was happening. On Monday, December 1st, Gleason followed with an article in the *San Francisco Chronicle*, which had a few more details, many of them incorrect, such as the name of the venue and the lineup of the bands. The radio stations started broadcasting about the free gig. That same Friday, the Stones made it official at the Rainbow Room press conference when the reporter asked about it and Jagger said yes, it would be held in San Francisco on December 6th. When another reporter asked him why they weren't doing a concert in New York, Jagger answered, "Because New York is too cold. We're going to do it outside, man. And San Francisco is really into that sort of thing."

Scully recommended an alternative site to Golden Gate Park because, as someone said, "The man can't bust our music." It was Filmways' Sears Point Raceway, which was located north of San Francisco in Sonoma County. Scully and Cutler were in charge of making it come together, wherever it ended up. Calvin Murray, the owner of Sears Point, said they could have it for free if they got all the permits, purchased insurance, paid for any expenses, and any profits from the film would go to a Vietnamese orphans' fund. Chip Monck, who'd handled staging and lighting at Woodstock and had set up the same for the entire Stones' tour, went to Sonoma and prepped the site. He was on schedule.

The San Francisco Hells Angels told Scully all bets were off if the show was moved. Sonoma wasn't their turf. They considered themselves the good Angels. No telling what would happen outside the City.

On late Wednesday, December 3rd, news was leaked that the concert was now taking place at Sears Point. Once word got out, the local AM and FM stations competed to see who could get the most "breaking news." They played Stones' songs, had contests, even loaned a traffic helicopter to help with setting up the venue.

With people crawling all over Sonoma trying to get the concert staged, Belli got a call from Dick St. John, the president of Filmways. Turned out, Filmways had bought the track from Murray and his partners in July. St. John had other ideas for this "free" concert. He wanted a $100,000 fee to cover any damage to the site and distribution rights to any film that was made. The film Filmways wanted was the film being made by the Maysles Brothers, Albert and David.

The backstory on the proposed film was as twisted as the site selection.

D.A. Pennebaker, a documentary filmmaker who had done Dylan's *Don't Look Back* and *Monterey Pop*, had originally spoken with the Stones about doing a documentary on the tour when plans for the tour were originally announced in June 1969. It didn't take long for Pennebaker to back out of the project, not digging the Stones' preference for commercial success over artistic vision. Jagger also spoke with Haskell Wexler, whose movie *Medium Cool* had opened to rave reviews. Jagger was attracted to the style Wexler used, combining fictional and real events. Wexler wasn't happy with the conversation, or Jagger. In his mind, too much was undecided. Finally, Wexler said he couldn't make the time to do the project. He suggested the Stones call the Maysles Brothers, fellow documentarians. He also called the brothers in New York to let them know the Stones might be calling. The brothers didn't know who the Stones were, but they trusted Wexler. Jagger did call and invited the Maysles to his suite at the Plaza in New York and outlined his vision for a feature film, not a documentary; perhaps something close to what Wexler had done. Jagger wanted to do the same thing Woodstock was doing, but bigger and better. The next thing they knew, the brothers were filming the band at their Madison Square Garden show. They documented the trip from then on.

The Maysles Brothers were born in Boston and raised in Brookline, Massachusetts, to Jewish immigrant parents. They both studied psychology – Albert at Syracuse, David at Boston University. Albert became interested in film while researching and photographing a mental hospital in Russia. David's interest developed as a result of working in Hollywood as a production assistant.

Around 1960, the brothers joined Drew Associates, a documentary film company founded by photojournalist Robert Drew, which included Richard Leacock and D. A. Pennebaker. Albert ran camera, David ran sound. In 1962, they formed Maysles Films, Inc. *Salesman*, their film about door-to-door *Bible* salesmen, was well received by critics like Vincent Canby and Gene Siskel. The brothers called their documentary style "direct cinema," which was similar to cinema vérité. In the direct cinema approach, the filmmaker tried to capture reality and represent it truthfully. What they did wasn't propaganda, or educational films. Direct cinema developed due to an interest in making more realistic films and the ability to create those types of films thanks to lighter, more portable equipment, which could allow the documentarian to be more involved with their subject matter.

There was some history with the Stones and Filmways. And bad blood. Filmways owned Concerts Associates, the company that had produced the Los Angeles concerts. The company was not happy with the Stones because of the way they handled negotiations for the concert and the fact that they cancelled a planned third show, which likely would have sold out, too. Because Filmways was also in the film and TV business, and knew about the Woodstock concert film, they sensed an opportunity to recoup the money lost on the cancelled concert. They had the Stones boxed in. They thought.

Jagger refused to give Filmways the rights to the film. Filmways said find another site.

CHAPTER 69

Stories were swirling that people from across the country and around the world were pilgrimaging to San Francisco with flowers in their hair and dreams of seeing the Stones for free. It was a few days until showtime and the site was, again, still undecided. DJs kept urging listeners to go to Sears Point anyway. Everyone in the Stones, except for Jagger, knew nothing about what was happening because they were down at the Muscle Shoals Sound Studio in Sheffield, Alabama, recording new tracks for their next album. They planned to arrive in San Francisco on Friday night.

Sheffield had been the home to FAME studios, which recorded Arthur Alexander, Wilson Pickett, and Percy Sledge. In 1969, four of FAME's session musicians – keyboardist Barry Beckett, bassist David Hood, drummer Roger Hawkins, and guitarist Jimmy Johnson – left to open Muscle Shoals Sound. This group of musicians were known as the Swampers. It was Keith Richards' idea to record there. He liked to schedule a studio session while they were in the middle of touring and playing tight. They picked Muscle Shoals because of its reputation and all the famous talent who had recorded there. They wanted that swampy, bluesy sound for these tunes.

The first night, they tracked "You Gotta Move," a traditional spiritual number recorded in 1965 by bluesman Mississippi Fred McDowell. Richards figured because they were in Alabama, they needed to do some McDowell. Next, they laid down "Brown Sugar," which had the funky sound Muscle Shoals was known for. The last tune was an acoustic song called "Wild Horses." They cut three tracks in four days, which was prodigious for these Rolling Stones. The Maysles shot it all.

Neither the Stones, nor Filmways, was willing to budge on the film rights. The search was on once more for a back-up site in case a compromise couldn't be reached and everything fell apart. Jagger wanted to do the show. Badly. He said, "Well, man, we'll play in the streets if we have to." That's when Michael Lang showed up. He had helped organize Woodstock and thought he could be of some assistance, even though Woodstock had moved sites four times and ended up being a free concert when they couldn't control the crowds.

At the same time, Belli was frantically negotiating with Filmways, even floating the idea of seeking a restraining order, so the concert could go on, and working out a deal later. Filmways knew better. They weren't bargaining.

That's when Dick Carter called and offered the Altamont Speedway.

Belli contacted Scully and Lang and told them about Altamont. The two choppered out to the site in a KGO traffic copter. Lang said they could do it. Altamont was a "go." The word went out. They had thirty-six hours.

On Friday morning, at a press conference in his opulent office on Montgomery Street in San Francisco's financial district, now filled with radio and film crews and people associated with the Stones, Belli introduced a middle-aged man with a pencil-thin moustache. His name was Dick Carter. He had heard about the last-minute need for a venue and he had volunteered his, an automobile and motorcycle racetrack known as Altamont Speedway. "I want the publicity," Carter told Belli. Carter was there to sign contracts. After the meeting ended, the free concert picked up momentum. Like a runaway train. People did things and asked questions later.

Richard Roy "Dick" Carter was born in Richmond, California, and lived most of his life in the East Bay. He served in the U.S. Coast Guard Special Services in World War II and was a NASCAR driver. He had been hooked on racing from an early age. He raced for pink slips, rode in a motorcycle club called the Richmond Ramblers, and worked as a stunt driver in a carnival. He raced in as many races as he could each week. When he retired from racing, he opened a used car lot in Hayward, California. He had purchased the Speedway about a year before.

The logistics of mounting a concert were daunting, let alone one that was switching sites mere days before the show. Staging, transportation, parking, security, toilets, and medical aid were the tip of the iceberg of the technicalities that had to be ironed out. This show was more than a singer and an acoustic guitar. Painfully more. The burden to make sure the show went on fell on the shoulders of Chip Monck and his crew. They had less than two days to move the Stones' traveling stage, sound system, and lights from Sonoma to Altamont, which lay on the western rim of the great Central Valley. It would take everyone working triple shifts to get it done.

A steady stream of choppers ferried equipment from Sears Point to Altamont. Someone, maybe Monck, would later refer to the operation as a rock 'n' roll Dunkirk. Instead of boats ferrying soldiers to safety, it was a caravan of copters, trucks, vans, and VW buses convoying stage, lighting, and sound. Like Dunkirk, there was no turning back. It was move, or die.

One of the first things done at the new site was encircle it with a chain-link fence and set up entrances. Those entrances were locked, or guarded, and nobody, who wasn't involved with setup, was allowed in until 8 a.m., the morning of the concert.

Radio stations were spreading the word and asking for volunteers to help set up. Anybody who was into music was planning to be there. It was going to be a once-in-a-lifetime experience.

Early Friday morning, the latest update was broadcast on KFRC, which was the most popular AM rock station in the City. DJ Frank Terry said the concert was on and it was happening at Altamont. Performers would include the Stones, the Grateful Dead, Jefferson Airplane, Crosby, Stills, Nash & Young, and some bands to be named later. The call had gone out for quality sound systems. That's when I had checked in with Zeff to see if he was planning to attend. Roberto thought it would be cool to offer up his gear; all that boss sound gear we had listened to on New Year's Eve. After all, he had already done sound for several Bay Area bands, including Boz Scaggs and Joy of Cooking. He had driven over to Altamont on Thursday in his Mr. Natural truck. We had arranged to meet once we got there.

Roberto's Mr. Natural truck was unreal. It was a 1930s-era Dodge ton-and-a-half flatbed with wooden cabinets on the back once owned by Leonard Sharp, who ran a cabinet shop. On the doors, he'd painted a musical staff with key signatures and the phrase, "b Natural – c Sharp." Sharp had done some modifications that altered its look and operation. Robert and Hal Flesher dismantled the wood cabinets and mounted an enclosed cargo box, which Hal had found at a turkey ranch in Coulterville, where he had worked. The truck had problems. It listed to the right, the U-joints kept falling out, the left turn radius was limited to 20 degrees, and the gas tank could be filled one-third thanks to a hole above that level.

On one occasion I knew of, the truck had overheated on the Altamont on our way to a concert. We pulled off the road to the right as far as we could go. Because the truck already listed to the right, it was unnerving. Robert hopped on his dirt bike, which he kept in the back for such occasions, and zoomed off. Every time a big rig roared by, the Dodge would rock back and forth on its creaky springs and be blown closer to the edge. Hal and I calmed our nerves with wine and weed. Robert returned with enough water to get us to Livermore. When Robert did a show for Boz Scaggs in Petaluma, Scaggs wondered aloud to Robert about the truck's reliability when he saw the U-joint fall out. Robert carried spares of those, too. The show went on without a hitch. Even with its many issues, the truck got Robert where he needed to go.

Robert had asked Andy Maurer to paint something on both sides of the cargo box on the back. He chose enlarged copies of illustrations by R. Crumb that had appeared in *Zap Comix*, an underground comic book first published in San Francisco in early 1968. Inspired by Mr. Sharp's clever wordplay, on one side Andy painted Mr. Natural striding across Death Valley, while thinking about a roast turkey on a platter. On the other side, he painted one frame from the original "Keep On Truckin'" cartoon strip, depicting a number of men strutting across different landscapes that also first appeared in *Zap*. It showed two characters walking down the road with the caption, "I said keep on truckin'." Crumb's inspiration was a line from the Blind Boy Fuller song, "Truckin' My Blues Away." Crumb, the publishers, and supporters of the comic, had several run-ins with the law over its controversial material. All I knew was, the truck turned heads and made dogs and Englishmen go mad when it rolled by.

The Chronicle ran a front-page story announcing the free concert. In his column, Ralph Gleason ran the wrong site and performers again, likely because he hadn't gotten the latest news before his Thursday afternoon deadline.

All we knew was that it was a go and we were going. We had missed Woodstock East, but we weren't going to miss Woodstock West.

CHAPTER 70

Gary and I drove out Highway 132, connected to Highway 50, jumped off on Patterson Pass Road, turned on N. Midway Road, and approached Altamont from the south. We didn't stay on 50, which was a four-lane highway, because KFRC and KGO were reporting a massive traffic jam ten miles long caused by abandoned cars; a congestion that had been building as early as late Friday night. A new freeway was being built to replace 50. That partially completed roadway had become a parking lot. Even Midway, which was a two-lane road mostly used by the nearby farmers and ranchers, was backing up. People had left their cars and hoofed it toward the speedway, like they'd done at Woodstock several months earlier. We parked at the first open spot, grabbed our blankets, food, and drinks, and joined the odyssey of rock fans streaming toward that moment's Mecca.

Thousands of people had arrived Friday night, camping out to make sure they got prime seats. Even Keith Richards. When the Stones had toured the site earlier in the day, Keith wanted to hang. He, and some others involved with the tour, walked the site, followed by a gaggle of the Friday-nighters. They'd stop at a campfire, drink some wine, take a toke or snort, rap some, and move on. It was laid-back and mystical. It portended a momentous day.

It was a hazy Saturday morning. The threads of remaining tule fog mingled with smoke from fires lit the night before by the early arrivers. We walked across the golden hillside feeling connected. Like Bedouins crossing a vast stretch of desert. The dry pasture grass crackled under our feet. This was going to be awesome. Our very own California Woodstock. We could do it better than New York. We walked in with hope, heartened by a communal vision of the world. We could see it and feel it in our fellow travelers, as they streamed in along the roads and railroad tracks.

That righteous vibe would soon become a total downer.

As we crested a slight rise, we could see the massive crowd collected in the parched and arid field adjoining the raceway. It was a massive bowl of people, wriggling in a dull and lifeless landscape. No trees, no grass, no green. Aircraft cruised through the skies. They weren't butterflies. Tie-dyed pennants fluttered in the wind. Brightly colored God's eye staffs wafted in the breeze. People were strumming guitars and tossing footballs. On the edge of the raceway was a collection of wrecked cars from past races and destruction derbies, rusted carcasses filling a heavy metal graveyard. Spray-painted on the side of one old black Chrysler were the words: "Hi-Fi Room, San Mateo."

As we passed two spaced-out cadets, one said, "Man, the moon is in Scorpio. You know what that means?"

"No idea," his buddy replied. "I'm not into that Astrology shit."

"Heavy days, man. Heavy days. Evil and violence. Evil and violence."

"Keep your eyes open, brother," his companion answered. "Keep your eyes open."

"Right on. Right on."

At the bottom of the bowl squatted the stage. Speaker towers had been erected on either side. Some people danced, but most sat, some on blankets, lawn chairs, or the dirt. A few had dragged in old mattresses to lounge on. It was a motley collection of families, couples, singles, hippies, kids, druggies, dogs, losers, straights, and college kids like us. They were having picnics, smoking pot, drinking wine, and rapping. Some people stood on top of cars they had somehow driven close to the stage. Coffee can lids were being zipped through the air like Frisbees, the same as they had at Golden Gate Park last November.

There were many spaced out cats – street people who were totally burned out. We had to be careful not to step on them. Others weren't so courteous. There were some ugly people, inside and out. There was this one fat, naked guy dancing alone. Oblivious to everything. The name "Oscar" was tattooed on his arm. Some concertgoers had scraped together enough debris to start fires to ward off the chill in the air. There were long rows of green portable toilets resting on green wooden frames with lines in front almost as long. There were dealers hawking grass, mescaline, and acid like they did every night outside Winterland and the Fillmore. Everyone was chilling out, waiting for the show to start. There was no joy here. No Aquarian optimism.

I noticed a number of men and a couple ladies with hand-held film cameras, capturing reality at 24 frames per second. We heard later that one, or two, had mistakenly ingested acid-laced drinks. That must've altered their point of view.

We connected with a few people from Modesto. Tom Myers, Doug Taylor, Dave Dolan, Don Bean, and Sonny Irwin, a kid I had played with on our Babe Ruth baseball team. And Dave Wherry, a Mud Bowl alum. They were sitting at various points along a hill, above and rimming the bowl, not far from where the action was.

Wherry bitched that he was sore from the Mud Bowl and was bummed he had missed the poker game and the opportunity to take my money. I commiserated with his soreness, but not his absence at poker. He related an incident he saw that was typical of the day. He said they wanted to be closer to the stage. They carved out a spot next to some jocks, who were drinking Red Mountain. With a little help from Wherry and friends, they finished the gallon jug. One of the dudes had to pee, so he moved off to the side, peed in the bottle, capped it, and set it down. At one point before the show began, someone on stage asked everyone to move back to ease the pressure on the stage, so this mass of people moved back. When Wherry inched forward again, he noticed that the cap was off the bottle and it was empty.

Another story sweeping through the crowd also heralded how the day might shake out. As Jagger exited the first helicopter that landed, some punk ran up to him, yelled, "I hate you," and punched him in the mouth. Someone grabbed the kid and Mick, fat lips growing fatter, screamed, "Don't hurt him." Someone hustled the kid off and Jagger continued on his way.

One more report making the rounds relayed that when the KSFO traffic helicopter pilot, who flew the band in, was told to stay, he said he couldn't. He had work to do for the station. About that time, one of the enforcers the Stones had hired for security, who was ex-FBI, sauntered up, pulled a gun, and said, "You'll stay." He did. Wild tales like that were flying all over the place.

CHAPTER 71

I went to find Roberto. I was thinking he'd probably parked his van somewhere near the stage.

Not too far down the hill from where we were sitting, I approached a guy filming a rusted-out '57 Chevy. The 16mm camera whirred. He was wearing a flannel shirt, Levi's, white tennis shoes, and a khaki hat with a yellow stripe down the middle. He lowered the camera and removed the hat. I recognized the familiar profile.

"Hey, dude," I said. It took him a minute to recognize me. I had changed from the evening when he picked up a thirteen-year-old hitchhiker and drove him to Disneyland in 1962. George Lucas looked the same. Except for the thick, black glasses and dark beard.

"Modesto?" he asked. I nodded. "On a quest to find Mickey Mantle."

"Bingo," I said.

"Mikey, right?"

"Right."

"Wow, that was a long time ago."

"It was."

"It really was," he echoed.

"What's new?" I asked.

"I got into film school."

"Which one?"

"USC."

"The one you wanted."

"Amazed even me."

"Your dad must be happy about that."

"I think he is. It's a prestigious school."

"Have you done anything I've seen?"

"Depends."

"On what?"

"Do you watch many student films, or documentaries?"

"I've seen a few."

"That's mostly what I've done. Some stuff on cars. Shot a few 'behind-the-scenes' docs on film sets."

"Which ones?"

"*Mackenna's Gold, Finian's Rainbow*, and *The Rain People*."

"I've heard of those."

"Ever heard of Francis Coppola?"

"Not really."

"He directed the last two."

"Busy guy."

"*The Rain People* was a 'seat-of-the-pants' film. No schedule. No studio. No plan. We had a shooting script, but that was about it. Francis just winged it. He likes working that way."

"That can get you in some trouble."

"He could talk his way out of anything. I was his third assistant director and 'go-fer.' I shot what was happening. I had a portable 16mm camera and a Nagra recorder. I was a 'one-man-band.'"

"Easy to do these days with cameras like that." I pointed at his camera. It was an Arriflex.

"I just finished a documentary about him and that film. Called *filmmaker: a diary by George Lucas*."

"Cool. An actual credit."

"Yeah, pretty boss. Oh, and we started a company."

"I recall you said you didn't think you wanted to do that."

"Francis can be convincing. He's like a big brother. Easy to follow."

"What's it called?"

"American Zoetrope. I wanted to name it Transamerican Sprocket Works."

"Both interesting names. What's a Zoetrope anyway?"

"It means 'life movement.' It's an optical toy. It has a spinning cylinder outside and a series of still images on the inside. As it spins, it gives the illusion of movement."

"Like animation?"

"Exactly. We wanted to create a place where we could make independent films outside the studio system. More like a guild of filmmakers, rather than a factory. Francis wants it to be like the Beatles' Apple Corps."

"Like a film school."

"We all missed that. The freedom, you know. We invited film school buddies and a few locals from San Francisco. It was Francis and his Merry Men."

"Where in San Francisco?"

"827 Folsom. What people called the 'warehouse and wino' district."

"Nice neighborhood," I smirked.

"A little seedy. I wanted another LA guy to join us, but Francis wasn't sure he was a good match for our little band."

"Have I heard of him?"

"Name's Spielberg. Steven Spielberg."

"Don't recognize the name. He done anything?"

"No, just a short, called *Amblin'*. I think he may have recently finished an episode for *Night Gallery*. You know, the new Rod Serling TV show."

"If he gets big enough, maybe they'll let him into the club."

"I hope so. I didn't realize it, but despite what he says, Francis wants to build a studio. I want a nice, small house. Or, a barn like John Korty has in Stinson Beach. Someplace small and quiet."

"It could still happen, right? He'll figure it out. So will you. Stick to your guns. Maybe you're more stubborn than he is."

"The first day we were at the Folsom Street building, we all went up on the roof with cameras and props, in costumes, and took a picture. It was neat."

"Like a class picture."

"The Grand Opening is next week. If you're in town, stop by."

"I don't know. I'll be back at school. Might be tough. 'Sides, I don't have an invitation, or anything."

"He's inviting everybody. One more person won't break the bank."

"We'll see."

"Francis made me vice-president of the company," he continued.

"Bet that made your dad proud."

"If we succeed."

"It's a terrific idea."

"But scary. My first feature film is going to be Zoetrope's first film."

"That is scary."

"The fact that this skinny kid with no track record is receiving almost a million dollars to make a film definitely got Mom and Dad's attention."

"I should say so."

"But, it's a lot of pressure."

"That's a lot of money."

"The budget was actually $777,777.00. That's what Francis told Warners it would cost. Seven is his lucky number. He was born on April 7."

"Where's the money coming from?"

"Francis promised Warners seven films. All less than a million to make. He has one called *The Conversation*, about a professional eavesdropper. He even sold the story John Milius and I have been kicking around about Vietnam."

"Timely subject."

"It was a concept. He shouldn't have sold it."

"Sounds like a good salesman."

"He is that. We described it as Stanley Kubrick's *Dr. Strangelove* meets Joseph Conrad's *Heart of Darkness*. A black comedy. It's called *The Psychedelic Soldier*."

"Great title."

"Our inspiration for all this was *Easy Rider*."

"Cool movie."

"When we saw it at a premiere last July, it made us realize films could be made anywhere. And they could make money. We all have that movie to thank. And blame."

"Why's that?"

"It opened a number of doors. And raised expectations."

"Yeah, but they gave you money to do what you want to do."

"Francis has signed on to do a film based on Mario Puzo's book, *The Godfather*."

"I read that one. It's a big book. Decent story."

"It's going to be a whale of a movie."

"You going to work on it?"

"No, I'm working on projects of my own."

"Like what?"

"One is an idea Francis got me thinking about. He told me to write something out of my own life. Something with 'warmth and humor' that people can relate to. I had already been thinking about something like that. Kind of a rock 'n' roll musical about growing up in the Fifties. About music and deejays and cruising. You know, the mechanized mobile mating ritual. I'm thinking of calling it *Another Quiet Night in Modesto*."

"Our hometown."

"Always will be."

"I did a little cruising last June when I was home for the summer."

"It's changed. It's not so innocent."

"It's better than nothing."

"Another story is something like a space opera. A throwback to TV serials like *Flash Gordon*."

"Got a name?"

"*Adventures of Luke Starkiller*."

"I dug those old serials. The acting and stories, sets and costumes, were so campy."

"That's what I loved about them."

"Working on anything now? Besides being out here in the middle of nowhere."

"The lucky $777,777 film. A feature-length film based on one of my student films."

"What are you calling it?"

"*THX 1138.*"

"Sounds even spacier than your other one."

"I call it 'documentary fantasy.' It's something different. Something abstract."

"Like *avant-garde*?"

"Sure. The style is 'immaculate reality.'"

"Never heard of that."

"I took it from Japanese director Akira Kurosawa."

"I know him."

"You do?"

"Hey, I get around. Sure, he did *The Hidden Fortress* and *Seven Samurai*. *The Magnificent Seven* was based on *Seven Samurai*."

"Wow, you do know your films. I'm impressed."

"His films played at the Strand while I was at JC. Plus, I love movies. Almost as much as music. Almost as much as you."

"We started shooting *THX* at the end of September in the Transbay Tube and tunnels of the Bay Area Rapid Transit system."

"That's the new SF subway system, right?"

"Yep."

"It finished?"

"Not yet. That's why we can get in there and get in cheap."

"Good for the budget."

"We shot it in Techniscope. Gave us a wide screen effect like Panavision without having to rent all the Panavision lenses and cameras."

"Expensive stuff, huh."

"It's not a real big budget, so we've had to do some serious improvising. We designed and shot it so it would be timeless. Nothing identifiable from a certain era. Past, present, or future."

"You sound pumped about it."

"I guess I am."

"What's it about?"

"The theme is the individual's loss of identity. Free will. It's about personal restraints. It's about being trapped in a cage with the door unlocked. It's about being afraid to open that door and go out."

"Timely themes."

"I think so."

"When's it going to be out?"

"We finished shooting a few weeks ago. November 21st to be exact. I wanted to be done before Thanksgiving."

"Home for the holidays."

"And turkey. I love turkey and all the trimmings."

"Me, too. Nothing better."

"We've been editing nonstop. Twenty-four seven. Walter Murch edits at night."

"Who's he exactly? I can't keep track of all your friends."

"He's a guy I went to school with. He's also part of Zoetrope."

"Another Merry Man."

"Lalo Schifrin did the music last October."

"Man, you got some heavyweights involved. He did *Mission: Impossible* and *Cool Hand Luke*, right? Impressive work."

"This scene is bumming me out," he said, gazing out over the scene.

"It's weird."

"It isn't Woodstock."

"Doesn't feel like it, does it? Some nasty *juju* floating around."

"And some bad drugs," he added.

"And some bad dudes. What's the deal with the Angels?"

"I don't know. Not people I want to hang out with."

I pointed at the camera. "I assume you're here for a reason. You working with the other camera people I've seen?" I asked.

He touched the huge lens on the front of the camera. "We used this monster to get the last shot for *THX*. When the protagonist emerges from the underground to see the rising sun."

"A brand-new day."

"A brighter day."

"How'd you get the gig?"

"I first heard about it from Haskell."

"So, you already knew him?"

"Yeah."

"How'd you connect with him?"

"I think I told you about Allen Grant on that long ride south in '62."

"You did. He was a buddy who had a racing team, or something."

"I used to help out on the pit crew and shoot some 8mm film with a camera my dad gave me. Haskell had his own racing team. Our paths crossed a few times. We talked cars and photography and film school. He knew some people at USC and said he'd put in a good word. I don't know if he helped get me in, 'cause I'd already been accepted, but knowing him sure didn't hurt."

"I'll bet."

"Anyway, Haskell was renting some office space at Zoetrope while he was helping some filmmakers do a project about this concert. Names are Albert and David Maysles."

"I heard of them, too. Do documentaries. I saw one, or two, of their films on campus."

"Haskell helped them get this gig. He told the Maysles about the Stones and how they wanted to do a documentary about their tour. They met with Mick Jagger and got the job."

"Funny how things somehow work out. It's a small world after all." He nodded at the reference to Disneyland, probably still his favorite place on the planet. Mine, too.

"They were looking for volunteers. Students, or free-lancers. They needed a bunch of shooters. They told Francis about it and he got busy recruiting. They had no money. All they could offer was film stock. Walter and I wanted to play around more with this lens, so we joined up. It's a one-thousand-millimeter lens."

"That sounds powerful."

"It is. And finicky. We packed our gear into a truck and came here on Friday. Spent the night on this hill. The lens can get crisp images from a mile away. So, they put us up here. We can get a full shot of the stage."

"Nice." He looked down at the stage and adjusted his glasses.

"I was sorry to hear about your dad," he said.

"That was rough."

"Sounded like a good man."

"He was the best."

"How's your mom doing?" he asked.

"She remarried."

"So you've got a stepfather now."

"He's a good guy, too. Not my dad, but he's okay."

"What about you?" he asked.

"What about me?"

"What are you up to?"

"I'm at UC Davis. First year. Did JC for two years, like you."

"Speaking of good schools."

"I like it. Close enough, but not too close, to home."

"What are you studying?"

"I've got a double major and a double minor. I'm studying English history and Russian history, English literature and Russian literature."

"Heavy load. Radical subjects."

"It is. And it is, but I've been able to handle it so far," I answered, thinking for a moment about what studying those subjects in this moment in time might appear like. No wonder the FBI had been bird-dogging me.

"What are you going to do with it?"

"I don't know. Teach, maybe. Someone mentioned the foreign service."

"You'd be working for the 'the man.'"

"I know how you feel about that. I remember that button you were wearing."

"'Question Authority.' Nothing's changed."

"You'll appreciate this. I've been working for instructional media."

"I kind of know what media is, but what's the instructional part?"

"Using television to teach."

"Educational films, like *Our Mr. Sun* and *Hemo the Magnificent*?"

"The same, but different."

"Good concept."

"I've learned how to run a studio camera. A bit about sound, lighting, and editing. I've even helped write a few things."

"Now that's scary. If you ask me, that's the toughest part. I wrote *THX*. With a bunch of help. It about killed me. Francis said I'd never be a good director until I'd written a screenplay. So, I did. Me, I'd rather shoot. Or edit. By myself. In a room with nobody around."

"I think writing's sort of easy."

"You're a storyteller," he commented.

"Like you."

"Well, it's been nice catching up, but I gotta go. Looks like things are heating up down there. Walter's waiting up the hill. He knows this lens better than I do."

"Be careful. It's nuts down there."

"I will."

"Carry on," I said.

CHAPTER 72

I continued my journey. As I walked beneath the light towers, I noticed the setup crew. They looked exhausted. With good reason. They had been up all night humping equipment from Sonoma to here. They were beyond tired. As I kept moving, I heard an eerie, electronic sound rolling across the hills. It was so weird even the weirds in the crowd took notice. I heard one Rapunzel redhead say, "That's a Moog synthesizer. Isn't it spacey?" I had read in *Rolling Stone* that the Moog had first been played at the Monterey Pop Festival in 1967. Steph had turned me onto it in the Browsing Room. He suggested I listen to a 1968 recording by Walter Carlos called *Switched-On Bach*. It had been a chart-topper that year. Unusual, but strangely captivating.

I passed the medical tents. People were lying in, and around them, with various injuries. Doctors were stitching up people and giving others meds to calm them. Nurses were bandaging people. Psychiatrists were trying to talk people down. It was obvious they didn't have enough people, facilities, or supplies to do their job. I had never been in one, but it resembled what I imagined a war zone would look like.

I pressed on. I noticed a small camper with some longhairs handing out *Rolling Stone* magazines. Jann Wenner, the co-founder and publisher, had sent a team to cover the show. They had done the same thing at Woodstock. They had been an underground rag when they published their first issue in 1967, but had now gone mainstream. I recognized *Rolling Stone* staff reviewer, Greil Marcus. He was moving down front to get a closer look. We walked together.

"Covering the concert for the magazine?" I asked.

"Wouldn't miss it," he replied.

"Me, either."

"My wife passed. She's pregnant."

"Congratulations."

"Thanks, man. When she heard the Angels were providing security, she decided to skip it."

"Can't blame her."

"No. There's crazy shit going down."

"I read your stuff about Woodstock. Nice work."

"Thanks."

"I didn't make it to New York, but from what I can see and hear, this ain't Woodstock."

"I'm afraid not."

"Can't wait to read the story about this one," I said.

"Me, either."

"Catch you later."

"Later," he said and pushed his way through the crowds.

I looped to the right side of the stage and around back. There was a quadrangle of dirt behind the stage, hemmed in and barricaded covered wagon-style by Hertz trucks and a chain-link fence. Trailers and tents had been set up backstage. One only for the Hells Angels.

I passed the trailer where the Stones were congregated. The eye of the hurricane. I knew that because the area around it was clotted with Angels, all wearing their colors. A stitched patch above their heart read, "Frisco." Spooky looking characters. A beautiful blonde lady came out for some air. I recognized her. It was Astrid Lundstrom, bassist Bill Wyman's Swedish girlfriend. She looked around and immediately ducked back inside.

The Angels had originally been contacted based on a recommendation from Jerry Garcia and the Dead's manager, Rock Scully. The Angels had a new peaceful reputation, largely thanks to their spending time at concerts in the Haight providing unofficial security. *Look* magazine had even hired famed fashion photographer Irving Penn to shoot photos of them and the San Francisco rock scene for their January 9th, 1968 issue. Scully said the Angels were "righteous dudes," who carried themselves with "honor and dignity." The Angels were guarding the Dead.

The Stones were fine with it, too, likely thinking these Angels were the same as the British Angels. who had provided security at the Hyde Park concert. Not even close. It showed how naïve everyone involved with the show was, and how badly they had underestimated how much the scene in America had changed since Woodstock. Pete Knell, vice-president of the San Francisco Chapter, who had been connected to Cutler by Rock Scully, told Cutler the Angels didn't do security. They weren't cops. But, like they had done at past free concerts for the Dead and the Airplane, they would kick back, have fun, keep people off the stage, and make sure nobody did anything stupid. They would be an "Honor Guard" and watchdogs like they had been at so many Bay Area free shows. When asked what they wanted to be paid, Pete said, "We like beer." Sam Cutler responded, "How about a hundred cases?" and the deal was done. At this moment, they were the rock barrier between the shore and the tide of people rolling downhill toward the stage.

The Angels had been streaming in throughout the morning. They took up positions on the stage and behind it. The San Francisco chapter had motored in on their own bus and now clustered on its roof, checking out the scene. They started partying early. And hard. The Angels were drinking beer and cheap wine. Others were dropping acid. I overheard a very young, very thin girl tell a friend that the Angels had been kicking the crap out of people and each other. When they weren't using their fists and feet, they used chains and leaded pool cues.

I found Roberto parked behind the stage, sitting in the front seat of his Mr. Natural truck, guarding his possessions. The passenger side door was locked when I yanked on it. Startled, Robert looked out and saw a familiar face. He unlocked the door.

"Roberto," I said. "How's it going?"

"Shitty," was the immediate reply.

"What's up?"

"There's no way I'm letting these assholes fuck up my stuff."

"It's not on the stage?"

"Hell no. It's in back."

"What happened?"

"I got here early. As I was driving back here, it was like I was looking at something out of a horror movie. All these tripped out zombies. I get backstage and there's nothin' but Angels. I couldn't find anybody in charge. So, I parked it and told anyone who asked that my speakers were on stage and I was waiting for the show to end."

"Don't blame you. That's expensive gear."

"They're my babies. I don't let anyone mess with my babies."

"You staying for the whole show?"

"Depends."

"On what?"

"How ugly the scene gets."

"Well, if you decide to leave, we're on the hill straight back from the stage between the two light towers. Stop by and have some wine."

"I don't drink."

"That's right. I forgot. Have a toke. Or an onion sandwich."

He smiled and said, "We'll see."

"Catch you back home."

"Damn right."

I jumped down from the truck and marveled again at the artwork.

CHAPTER 73

I walked around the other side of the stage, figuring I might see somebody I knew. I did.

It was Motown. The bad penny had turned up again. He was standing at the front edge of the stage. He was groovin', like he had at the Moratorium March and always had. The music hadn't started yet, but he was tripping on something. I got closer and, knowing better than to startle him, inched around to get into his peripheral vision. I had to move through, around, and over some bodies to get there. It took a moment, but he saw me. He did a double-take. He recognized me, but it was out of context. I pulled the chrome bolt from my pocket. He smiled and motioned me to come closer. I did.

"You still got it," he said.

"Yep. I brought it thinking I might see you."

"I'm here. Diggin' it."

"You helping out?"

"Totally. Keepin' the losers off the stage."

Now that I was closer to the stage, I couldn't believe how low it was. Maybe four feet, if that. The stage at Woodstock had been fifteen feet high with a fenced chasm between the stage and the crowd. Here, the only thing holding the crowd back was a piece of thin cord. *Pretty damned optimistic*, I thought.

"Everything good?" I asked.

"So far. Got some yahoos keep tryin' to jump on stage. I wish the bands would get their shit together. These people are losin' it."

"Things are intense," I said. "Watch your back."

"Here's the way I see it, my man. If you treat me right, I'll treat you better. If you treat me bad, I'll treat you worse."

"You might need this." I offered him the bolt. His face darkened.

"Don't disrespect me, man. It was a gift."

I tucked the bolt in my pocket. "Looks like they're close," I said, noticing roadies on stage tuning guitars. "We're up on the hill. I'm going back."

"I heard the owl call my name," he said. "Catch you on the flip side, brother." He faded into the crowd.

I had moved a yard, or so, away when I heard a commotion behind me. I turned back and the Angels were in the face of some strung out space cadet.

He was dancing, oblivious to what was looming right in front of him. An Angel popped him and he went down. When he tried to get up, a second Angel came after him with a bike chain. Motown stepped in. He whipped a pool cue out from behind his back and raised it over his head. We made eye contact. For a moment. He brought the stick down. I turned and hustled up the hill.

As I was working my way back, I saw and heard a pick-up truck rumbling toward me. People were shouting and diving out of the way. As it approached, I thought I heard, "CSNY coming through! CSNY coming through!" Sure enough, I could just make out Stephen Stills and David Crosby sitting on the front bumper. Hanging onto the passenger side door, his hair flying, was Neil Young. I had no idea who was driving, but it looked like Melvin Belli.

As they navigated by me, I held up a hand. Young glanced at me for a moment. It took a second, but he recognized me. Again, out of context. He raised his arm in question. I raised both my arms in response, indicating I didn't know any more than I had the last time I saw him in that diner in San Francisco.

He hopped off the running board and landed with a thud in front of me, looking all Neil the Loner in his flannel shirt and patched jeans.

"I heard you were going to be here," I said.

"Croz wanted to do it bad, so we're here."

"It ain't Woodstock," I said.

"I guess that's good and bad."

"Be careful," I cautioned. "There's weirdness everywhere."

"I can dig weird. I can't handle violent."

"That's here, too."

"I'm getting a sick feeling about this show."

"I'm feeling the same about this whole scene."

"You a dodger yet?" he asked.

Confused, I said, "I hate the Dodgers."

"No, I meant draft dodger, dude."

"Not yet."

"What number you get?"

"Twenty-four."

"Damn," he replied.

"Damn is right."

"What now?"

"Working on it."

"You going to be a Canadian like me?"

"Maybe."

"Sorry you got to deal with this shit," he said.

"Me, too."

"Better to burn out than fade away, right?"

"I'll let you know."

"You do that, brother. You do that."

"Have a good one."

"Go in peace," he said, and ambled down the hill, in the wake of the careening truck.

I arrived and sat next to our small band. We were far enough back to be out of the craziness, but close enough to see and hear most of what was happening. Gary brought some binoculars so we could view some things up close. It was time for another "junk food picnic." Not a vegetable to be seen. A repast for a king.

At various times during the morning, Sam Cutler had asked people to move back. Obedient children that most of them were, they dutifully packed their stuff and shuffled away. But, the area nearest the stage remained packed. He also pleaded with the people, who had climbed the scaffolding erected for the light towers, to get down. Unlike what Chip Monck had done at Woodstock, Cutler didn't make any personal announcements, or warn that bad drugs were going around, even though we'd heard some of the wine being passed out was spiked with acid. He later justified it saying he didn't want to lay any more bad trips on people. He thanked all the people who had made this miracle happen. He reminded everyone that despite all the challenges, they were ahead of schedule. The show was supposed to start at 1 p.m. and it was almost noon. With that, he said, "Let's have a party and let's have a good time. Ladies and gentlemen, we give you Santana."

The crowd jumped to its feet. It was showtime. At last. San Francisco's own Santana opened their set with "Savor." The drums and congas floated up the hill. The crowd was swaying in rhythm with the Afro-Latin beat. Maybe we were going to have our own Woodstock. The band was into their sixth song, "Soul Sacrifice," when something in the crowd forced them to stop.

The naked fat guy I had seen earlier, who was high and clueless, kept stepping on people. He was bouncing off people like a pinball. He made the nearly fatal mistake of coming too close to the Angels. They pummeled him until someone jumped off the stage and convinced them to stop. The fat guy wobbled to his feet and turned to leave. As he did, he punched an Angel and disappeared into the crowd. Pissed, the Angels thumped the guy who stopped the fight with pool cues. People flashed the peace sign and yelled, "Peace!" It didn't matter. As the band's set ended, a kid dashed across the stage chased by two Angels. They caught him and beat him in front of the band.

The California Aqueduct collected water from the Sierra Nevada snowmelt and carried it from the abundant and generous north to the parched and avaricious south. The aqueduct was built by Governor Edmund G. "Pat" Brown. Initiated in 1963, the 700-mile system of canals, tunnels, and pipelines originated in Contra Costa County before splitting into three branches. The Coastal Branch ended at Lake Cachuma in Santa Barbara County. The West Branch carried water to Castaic Lake in Los Angeles County. The East Branch spilled into Silverwood Lake in San Bernardino County. One section of the aqueduct ran near Altamont. A report was speeding through the crowd that a kid had jumped the cyclone fence, stripped down to his skivvies, slid into the freezing water, and drowned. They found him in a filter trap two hours later.

Drugs were being handed out freely and people were lapping them up, trusting whoever was playing Dr. Feelgood that they were safe. The Angels kept drinking, popping, and having a fantastic time. The crowd kept inching forward, pressing against each other and the stage.

Next up was the Jefferson Airplane. My favorite SF band. Terrific songs, singers, and musicians. *Surrealistic Pillow* was an incredible album. They had played Woodstock and about every other free and ticketed festival during the year. They were veterans of this scene. The past November, while the Stones were playing Madison Square Garden, the Airplane was playing Fillmore East. They had followed the Stones to Miami, also playing the Palm Beach Pop Festival.

Jagger wasn't happy that they were on the Altamont bill because they were popular locally and they had vastly outplayed the Stones in Miami. The Airplane had arrived from the East Coast late Friday night. When they took the stage, it was crowded. More crowded than it should have been. Cutler ordered anyone who wasn't supposed to be there, to clear the stage so the music could continue. A few civilians complied. The Angels didn't.

During "The Other Side of This Life," a psychedelic version of a classic Fred Neil song, lead singer Marty Balin got pissed at what was happening in front of the stage. He threw a tambourine at somebody. He jumped into the crowd to help a black dude, who was being thumped by the Angels. He said something he shouldn't have. An Angel wearing a dead coyote skin cold-cocked Balin. He went down. The band kept playing.

The crowd was stunned. Nobody hit rockers. They were royalty. They weren't to be touched. It seemed such a contradiction. I later learned the biker's name was "Animal." Balin came to, pissed and probably woozy.

Someone drug him back onto the stage and escorted him backstage. Sam Cutler talked Animal into going backstage and apologizing to Balin. When he did, Balin went nuts again and the guy knocked him out again. Balin made his way out front in time for the last song, which was "Volunteers," the title song from their new album. Everyone knew who was in charge now. It was the Angels' party and it was our turn to cry. It was their stage and nobody dared take it without some serious damage being done. The crowd looked on in dazed disbelief.

CHAPTER 74

Those sitting up the hill like us were puzzled by the constant interruptions, especially in the middle of songs. We thought it might be something to do with the sound, which wasn't all that good to begin with. As we'd learn, there were two concert experiences happening simultaneously. Those like us in the outer circle were kicked back and half listening to the music. We wanted to kick back and be a part of an historic happening. It was all mellow and cool. We partied on. Those down below in the inner circle were experiencing a personal nightmare, either because of bad drugs, bad vibes, or bad asses.

Next up was a new band made up of old hands. It was the first public appearance of the Flying Burrito Brothers, a goofy name for a talented band. Gram Parsons had assembled this group of accomplished musicians, which featured Chris Hillman of the Byrds and Bernie Leadon of Dillard & Clark. The front man for the band, Parsons wore a Nudie suit jacket with Thunderbirds and an Indian warrior.

Nudie Cohn was a Ukrainian Jew who became a professional tailor. Working out of his shop in North Hollywood, he designed wild rhinestone-covered suits, known as "Nudie Suits." His early clients were country-western stars like Tex Ritter, Hank Williams, and Porter Wagoner. As the suits gained popularity, celebrities like Elvis Presley began wearing his custom-made outfits. That's when Gram came calling. The Burritos wore Nudie suits on the cover of their first album. Parson's featured pills, poppies, marijuana leaves, naked women, and a huge cross.

The Burritos played country-rock, inspired by Parsons' work with the Byrds on *Sweetheart of the Rodeo*. They were on the bill because Parsons had been hanging out with Keith Richards after leaving the Byrds, having been part of the Stones' entourage from the moment their tour launched in Los Angeles.

Parsons was born Ingram Cecil Connor III in Winter Haven, Florida. He got into country music after meeting Merle Haggard during a short flirtation with Harvard. He founded the International Submarine Band in 1966 and released *Safe at Home* in 1968, after the band had broken up and its members gone their separate ways. He joined the Byrds that same year, after David Crosby and Michael Clarke quit, and worked on *Sweetheart of the Rodeo* with Chris Hillman and Roger McGuinn. Parsons left the Byrds in late 1968 and spent some time with Jagger and Richards. The following year, he returned to Los Angeles, tracked down Hillman, and formed the Burritos, releasing their debut album, *The Gilded Palace of Sin*. I owned *Sweetheart* and *Palace*. Country rock was becoming my music.

While many people considered country to be square, reactionary, and redneck, I thought it was darned good. It was the heartbeat of my hometown. I loved the tempo, the harmonies, and especially the pedal steel guitar. Country was big in the valley. We had been home to the Maddox Brothers and Rose and Chester Smith. My dad liked all music, but he seemed partial to the country music of Hank Williams and Eddy Arnold. That's what I grew up listening to. Paul enjoyed it, but not as much as Dad, or me. Even little brother Willy was into it thanks to a few early Beatles' tunes, some Dylan, *Sweetheart*, CSNY, and Poco.

The Burritos played a forty-five-minute set. They opened with a countrified version of Little Richard's "Lucille," followed with a cover of the Bee Gees' "To Love Somebody," then tore into Dave Dudley's "Six Days on the Road." Their laid-back, sweet, steel-guitar sound must have brought back pleasant memories of childhood, or a simpler time, because the crowd and the Angels all seemed to mellow out. Chris Hillman later said playing at the Monterey Pop Festival and Altamont was like playing in Heaven and Hell.

Up where we were, the sound was fuzzy and the view blurred. We were oblivious to what was happening below at the bottom of the bowl. What we heard sounded like it was coming out of a transistor radio, and what we saw looked like a squirming school of fish. Little did we know how hell-bent on crazy the crowd really was. It wasn't rational. Drugs, alcohol, paranoia, close quarters, panic, and violence were a lethal cocktail. Instead of hippies filled with peace and love, it was a bunch of assholes tripping on bad drugs, cheap wine, and dangerous attitudes.

Crosby, Stills, Nash & Young took the stage next. Crosby, an old friend of the Dead's Jerry Garcia, had been asked by Garcia to talk the rest of the band into participating. They agreed. Reluctantly. I peered at my new favorite band through the binocs. They looked scared shitless, like Stills had said at Woodstock. This time, it was real. Stills flinched every time there was a loud noise. They played a short set, likely because they wanted to get out of there as fast as they could. They opened with an acoustic song, Stills' "Black Queen."

Almost as quickly as they started playing, the Angels started fighting. "Please stop hurting each other," Crosby pleaded. Nobody listened. The band followed with "Pre-Road Downs" and "Long Time Gone." They closed with Neil Young's "Down By the River" and a guitar-driven jam. The moment they finished their set, Stills yelled at people to wrap. He picked up two guitars.

Crosby grabbed some. A woman, maybe Neil Young's wife, Susan, helped and everyone hustled toward a waiting chopper. They had a gig that night at UCLA and they were already gone. It was a far cry from the concert we'd seen last night. On Friday, they were filled with bravado and were bulletproof. On Saturday, they were no longer invincible. The spell of Brigadoon had been broken.

The parallels between Brigadoon and Altamont were eerie. The legend of Brigadoon was the story of a mythical village in the Scottish Highlands. The village became enchanted centuries before, remaining unchanged and invisible to the outside world, except for one special day every one hundred years, when it could be seen, and even visited, by outsiders. This magical day was spent in joy and celebration. Those who happened upon Brigadoon could remain in this beguiling place if they loved one another enough to give up the outside world. If anyone left the village during the special day, the miracle would be broken and it would be the end for them all. At Altamont, the enchanted miracle was being kicked in the teeth.

Concert security was a joke. Michael Lang had hired off-duty NYPD officers to patrol Woodstock. At Altamont, the only security, in addition to the Angels, was five plainclothes Alameda County Sheriff's deputies. They were so badly outmanned that they kept a low profile and their guns in their holsters.

The Dead had played Fillmore West the night before. They arrived during the Burritos set. They were scheduled to play after CSNY. They decided not to because things were officially out of hand. They were stunned to find the Angels had beaten up musicians. They weren't as surprised that they were out of control. It was a runaway train. Some of the Angels were grumbling that there were too many people and too many responsibilities. They'd been expected to do something they hadn't volunteered for and weren't equipped to execute. They thought they were there to drink beer and keep some hippies off the stage. What they were now expected to do had become a thankless and impossible task.

The Dead had another show that night at the Fillmore and, fearing for their safety, packed it in. The musicians who had lobbied to have a free concert, so the Stones could experience the best of the San Francisco music scene, were too scared to see it through to the end. They had opened Pandora's Box and didn't have guts enough to close it. At least the Stones stuck it out. By leaving early, the Dead might have been thinking the Stones could start earlier and bring this nightmare to an end. They were entitled to the benefit of the doubt. Unfortunately, that's not the way the Stones did things. The Angels had scared the Dead.

CSNY finished around four in the afternoon. With the Dead way gone, it was the Stones' turn. And our turn to wait, which the Stones liked their fans to do. They wanted everyone to want them. Badly. They wanted this to be more memorable than Woodstock. They had missed Woodstock and they were going to make up for it. They wanted to play under the cover of darkness. Silhouetted by the blazing lights. They wanted it all to go down in history. We were all here to bear witness. So we waited. And got more wasted and pissed.

CHAPTER 75

The sun went down. The day got colder. The wind kicked up. We bundled up as best we could. I stood and stamped my feet. I looked around. It was something out of a Salvador Dali painting or George Romero movie.

"I don't know how much longer I can wait," Gary said.

"Be patient," I counseled.

"I love music, but this is ridiculous," Gary continued. "That's why I love the Beatles. These guys are arrogant assholes."

"Beatles could be, too."

"Sometimes."

"Don't give up. This may be the one chance we get to see them."

"See is about all you can do 'cause you sure can't hear much," Gary groused.

"Let's give them more time. It won't be long," I said.

My last word was drowned by the deep-throated rumble of a posse of motorcycles. A pack of Angels roared over the hill, throttled back, and drove slowly to the front of the stage. The Oakland Hells Angels had arrived, led by chapter president Sonny Barger, who had been born in Modesto. They parked their hogs down front and added reinforcements to their biker brothers. They had been asked to do a job and they were going to finish it. One way, or the other.

It had been two hours from when CSNY had finished playing. The Stones were waiting, too. For bassist Bill Wyman. He had been shopping in the City and had finally arrived.

The Stones left their trailer and went into a small tent to tune their instruments and prepare for the show. Some kid was leaning against the tent. The next second he was flat on his face. Someone inside had hit him with something.

The stage was sagging from the weight of equipment and bodies. Angels were roaming from side to side, trying to keep people off the stage or from getting too close. It was growing dark, as the roadies set up. Spectators were leaning on the edge of the low stage, wedged between the monitor speakers – a tide of fans lapping at the feet of the musicians. Someone scattered rose petals across the stage. Flaming lights created a hypnotic backlight for the band, illuminating the youthful upturned faces of the crowd. Their bright eyes shined like wolves.

Cutler stepped to the microphone. He looked exhausted. He tiredly asked people to clear the stage so the Stones could start. Nobody listened. Until Sonny Barged stepped up and barked for everyone to move their asses off the stage, including Angels. Everyone moved their asses.

Backstage, the Angels cleared a path from the tent to the stage, ruthlessly parting the crowd. The Stones followed in their wake, walking through a gauntlet of bikers. Jagger led the way, signing a few draft cards as he went. On the front of his black shirt was the Greek letter omega, the last letter in the alphabet. A symbol for the Apocalypse. The end of days. Judgment Day.

Cutler, barely able to stand, in contrast to his usual hearty, overblown introduction of the band all tour long as the "World's Greatest Rock 'n' Roll Band," could only whisper, "The Rolling Stones."

The Stones took the stage. The crowd surged forward. It reminded me of the mob scene in Nathanial West's *Day of the Locust*: the crazed mob devouring its idols.

"Really great to see y'all here!" Mick shouted.

The Stones led off with "Jumpin' Jack Flash," followed by the Chuck Berry tune, "Carol." The monstrous backlights bathed the stage, so intense you could barely see. It brought back memories of a Who concert in Berkeley. The light was blinding and the band cripplingly loud.

The Stones kicked into "Sympathy for the Devil." As I listened to the lyrics, "Just as every cop is a criminal, And all the sinners saints," it occurred to me that every villain was a hero in his own mind. He was convinced that his view of the world was the right view; that what he did was for the benefit of everyone. I was sure the Stones felt that way, as did Motown. So did Reagan and Nixon. And any number of other people, famous and infamous, known and unknown. Their perception of reality had been warped by power and money and privilege. They were isolated in their delusion, perpetuated by everyone around them.

My thoughts were scattered when a fight broke out in front of the stage. Someone was messing with an Angel's bike and Barger was taking care of business. The band stopped. Richards kept playing, totally absorbed. Jagger finally stopped him and pleaded with the crowd, "Hey, people. Sisters, brothers and sisters! Brothers and sisters! C'mon now, just cool out a minute!" He continued, "Everyone just cool down. Is there anyone there who's hurt? Okay, I think we're cool, we can groove." They fired it up again. And rocked the place. The song ended. Finally. The Stones realized it wasn't their show anymore. "Something very funny happens when we start that number," Jagger said to no one and everyone.

The Stones shifted gears into a mellow version of Jimmy Reed's, "The Sun is Shining," to cool out the crowd. They played "Stray Cat Blues" and a cover of Robert Johnson's, "Love in Vain." Things seemed to move back into the Stones' sphere of influence. Momentarily.

We found out later, after Keith Richards said they weren't going to play if the Angels didn't cool it, Barger had stuck a pistol in his side and told him to start playing his guitar, or was a dead man. He didn't have to ask twice. Richards played like a madman.

People were packed so tight, there was no space between. Until a fight erupted. A small circle would widen and people would back over each other, like cascading dominoes. At the center would be several Angels hitting somebody with pool cues, or stomping them with their heavy boots. Each time, the Stones would stop. The scene resembled something from *The Lord of the Flies*. People feasting on each other. Or, *Huck Finn* on acid. The flip side of Aquarius.

The Stones jumped into "Under My Thumb" when a fight broke out near the stage to the band's left. Jagger pleaded with the crowd to sit down and be cool; to get it together. Nobody listened. The band looked lost. Swallowed up by the enormity of it all. They had never lost control like this. They re-started the song.

A whip-thin young black man in a lime-green suit and hat tried to climb up on a speaker box at the edge of the stage to the Stones' left to get a better view. An Angel standing next to the stage, playfully grabbed him by the ear and hair. Laughing, the Angel shook his head, a gentle warning. The young man pulled loose and gave the biker a cold, hard stare. The Angel grabbed the kid's arm, the gentleness a distant memory. The dude yanked his arm back, glaring at the Angel. The Angel popped him once, knocking him down. The guy jumped up and tried to escape, but several more Angels tackled him. He ran into the crowd, shoving and pushing and trying to get through to the scaffolding edging the stage. He stumbled, but remained upright. The crowd had him hemmed in. He pulled a gun from inside his coat with his left hand and held it up a moment, as if warning the Angels not to come closer.

"Don't shoot anyone," a female voice screamed. A big hole opened, people scrambling to get to safety. Some hit the dirt. Jagger stopped singing. The band kept playing. Then just Keith was playing. He stopped. All they could see was a hand filled with a big knife raised in the air and slicing down. The kid in the green suit went down and the man with the knife went down with him, stabbing again and again. An Angel pulled the gun from the dude's hand. The guy got up and stumbled a few steps before going down to his knees near the scaffolding on the side of the stage. Another Angel kicked him in the head, knocking him down. The guy rolled over and looked up at his attackers, wondering why they had done that.

"I wasn't going to shoot you," he said.

"Why did you have a gun?" one of them asked, before grabbing a garbage can lid and smashing the kid with it. More Angels jumped in, kicking the dude. They stopped and walked off. Somewhere in the dark, a hysterical woman was screaming, "Is he dead? Is he dead?"

The Stones played the final chords of the song and stood in shocked silence at what they'd witnessed. The show was dead in the water. The Stones were flipping out. They had seen the wounded man up close, when people in the crowd had lifted him onto the front of the stage, hoping he would be taken backstage to see a doctor. The Angels pushed the body into the crowd, until a doctor carried him away.

Like the pros they were, the Stones talked for a moment, regrouped, and played a song we hadn't heard before. Jagger told the crowd it was new. It was called, "Brown Sugar." They continued with one of their best live tunes, "Midnight Rambler," hoping to get the show back on the rails. It wasn't lost on me, and probably the rest of the crowd, that both were dark songs. They rolled into "Live with Me," which was off *Let It Bleed* and had been released the day before. A naked girl was dancing in front of the stage. When the song ended, she tried to climb over everyone in front of her to reach the stage. Several Angels tried to stop her, but she was determined to reach her goal. Barger strutted across the stage and kicked her square in the face, knocking her into the masses. The Stones rocked into "Gimme Shelter." They played like there was no tomorrow. I grimaced at the irony. Looking through Gary's binoculars, the band looked freaked out. Not from drugs, but fear. They had conjured up this devil and now he wanted what was due him. Murder had truly been just a shot away.

But, the Stones couldn't stop. They had more songs in the set list they were determined to play, regardless of what had happened; in spite of the fact they may have witnessed someone's death. They chugged through Chuck Berry's "Little Queenie," a staple of their early pub band days. Next, the instantly recognizable intro to "Satisfaction." There was no doubt these Limeys could play. It was almost like they had channeled their horror and fear into their music because that was the one safe haven left. They were their music.

Jagger tried to rally the crowd between each song, hoping to reach some level of normalcy in a day filled with lunacy. The band power-chorded their way into "Honky Tonk Women," a killer song that had been released as a single this past summer. It was a quintessential Stones song. Sassy and primal. The Stones could see the light at the end of the tunnel. They still weren't sure it wasn't a train. Jagger said, "good night," and they closed with "Street Fighting Man," a song off *Beggar's Banquet* and another bit of fearful irony. They were ready to get the hell out of Dodge. As the song thundered to a close, the Angels tossed long-stemmed roses into the crowd, camouflaging the band's panicked exit.

As soon as the music ended, the Stones sprinted backstage, through the cyclone fence, into waiting vehicles, and worked their way slowly through the murmuring crowd to a waiting KFRC copter. The nasty boys of rock didn't look so nasty. They looked like scared kids. Sam Cutler followed, with what looked like blood on his white sweater. There wasn't enough room for everybody who wanted to escape, but they piled in anyway. The copter tried to lift off, but couldn't, likely because there were too many people onboard. The engine revved higher and it almost got airborne. The engine revved higher yet and the bird lifted off and barely cleared the low-lying hills. A witness would later say it looked like the last chopper out of 'Nam.

CHAPTER 76

The crowd stumbled through the pitch-black night trying to reach civilization. Or, what was left of it. Some stayed behind, not ready to brave reality. Roadies remained to do what they do. Clean up. A few Angels partied on.

We plodded the many miles back to our car, hoping it was intact. As people streamed into the moonlit night, I passed George on the way out. He looked shaken.

"We finally got the camera to hold focus," he said. "We might have gotten one good shot."

"I hope they use it," I said, tired and bummed out.

"Me, too," he replied.

We got more of the story, while listening to KSAN on the way home, and on TV and in the papers over the next few days. Meredith Hunter was the young man the Angels had attacked. He was a black kid from Oakland. He had come to the concert with Patty Bredehoft, a seventeen-year-old white girl. He had told her he wanted his gun in case things got psycho, so he had gone to his car to retrieve his .22 caliber pistol and returned to the show. When the Stones started, he moved closer to the stage. When Hunter pulled the gun, an Angel named Alan Passaro saw it and pulled his knife. He stabbed Hunter in the neck and back. Multiple times. Hunter had been pronounced dead at 6:30 p.m., while waiting for an ambulance, after the pilot of an empty helicopter said the chopper was reserved for the Stones.

Back at their suite in the Huntington Hotel on Nob Hill in the City, the *Chronicle* called Jagger for a quote. He said, "I thought the scene in San Francisco was supposed to be so groovy. I don't know what happened. It was terrible. If Jesus had been there he would have been crucified."

I was done. With Altamont. With it all. It was a long, silent ride the rest of the way down into the valley.

That night, the Dead played their second show at the Fillmore. Hardly anybody showed because, like often seemed to happen, word had spread in no time on the informal grapevine about what had gone down at Altamont.

Nobody expected the Dead to play. Backstage, Bill Graham confronted Rock Scully and the Dead, telling them, in his colorful language, they had blown it. He called Scully a murderer, at which point Scully shoved him down the stairs of the dressing room. Violence begat violence.

CSNY had a gig at UCLA's Pauley Pavilion. Stills was so shaken by the day's events that he passed out at one point. The dark day kept getting darker.

"300,000 Say It With Music" was the headline the next day for the Sunday edition of the *San Francisco Examiner*. They got a bulk of it wrong. Their reporter, a veteran named Jim Wood, was there, but his deadline had forced him to miss most of what happened later. He made it sound like this Woodstock West was even bigger and better than the original.

Ralph Gleason called them out on it, even though he was partly responsible for the whole affair, thanks to having guilted the Stones into doing it with his comments about ticket prices. In his *Chronicle* column, he wrote: "Is this the new community? Is this what Woodstock promised? Gathered together *as* a tribe, what happened? Brutality, murder, despoliation, you name it. . . . The name of the game is money, power and ego, and the money is first and it brings power. The Stones didn't do it for free, they did it for money, only the tab was paid in a different way. Whoever goes to see that movie paid for the Altamont religious assembly."

The same day, DJ Stefan Ponek, who helped organize the event, hosted a special and a call-in show on KSAN, so people could tell their version of what had happened. Ponek had been there doing live updates. The live show was called, "Tower Records Presents a Saturday Afternoon at Altamont Speedway." It made the event sound like a concert at Stern Grove or Tanglewood. The original plan for the broadcast, and what Tower had agreed to, was a replay of the concert and Ponek's real-time stories. Unfortunately, reality took charge and people wanted to talk about what had happened, not what Ponek or the media had reported, which was decidedly different. Ironically, an ad at the top of the show reminded people that the Stones' new album, *Let It Bleed*, was on sale at Tower for $2.77.

I listened from my bedroom. I heard as many opinions about what had happened and why, as there were spectators who participated. It was almost as chaotic as the concert. Pete Knell of the SF Angels called. He explained how they had gotten involved and that they were there to protect the Stones and their gear. Frisco Pete added, "Now if these people asked us to do this thing, we did it. What are we supposed to do? We ain't cops. We're not into that thing. We decide to do somethin', it's done, no matter how far we have to go to do it."

Ponek was able to reach Sam Cutler by phone. Cutler didn't blame the

Angels for the violence, saying, "they tried to help in their own way." He also asked for volunteers to help remove the tons of garbage left behind. Another caller was Sonny Barger. He said the fans were out of sight. That the Angels did what they were asked to do. He added that Cutler and the Stones had given them an impossible job to do. "Mick Jagger used us for dupes, man." He explained the heart of the matter for him and his fellow Angels. He pointed out that way too many people were out of it. They were messing with the Angels' bikes, thinking they could get away with it because there were so many people around. "I just went there to sit on the front of the stage and drink beer and have a good time, like we was told," Barger told Ponek. "But when they started kickin' our bikes, man, that started it. I ain't no peace creep, man, but if a cat don't wanna fight me, I wanna be his friend." Barger made it clear you didn't mess with an Angels' bike and, if you did, you paid the price. If you got into it with a brother, you started into it with all the brothers, and there were consequences. It was that simple, that cut and dried. Promoter Bill Graham also chimed in. Ponek closed the show saying there were no conclusions to be drawn and it was "a very weird experience." No shit, Sherlock.

When asked later if he thought Altamont was the end of the Sixties, guitarist Mick Taylor responded, "Well it was the end of the sixties [sic], wasn't it? It was December 1969." He was chronologically and metaphorically correct. He added, "I really don't know what caused it but it just depressed me because it could have been so beautiful that day."

When he was interviewed five days later, Ralph J. Gleason said, "we're a violent society – the violence is part of everything." He continued, "A poet that I know said that violence occurred every time there was a violent song. If these people are going to sing about violence, then they've got to handle and understand and expect violence." He called Altamont, "a controlled riot." He finished by saying, "God is dead. There's nothing to believe in any more [sic]." It was sad to hear because he was the harbinger of it all.

Most of the news stories that came out in the papers, like the *San Francisco Examiner* and the *New York Times*, or on radio stations like KFRC, didn't get it right. They hadn't seen the same concert most of us had. The only one that did was the one I relied on for my news; the only one that promised, "All the News That Fits." That was *Rolling Stone*. It would take several weeks for the journal to sort through it all – personal accounts, newspaper articles, radio and TV broadcasts, eyewitness accounts, participant interviews. The finished article wouldn't come out until January 21st, 1970, and it would be entitled, "Stones Disaster at Altamont: Let It Bleed." For this story, they could have easily changed their tag line to, "All the News That's Fit." Their version was substantially different from what had already been published, or broadcast. Their conclusion: "Altamont was the product of diabolical egotism, hype, ineptitude, money manipulation, and, at base, a fundamental lack of concern for humanity."

Meanwhile, deep in the labyrinth of the Ed Sullivan Theater building at 1697 Broadway in Manhattan, the Maysles brothers and their editors were piecing together their version of the story. David Maysles had told the crew on the day of the shoot, "We only want beautiful things." The violence and the death of Meredith Hunter turned a concert film, which would have given those who couldn't attend a glimpse into the world of the Stones and the biggest tour in decades, into a completely different experience. It was now the story of good intentions gone bad; of hope and optimism crushed under the weight of arrogance, celebrity, and avarice. It would be a tough story to tell. And sell.

Jagger wanted it done now, so his film could beat the Woodstock film to the market.

There was plenty of guilt to go around. The Stones had been cocky and irresponsible. They let too many of the wrong people make important decisions. The smart asses weren't so smart; the tough guys weren't so tough; the bad boys weren't so bad. The Dead and their people were too optimistic, and gullible, in pushing to use the Angels. Then they hit the silk when things fell apart. The Angels did what they were hired to do. With a vengeance. They did what they do and nobody should have been surprised. The authorities were neglectful. How could they, in good conscience, abdicate their responsibilities for security and public safety to the Angels? The crowd was selfish, which was also no surprise, and too stoned to behave the way civilized people should behave. We were watching out for ourselves, as we Baby Boomers had always done. "I got mine. The rest of you are on your own." Anonymity reigned supreme. People faded in and out of each other.

Ultimately, Meredith Hunter and the concert at Altamont were killed by the weight of expectations – expectations that peace and love and music would win over humanity's most base instincts and behaviors: hate, mistrust, violence, and selfishness. The seven deadly sins had been resurrected and triumphed over the seven cardinal virtues. Pride, greed, lust, envy, gluttony, wrath, and sloth had vanquished prudence, justice, temperance, courage, faith, hope, and charity. As someone said, or wrote, tongue firmly planted in their cheek, Altamont had failed the acid test. *Rolling Stone* reported that, early in the planning stages, one of the staff of the Grateful Dead had pinned a poster to a bulletin board in their Marin County offices which read: "First Annual Charlie Manson Death Festival." Woodstock could have been Altamont, but it dodged the bullet, only by the luck of the draw and being slightly better organized. Altamont made us realize we weren't bulletproof. The dark side had won.

The music had been amazing, even anthematic. People had been energized and had gotten involved. There was a chance we might end the war. We were influencing politicians and political decisions and presidential campaigns. It appeared we were going to be able to make a difference. In the world. Then Altamont happened. Four people had been born. Four people had died. Hundreds were injured. Property was damaged or stolen. All the good intentions, now suddenly gone bad, had been focused in on one spot. The barren landscape of Altamont, California. We realized we couldn't make any difference. We couldn't change people's hearts and minds. We couldn't wish away the violence and darkness.

Our dreams had been too big. Our naïve idealism too powerless. That was truly the day the music died – the day the myth of the counterculture died. As did our hope. We were no better than our parents. The parents we thought we were better and wiser than. The parents who, as Ginsberg had written in *Howl*, had destroyed the best minds of its generation with madness. Instead, a new and frightened world had been born.

CHAPTER 77

The Sunday after the concert was a rough one. Almost as brutal as the concert itself. We had to get back to Davis because I had tickets for a poetry reading by a Central Valley poet named Brother Antonius. He was appearing at 194 Chem at 3 p.m. It was a packed house, likely because the Brother was a well-known and vocal conscientious objector. That's one of the reasons I was there, plus the fact that he was a valley boy.

I had read the Brother's poetry in Gary Phillips' English class at Modesto Junior College. One of my favorite poems of his then, and now, was about the valley. It was entitled "San Joaquin."

This valley after the storms can be beautiful beyond the telling,
Though our city-folk scorn it, cursing heat in the summer and drabness
  in winter,
And flee it – Yosemite and the sea.
They seek splendor, who would touch them must stun them;
The nerve that is dying needs thunder to rouse it.

I in the vineyard, in green-time and dead-time, come to it dearly,
And take nature neither freaked nor amazing,
But the secret shining, the soft indeterminate wonder.
I watch it morning and noon, the unutterable sundowns;
And love as the leaf does the bough.

Another Central Valley patriot, Brother Antonius loved this valley. It was his touchstone, not a flat spot on the map you viewed in the rear-view mirror, while on your way to someplace else. Many of us had lost our connection with it – with what made us who we were. In all its kaleidoscopic glory. The familiar sight of the sun low on the flat horizon. The soft sound of rustling grape vines. The cool touch of flowing rivers. The sweet taste of a fresh peach. The memory-etching smell of irrigated soil. Here in this part of the planet, we were all linked by the land and this place we called home. The valley was, and has remained, my tap root. From it, I drew sustenance and inspiration.

Brother Antonius was born William Oliver Everson in Sacramento. He was raised on a farm outside the small town of Selma, California. He was a literary critic, a social activist, teacher, Dominican brother, and small press printer. His poetry focused on themes of nature, eroticism, and religion. He published thirty-seven books of poetry and five prose collections. He was a Guggenheim fellow and a Pulitzer Prize nominee. Everson was an early disciple of Robinson Jeffers, another well-known California poet. Like Jeffers, Brother Antonius was obsessed with the notion of mankind tormented by the evil residing in itself. His poetry combined his Christian faith with his love of the native beauty of the American West.

In 1940, Everson registered as an anarchist and a pacifist with his draft board. In 1943, he was registered as a conscientious objector and sent to a Civilian Public Service (CPS) work camp in Waldport, Oregon. He spent three and a half years there, where he learned the craft of fine printing. Of his time there, he wrote that his stand was "so personal and so drastic as to be unintelligible to all but the handful of us, and our supporters, who found ourselves in the isolation camps and the penitentiaries of the government." After his release, he settled in the Bay Area and became identified with a group associated with poet Kenneth Rexroth.

He became nationally recognized in 1948 with the publication of The Residual Years. In 1951, he converted to Catholicism. He took the name Brother Antonius, when he joined the Dominican Order as a lay brother in Oakland in 1951. By definition, a "lay brother" was a "man who has taken the vows of a religious order, but is not ordained or obliged to take part in the full cycle of liturgy and is employed in ancillary or manual work." His poetry reflected his personal struggles and his counterculture world. As a poet of the Beat Movement and the San Francisco Renaissance, he immediately became known as the "Beat Friar."

His presentation at Davis that night, which was entitled "The Savagery of Love," had been well-publicized. The Brother was known for his dramatic readings, so the auditorium was packed with students, locals, and out-of-town fans. The room was buzzing with an electric tension. People seemed to sense that something momentous was about to happen. I had gotten there early, so I had a front row seat on the aisle close to the door used by professors and lecturers to enter and exit. The Brother entered. There was a long pause. He paced, stopped, stared at us sitting there, waiting. He read the prologue to a new poem he called, "Tendril in the Mesh."

Persephone smiles,
The pomegranate seed in her pouch, her jewel of rape, and the stain
Of his lust on her lip. She measures his term. Cringing,
He sleeps on unappeased, in the hush of the solemnly slain . . .
Oh my God the terrible torch of her power!

"Thus far," he said, "I've been talking about Plato and Persephone, but I can no longer do that. I was writing about myself, and when this reading is over I am going to remove my habit and leave the Dominican order to marry."

The stunned silence was deafening. He pierced it with the next lines of the poem.

In the glimmer of night a wedge of fern configures her croft.
Maidenhair snuggles the cleft. Its shadow conceals and defines.
When I dip my lips to drink of that spring I throat the torrent of life . . .
I have fastened my heart on the stitch of your voice.

He paused between parts of the poem and spoke of his life. Of being a Dominican. Of the reasons for leaving the Order. The soliloquy of his life was truly Shakespearean. He concluded by reading the poem's epilogue.

Call to me Christ, sound in my twittering blood,
Nor suffer me to scamp what I should know
Of the being's unsubduable will to grow.
Do thou invest the passion in the flood
And keep inviolate what thou created good!

Finishing, he carefully removed the black and white Dominican robes he had worn for so long and said, "This is my habit, and when I take it off, I take off my own skin. But I have to take it off to find my heart."

As he strode past me in his street clothes, a transfigured man, I caught his eye. There was a brief moment of recognition. Two men on the verge of life-changing decisions – one made, one about to be made. He nodded, smiled, and swept out of the room, the thunderous standing ovation echoing behind him.

I sat there, exhausted by recent events, the excited crowd swirling around me. I thought, here was a man who moments before had given up his entire previous life for the love of a woman; for something he truly and deeply believed. Here was a man who had cultivated peace, love, and non-violence. He had chosen to be a dove, not a hawk. Gandhi, not Hitler. He had made a stand. It was humbling. And inspiring.

The next day, when class was over, I returned to Altamont. I was curious what it looked like without the people and the bizarrity. I wanted one last look before I wrote my own epitaph. It was overcast and felt like rain. The parched hills would welcome it. The auto carcasses loomed like industrial Stonehenges. The flotsam and jetsam of the concert clogged the landscape. I picked up a plastic coffee can lid and spun it through the air. I stopped at the top of the hill where we had sat and surveyed the bowl below. It was an eerie sight. I pictured it full of people and music. I tramped slowly toward where the stage had been. I passed the rusted-out Chevy where I'd encountered George. It was no joke. I felt like a dream-walker. I continued past where the medical tents had been located. I paused near the spot where Meredith Hunter went down below the speaker towers and the Angels' knife.

A chill ran through me. I moved to my left and stood in front of where the stage would have been, its outline still visible. I could hear the Angels' choppers roaring and the Stones' music soaring. I circled behind, reimagining where the chain-link enclosure would have been, as well as the tent where the band tuned and the trailer where they waited and made us wait. I continued around where Roberto had parked in Mr. Natural. I gazed back toward our perch. Fools on the hill. It was a grim ride back to Davis.

It got worse. The letter from the draft board was waiting. I was to appear in Fresno for my induction physical on Thursday, December 18th. Secretary of Defense Laird had gotten his way. It was sooner rather than later. Gary and Gover had gotten theirs, too. The boat was sinking fast.

That week, I learned a performer I enjoyed had been humbled. Bob Hope was an entertainer I admired. I had watched most of his movies, especially the *Road* pictures with Bing Crosby. I never missed his television specials, or the broadcasts of his golf tournament in Palm Springs. Although I didn't agree with his politics, I respected his dedication to our servicemen and his efforts to entertain them, which he had been doing from the time we entered World War II. His first trip to Vietnam took place in 1964. Traveling with him this year were Connie Stevens, The Golddiggers from *The Dean Martin Show*, and astronaut Neil Armstrong. Most of the audience loved seeing Bob and were thankful for his tour. But, this year, there were more peace signs and, for the first time ever, the crowd booed. Connie Stevens silenced them with a heart-wrenching rendition of "Silent Night." Things were definitely changing.

On Friday, an end of school concert was held at Freeborn Hall featuring The Kinks. Although they were a slightly less popular part of the British invasion, I had been a fan from the start. I knew their early songs, but appreciated them more when one of our local bands played their songs at the YMCA dances we attended in high school. The Ratz were a talented group of young musicians. The bass player was a kid named Rick Edmond, who was a classmate I had known starting in junior high. Danny Johnson, the keyboard player, was another Davis Spartan, who was a few years older than us. Pat Durr was the guitar player. He was a Modesto High kid and a few years younger. Ray Rector was the drummer and founder of the band. They all wore their hair long and dressed in Carnaby Street-style clothes. They had performed at several clubs in and around town, did shows in the Bay Area, and opened for touring acts when they came through town. They rocked.

Sooner than expected, the fall quarter and school year were over. Finals were upon us. It was time to hit Olsen Hall, pack my pockets with change for the bad coffee, and start going over the meticulous notes I had taken throughout the quarter.

As I always did, I scheduled my finals early in the week so I could start my Christmas vacation right away. My roomies did the same. I finished my last final Tuesday afternoon, December 16th. I felt good about them. I thought I had a shot at all As, but we would see what the professors thought.

CHAPTER 78

Gary and Gover followed Ugly Orange in the VW. Gary wanted to get home to La Grange, so he didn't stop. He dropped Gover and headed for the hills.

I pulled up in front of 1532 Del Vista right before dinner. I entered through the garage and dropped my bag of dirty clothes by the washer. I could hear a Bing Crosby Christmas song playing. I clomped inside. Mom was making my favorite dish, which was ground beef tacos. She stopped what she was doing and hugged me.

"Welcome home" was all she said and needed to say.

As I entered the dining room, I was immediately wrapped in the arms of my two little sisters, who had gotten out of school for the Christmas break the previous Friday. I pried myself loose and went to my old room. I dumped my backpack on the floor. Willy was sitting on the top bunk. His high school holiday break had also begun on Friday. KSAN was on the radio above the small desk tucked against the wall.

"Hey," he said.

"Hey," I said. "Good to be home."

"Cool."

"Where's Tim?"

"The usual place." He was at Laura's. They had wrapped up their finals at MJC the week before also. Everyone was on vacation, except Paul, who entered the dining room as I came out of the bedroom.

"Good to see you," he said, and extended his hand.

"You, too," I said and shook it.

"Good quarter?"

"I think so. I'll know better in a week. or so. when I get the postcards with my grades."

"You've always done well. I'm sure you have again."

"I hope."

"Any news on the other front?" I handed him the letter. Mom had joined us at this point, also curious. Paul handed it to her.

"It's a waiting game now," I continued

"Dinner's ready," Mom said.

We lined up in the crisp morning waiting to board the bus that would take us to the induction center in Fresno for our physical. Gary, Gover, Gant, and me trooped on together after showing our driver's license and draft card. I noticed a number of other high school classmates I hadn't seen in a while, ones I didn't hang out with. There were several others from Modesto and Downey High. I saw many pale, worried faces that morning.

Many slept on the bus ride down. Others stared out the window. More, like me, went over what they were going to say to convince the doctors they should be classified 4-F. I didn't have any obvious physical issues. One thing I had going was my missing spleen. I'd heard that was cause for disqualification, which was reinforced by the lyrics of the Phil Ochs' song, "Draft Dodger Rag."

Sarge, I'm only eighteen, I got a ruptured spleen
And I always carry a purse
I got eyes like a bat, and my feet are flat, and my asthma's getting worse
Yes, think of my career, my sweetheart dear, and my poor old invalid aunt
Besides, I ain't no fool, I'm a-goin' to school
And I'm working in a DEE-fense plant

I was also carrying a copy of the sealed letter from my dentist in Davis I'd gotten from my draft board. I'd asked him to write a letter about my dislocated jaw, which I had incurred during a rain-soaked intramural football game on the main I.M. field last October, while playing my first season with FYNC. I had gotten tangled up with a defender and fallen face-first. I felt something pop on the left side of my jaw. It hurt like hell, but I was too wrapped up in the game to sit out. I would learn later that the dentist believed in the war because he had written there was nothing wrong with me physically, but perhaps there was an issue mentally. Of course, I could've gotten out on a mental, if I was willing to pretend I was eating my feces.

There were three things the screeners looked at. Aptitude for military service, physical qualification, and background. To assess that, there would be a physical and mental evaluation.

We lined up single file, checked in, and trudged inside the induction center. It was desolate. Concrete walls, concrete floors, acoustic ceiling tile, and harsh fluorescent lighting. We sat in a holding area, while a sergeant named off names and we collected our paperwork.

Next, we went to the clothes changing room, which was a dreary locker room, not unlike the room at Playland pool in Modesto. We were told to strip to our T-shirts, underwear, and socks. It was Klondike cold. I guess they wanted us awake. We stored our belongings in a wire basket. I was feeling déjà vu-ish, except there were no Zero bars. We were given a bag to store our valuables and the key to the basket. After providing a urine sample, we were subjected to a chest X-ray.

Then it was the written test. Once we completed that, we lined up to be examined by a physician. We sat, listening to the physicals taking place in the next room, while waiting our turn. When our name was called, we entered the examination area. On either side of the main aisle, there were rows of cubicles separated by cloth curtained portable screens. There were colored striped lines on the gray linoleum floor leading to the various stations. We were told what line to follow, which would take us to each testing area.

Our blood pressure was checked. Mine was absolutely normal. Our reflexes and hearing were tested. We took a color blindness and eye test. I had to remove my glasses. I was hoping my vision was bad enough to disqualify me. I heard later that nearly everyone got the same score, no matter how blind you were. The same was true for the hearing test. Everyone passed, even one guy I knew, who had been deaf since birth. The game was obviously rigged. The next station was height and weight. A normal day at the meat market.

The last station was an interview with a physician. This was when you told your story and provided any supporting documentation. The key to success was rattling off as many maladies as you could before your time was up and he stamped your form.

My doctor was middle-aged and kindly looking. He didn't appear too bored. He was the guy I had to win over. I handed him my paperwork and told him about my spleen and jaw. As I talked, he glanced over the letter from the dentist. I knew the odds weren't in my favor. He didn't say anything, or give any indication one way or the other. No questions, no comments. He stamped my forms, handed them to me, kept the letter, and motioned for me to move on.

My fate had likely been decided.

Routed back to the changing room, we got dressed, picked up our X-rays, and had our forms signed before turning them in.

We were all given meal vouchers for the cafeteria. After a hasty lunch, we returned to the main room and took an intelligence test. Following that, we had to fill out and sign a loyalty oath. We returned to the main desk where the sergeant stamped our papers and told us to board the bus.

The ride home was much more animated. Guys recounted their experiences, a few of which were true, many of which were bravado. We all pondered our fate, knowing some would get out, others would have to go back for more tests, and still others would be taking the first step on a journey that might lead to death, or permanent disability. It was a day I wanted to put behind me.

I heard some wild stories from those who were there and supposedly witnessed it. One guy from Downey High, who we all knew was nuts, reportedly slathered his butt crack with peanut butter. When it came time for him to drop his skivvies, he reached back, scooped a handful of peanut butter, and ate it. Another guy, equally known for his craziness, hopped up on the exam table in one of the cubicles and popped his hemorrhoids. Someone else had heard that eating eggs could increase the levels of albumin in urine, which might exempt you. I knew one who ended up taking speed, hoping they could make that fly. Of course, all the docs had to do was look at their pinpoint pupils to know what they were up to. The docs had seen pretty much everything and were hip to most of the tricks.

The next day, I went Christmas shopping. It was the end of the quarter, so I was short on cash. I needed to be creative. I bought Tim *Ballad of Easy Rider* by The Byrds. For Willy, I found a cool greeting card of a blonde-haired mythological character, who looked like him, and framed it in a plain black frame. For Diane, I got a book on how to make western shirts and vests. For Cheryl, a songbook of Joni Mitchell songs because she wanted to sing and play guitar like her youngest older brother. For Mom, I framed a photo of the family that had been taken for a telephone company publication celebrating Valentine's Day. It showed Mom and Dad staring at the five of us kids, who had Valentines hidden behind our backs. I hoped it wouldn't offend Paul, but it was a gift I knew Mom would appreciate. Paul was difficult to buy for. He had recently taken up smoking a pipe, so I bought him tobacco from a local tobacconist.

Over the next few days, with everyone home for the holidays, I made the rounds around town. It was wonderful seeing the city decorated and people in the holiday spirit. Downtown Modesto had been undergoing redevelopment. It had looked bad for a while, but was now coming back, thanks to several new businesses. I caught up with Bob Buzbee at his mom and dad's place. He and his brothers were listening to *Let It Bleed*. I sat in for a few hands of poker with Decker and Gover at the smokehouse. Zeff was working on sound systems at his parents' house in Northgate. Chuck Horne was on leave and visiting his parents. I stopped to say hello to Nancy Ogden at her mother's house and dropped in on Linda Bacciarini at the apartment she was now living in on Needham and Magnolia. I tossed the football around with Si and Brad at Roosevelt. I visited Threlfall at neighbor Andy Maurer's house. I stopped by Bob Sims to listen to Willy's band practice.

The following Saturday was December 21st, the Winter Solstice. Once again, the sun stood still. The longest night and shortest day of the year. The sun lowest in the sky. A bleak midwinter's day. In the dark and cold, we sought warmth and solace in family and community. Feasts, festivals, and celebrations were held because it meant the return of the sun. The return of hope. It was a good day to reflect. A good day for optimism and resurrection, as the days grew longer.

I met Kelly in the basement of Sears, which had been sprinkled with Santa dust and magically transformed into Santa's Toyland. My family had been visiting that basement for as long as I could remember, hoping Santa would bring us one or two of the things on display. I had taken Kelly there our first Christmas together and it had become one of our holiday traditions. We wandered the aisles. We went for coffee at the Old Mill Café, which sat next to the railroad tracks on Ninth Street.

I sat facing her. She gazed into the darkness of her coffee. I touched her sleeve.

"To old times," I toasted.

"To now." As we nursed our coffees and waters, we danced around our futures. She was worried.

"That's a bad number," she said.

"Tim's is worse. Gary's isn't much better."

"What are you going to do?"

"I don't know yet."

"Do you have a choice?"

"A few."

"Canada?"

"Maybe."

"I wouldn't like that."

"Would you go?"

"If that were the only option."

"It might be."

"I love you, but I have a life here."

"We could make a life there."

"That blind optimism again."

"Like you've said before, that's why you love me."

"It might get you in trouble someday."

"It's guarded, not blind."

"What about the reserves?" she asked.

"It's not my first choice, but it's a choice. It's a long shot."

"What's your first choice?"

"That it will end. That the government will realize they can't win and stop the war."

"Even if it ended tomorrow, they'd need soldiers to finish things. You could be called up anyway."

"I'll do what I have to do," I said.

"I see."

"There are some things a man can't run away from," I said, repeating what Wally had said after watching *3 Godfathers*.

"Even if . . ."

"Even if." That possibility was heartbreaking.

"Let's wait and see," I said. "Roll the dice."

"Let the chips fall."

"Exactly."

"I wish it was more certain than that."

"Me, too."

"To innocence," she toasted.

"To time," I replied.

The weather during the week leading up to Christmas alternated between chilly rain and dreary fog. Of course, the fog made the Christmas lights shine in a brightly muted way. There were open houses and craft fairs selling hand-made and home-grown gifts. The annual Christmas parade wound through downtown and featured marching bands, children, city leaders, and civic groups. There was a production of *The Nutcracker* at one of our three high schools and *The Messiah* at one of our churches. I wasn't a skier, but I made time to run up the hill to the snowline at Twain Harte, which looked like a postcard, Alpine village this time of year. I paid my annual visit to see Santa at the North Pole in McHenry Village, where he was housed in a tiny red and white shed. A few times as an adult, I had stood in line so I could tell Santa what I wanted. In recent years, I had asked for peace and the end to the war. This year, I asked Santa to see what he could do about the draft.

Unfortunately, my Christmas wish didn't come true. Five days following my physical, I received the results in the mail. I had been reclassified 1-A. I was cannon fodder. Gary was 4-F. The doctors confirmed he had done damage to his cornea during a mud fight we'd had at Modesto Reservoir a couple summers before. He had been seeing double all this time. I felt terrible about giving him a hard time about it. His vision was bad enough to save his skin. Gover was classified 4-F thanks to his football injury.

It was promising to be a long, cold winter. And not a very holly, jolly Christmas.

Reality had come home. I had to get serious about what I needed to do.

CHAPTER 79

Christmas morning 1969 wasn't much different from any of the Christmases I had spent with my family. I wasn't complaining. Lots of gifts, lots of food, lots of music, lots of friends. Everything but Dad. Paul even dug up the old 8mm film camera and light bar Dad had used to capture Christmases past.

In the movie, *The Bishop's Wife*, there was a scene between the Professor and Julia inside Maggenti's Flower Shop. Wistful, the Professor said, "I like to have a Christmas tree because it reminds me of my childhood. I find, for some good reason, that this is a good time of year for looking backward. Can you imagine me ever having been a child?"

My mother was so much the child at Christmas that she had two trees. A living green tree in the family room and an artificial 1960s silver Alcoa in the living room. Each year, when Christmas was over, she asked Dad, and then Paul, to plant the green tree outside the family room window, so she could continue to enjoy it until it turned dead brown.

Like most families, our Christmases were a collection of rituals. As expected, Mom wanted to decorate seconds after the Thanksgiving pilgrims and turkeys were exiled. It began with Dad stringing the large, multi-colored bulbs around the house exterior. It wasn't precise, but it was festive. Next, he staked a flat plastic Santa in his sleigh and eight tiny reindeer on the front lawn. The Alcoa landed first, with the rotating color wheel and red bulbs. The nativity was next. The green tree was purchased, situated in the family room, and covered with Shiny Brite and home-made ornaments and tinsel. The front and family room windows were stenciled with snowmen, Santas, and snowflakes. Our matching Christmas stockings, and red plastic stockings filled with assorted candies, were hung on the fireplace mantle. The Christmas cards were clipped to a metal Christmas tree hung over the desk in the dining room.

Dad would bake his peanut butter, chocolate chip cookies and make his nutty fudge. Mom would purchase her favorite fruit-filled and ribboned hard candy, which inevitably ravaged someone's tooth. We'd write our letters to Santa, mark the gifts we wanted in the Sears and Penny's catalogues, and visit Santa's Toyland. When the Sears & Roebuck "Wish Book" arrived wrapped in brown paper, Cheryl would use a Bic pen to circle and circle the things she wanted until the circle was imprinted on the following pages. It didn't matter. Mom bought us almost everything we asked for.

Then the Santa games would begin. As the oldest, I became the first non-believer. Tim and I would look for the gifts our parents had squirreled away. In closets, in drawers, in the garage. We'd try not to leak the deflating truth to our younger sibs. They religiously continued to put out milk and cookies for Santa and Santa ate them. On Christmas morning, for some reason, Dad couldn't look another cookie in the eye. Cheryl remembered Laura's dad, Marco, playing pinochle on Christmas Eve with Mom and Dad and threatening to start a fire. Cheryl was on the verge of realizing that Santa was a myth, but she made sure there was no fire that night before she went to bed to dream of sugar plums.

My father would have to assemble something each year. The directions were horrible, generally written by someone in Taiwan, or the Philippines, and the toddy for the body didn't help. From bicycles to cardboard kitchens, he put them together on countless Christmas Eves. If needed, I helped. I passed the task to Paul, with assistance from Tim and Willy.

One Christmas, after rousting Tim out of bed, we scurried down the hallway and peeked through the hallway door into the kitchen, where my dad was busy wrapping gifts on the gray Formica table in our small kitchen. Another year, he tried unsuccessfully to wrap our oddly-shaped football helmets. None of us could forget waiting in breathless anticipation when Mom made us stay in our rooms, so the parents could get their coffee, have a cigarette, and make sure everything was lovingly set up before we could burst into the wonderland of gifts. Only to be blinded by four white-hot lights.

Dad had bought an 8MM camera with a light bar to capture the times of our life. The lights were so bright, every movie he shot featured people squinting in pain, their hands covering their faces. His coverage was almost the same each Christmas. Up the tree and down the tree. Shots of presents piled under both trees. Close-ups of sleeping animals and passed-out humans. One year, somehow, my father double-exposed the film. He must have forgotten he had already recorded Christmas when he shot the family vacation to SeaWorld. After the film was developed, it featured dolphins and orcas dancing through the Alcoa.

Christmas was all about the music. I could never get enough of Bing singing "White Christmas," Brenda Lee's "Rockin' Around the Christmas Tree," "Run Rudolph Run" by Keith Richards, or "Little Saint Nick" by the Beach Boys.

Then there were the movies. *Holiday Inn, White Christmas, The Bishop's Wife, A Christmas Carol* with Alastair Sim, and *It's a Wonderful Life.*

And the wonderful, every-kid-had-to-have-one presents, like the testos-terone-fueled, hand-to-hand combat of the Rock 'Em Sock 'Em Robots; the eloquent, loquacious Chatty Cathy; or the trendy, just-like-the-movies 007 gadgets. There was athletic gear, including the full football uniforms we three boys got which, Willy reminded me, let us beat the crap out of him without getting into trouble. There were gifts that changed everything, like the year Willy got his first guitar and amp. A Sears Silvertone. Cheryl was especially excited the Christmas she and Diane received their vanity sets, which were full-sized, hard plastic make-up tables with flip-up mirrors, tiny side drawers, and fake make-up. And who could ever forget the bright shiny spokes of brand-new bikes flashing in the winter's sun.

Each year, Cheryl and Willy would stage their annual who-gets-to-open-the-last-present contest, with both of them tucking away at least one present to be "discovered," after everyone had opened their last gift.

Then there was the food. Turkey stuffed with oyster dressing prepped in an old hand-cranked meat grinder. Dips that made our mouths water. Clam, onion, bacon. Crackers, chips, pretzels. A salt overdose. Egg Nog, hot chocolate with marshmallows, Tom and Jerries. A sugar overload.

And the rest of the traditions. Marco coming to the house dressed like Santa Claus and stealing presents from under our tree. Gary making sugar-covered walnuts, which seemed to have a shell, or two, left intact because he'd had a few too many Buds while making them. Serenading the neighborhood with Christmas Carols. After going off to college, when I came home for the holidays, instead of attending Christmas Eve service at the Congregational or First Methodist Church, I made myself comfortable on the couch in the family room, squinting at the colored Christmas lights and watching old Christmas movies until I nodded out. I inevitably awoke around midnight to the Vatican's annual Christmas celebration.

It had long been said that Christmas was for kids. At this time of year, I wished I were a kid again.

The routine was comforting. I knew I could count on Christmas to make me feel better, even to make me happy. I could taste, touch, hear, smell, and see all the cheery things that made me enjoy and appreciate this special time of the year. I wished the feeling could last all year long.

I had been accused of expecting too much, of perhaps being naïve – of hoping the holidays would make up for the problems that existed the rest of the year. I could only wish.

I sat in Mom's recliner, scratching the ear of Gilbert, one of her many kitties, who had been named after the Oakdale feed and seed company where they found him. The Vatican sermon was about to begin. I glanced at the framed photo of John F. Kennedy hanging on the smoke-stained fireplace and the rustic nativity to its left. I took another bite of Dad's peanut butter, chocolate chip cookie, which Paul had made in remembrance, with help from the girls.

"Are they as good as mine?" a familiar voice asked from Dad's matching recliner. I wasn't shocked. I was expecting him.

"Pretty close."

"I appreciate Paul doing that," Dad said.

"He tries." I looked past the pole lamp at my father relaxed in his recliner, looking like he did the last time I saw him in 1962.

"You made any decisions?" he asked.

"At least one."

"What's that?"

"I need to appreciate what I have. To be grateful for how lucky I am."

"I don't think many of us do that enough."

"I need to begin living in the moment. To not anticipate the future, or regret the past."

"That's hard, too, but healthy."

"Most of all, I need to stop living in fear. Fear of what may come. Fear of what the government might do."

"Fear can be paralyzing. It can keep us from doing what we need to do. What's right. And right for us. It can pit us against each other."

"It's time to live my life. To be optimistic that things will work out."

"Time will tell."

"As much as I want to, I can't control any of it."

"At this point, it's probably out of your hands."

"I've got some tough decisions ahead."

"Let your good judgment be your guide." The familiar words of advice brought a smile to my face.

"Remember," he continued, "things turn out best for those who make the best of the way things turn out."

"I feel sorry for those who don't understand that."

"It's a gift," he said. "Merry Christmas, son."

"Merry – " I turned to tell him, but he was already gone.

CHAPTER 80

On December 27th, the Weatherman faction of the SDS assembled in a boarded-up hall called the Giant Ballroom in Flint, Michigan. One of the first orders of business was to change their name to the Weather Underground Organization (WHO). It was later reported that Weather Underground leader Mark Rudd said during the group's "War Council" meeting that people should expect violence that will make "the '60s look like a Sunday school picnic." The group decided at this meeting to go underground and actively engage in guerrilla warfare against the U.S. government. The other decision they made was to disband the SDS and close its national office.

The meeting ended with a speech by John Jacobs. He called out white middle-class kids for their apathy and pacifism, saying they were clueless about the violence experienced by their black and poor brothers and sisters. He believed America's youth were moving toward a new culture of "repersonalization" brought about by drugs, sex, and armed revolution. He stated, "We're against everything that's 'good and decent' in honky America. We will burn and loot and destroy. We are the incubation of your mother's nightmare." As New Year's Eve approached, the Eve of Destruction was upon us.

That Sunday, Kelly and I went to a Wild West film festival at the Strand Theatre. One of the films it featured was *Red River*, directed by Howard Hawks and starring John Wayne. The one film the John Wayne-birthday-movie-marathon hadn't shown and I had wanted to see. It reflected many of the same themes Wayne and John Ford had included in their many collaborations. In particular, the individual in relation to the community. To survive in a hostile environment, individuals had to become a community to get through. They had to work together to endure. The ability to achieve that balance was what was remarkable about America. Our country's singular yin and yang was all about how different individuals decided to become a community for the purpose of common survival. In Ford's and Wayne's films, as well as this one, the individual was faced with a decision. They could join the community and build a future together, or remain a lone wolf and walk away to meet their particular destiny. Wayne's character in *The Searchers* had done that. In this one, he hadn't.

I stared at the big screen as the final scene of *Red River* played out.

Joanne Dru's character Tess Millay, the woman who loved both John Wayne's character, Thomas Dunson, and his adopted son, Matthew Garth, played by Montgomery Clift, threatened to shoot them both if they didn't stop fighting. They did, and in so doing, these two, strong individuals rejoined the community for the greater, common good. The "we" became more important than the "I." It was a uniquely American resolution.

The next day, I re-visited my ever-present past. The people and places, sights and sounds, memories and mementos that were, or symbolized, the then, now, and yet to be of my life. The Beatles' "In My Life" played in my head. Again. I ended my pilgrimage standing on Dry Creek Bridge, staring at the water and remembering my visit to a river almost exactly a year ago. I looked upstream to where it had been, gazed below at where it was, and swept my eyes downstream to where it headed, into the Tuolumne. The past fed into the present and flowed downstream into the future and out of sight.

I recalled what I had said to Gary about learning from yesterday, living for today, and hoping for tomorrow. I thought of America, of my family and friends, of the future. I was saddened by the culture of fear that forced us to remain isolated individuals; that didn't allow us to become a community; didn't allow us to work together to do what was right; didn't allow us to collaborate and compromise for the common good. For us, for our community, for our country. As Martin Luther King, Jr. said, "We must learn to live together as brothers or perish together as fools." It seemed so obvious to me that the one thing that would guarantee we would perish was not learning from history; not learning from our past mistakes; not listening to the better angels of our nature.

War was never good. Never acceptable. It never solved anything. Too many things were irretrievably destroyed due to war. Vietnam was an inexcusable war. We were there for the wrong reasons. Much of the nation was against it. The government didn't know that, or didn't want to. They weren't listening. A small minority of people were making decisions that affected the rest of the country and the rest of the world.

That arrogance, that hubris, would be our demise. All the noted empires of the past, including *Pax Romana* and *Pax Britannica*, had fallen when they had become too imperious and too extended, when they were convinced that their way was the only way and the rest of the world be damned, when they were fighting too many wars on too many fronts. If we didn't change course, *Pax Americana* would suffer the same fate. Perhaps the government would collapse under its own evil. As Mr. Gordon had said, quoting Napoleon, "Never interfere with the enemy when he is in the process of destroying himself."

I spent the next to the last day of the year at the site of many significant events in my life. The Little League diamond at Pike Park looked sad in its emptiness. It, too, couldn't wait for spring, when it would be filled once again with kids playing baseball. Sitting on the worn, wooden bleachers, I was imagining all the possibilities that lay before me. I knew it would take many years to recall and assess all that had happened in this past year. Someday, a song would sneak up and hit me from behind, conjuring everything I had experienced. I would try to capture it in some way so I would never lose it. Because, as someone had said, to remember is to live again.

Those significant events were filled with people – people I had known my entire life and people I had met this year. Family, friends, chance encounters, passing acquaintances. My family was a given. The friends weren't. I had become friends with Gary, Gover, Wally, Steph, and Rod for a variety of reasons as different as they were. Could that friendship sustain the changes that were bound to come? Would we go our own ways and become strangers? Time would tell.

Another year was nearly over. Where had the time gone? January was upon us. Named after Janus, the Roman god of doorways. It was the month of new beginnings, comebacks, and second chances. Janus was the god of doors, transitions, gates, and change. A two-faced god, he looked at what was and what will be. Janus was the master of time because he could see into the past with one face and into the future with the other. As the god of beginnings, he represented the harvest, marriages, and deaths, as well as the limbo between barbarism and civilization, rural and urban, youth and adulthood. Like Janus, I was suspended between two worlds, two realities. I stood here in the now contemplating the road behind and the road ahead. One face looked backward, one face looked forward. *There were no endings in life, only new beginnings*, I thought to myself.

The new year meant a fresh start. Every ending presaged a new beginning that constantly renewed itself, which spawned an ending that never ended. I was reminded again of the *ouroboros*, the serpent of mythology that devoured its own tail, gave birth to itself, and devoured itself yet again. The future would not unfold until we had devoured our past. The dawn of the new year meant a never-ending present. What would it hold for me?

As I sat staring at the open field, an errant thought came to me, spurred by all I been through in the past year; all I'd witnessed; all the people I'd spoken with; all I'd done. Revolutionaries wanted to change the world and make it better. So did teachers.

Another random notion crossed my mind. I had heard of a new housing development scheduled to be built on the west side of the Davis campus. It was a community of geodesic domes, inspired by Buckminster Fuller and fabricated with a fiberglass exterior and polyurethane foam interior. Each had a kitchen, bathroom, downstairs sleeping area, living room, and a loft. It was to be called Baggins End, a variation on the name and home of Bilbo Baggins in *The Hobbit.* It was eco-friendly, cooperative living. They cultivated their own garden. I wondered if there would be a vacancy.

On a cool, clear New Year's Eve day, I helped Paul and Willy plant a winter garden. From inside the family room, I could hear "Woodstock" by Crosby, Stills & Nash. I peered through the fading, Christmas-stenciled windows and saw Mom's Christmas clock ticking down the hours on their way to midnight. And a new year. I had a date to celebrate Wally's 21st birthday back in Davis with the boys.

As I had done my entire life, and would continue to do, I would hope for the best, but prepare for the worst. I had a decision and plans to make.

I touched the silver bracelet on my wrist and went to work.

With that, 1969 came to an end.

"Hope smiles from the threshold of the year to come, whispering, 'It will be happier.'"
– Alfred, Lord Tennyson

POSTLUDE

Mark Twain was quoted as saying, "The two most important days of your life are the day you are born and the day you find out why." December 31st, 1969 was the day I found out why. Like Candide, I was amused and confused, mystified and motivated by Pangloss' pronouncement, "In this best of all possible worlds, everything is for the best."

Thank you for joining me on this journey through a pivotal year for me, my peers, and my country. The year that changed everything and everything changed.

"When I was a young man, I wanted to change the world.
I found it was difficult to change the world, so I tried to change my nation.

When I found I couldn't change the nation, I began to focus on my town.
I couldn't change the town, so as an older man, I tried to change my family.

Now, as an old man, I realize the only thing I can change is myself.
And suddenly I realized that if long ago I had changed myself, I could have made an impact on my family.

My family and I could have made an impact on our town.
Their impact could have changed the nation, and I could indeed have changed the world."

– *Unknown Monk, 1100 A.D.*

ABOUT THE AUTHOR

Ken White retired from the worlds of advertising, corporate communications, and interactive entertainment to concentrate on writing and community service.

He received his A.A. degree at Modesto Junior College, his B.A. and teaching credential at UC Davis, and his M.A. at San Francisco State University. He has taught mass communications and film appreciation at Modesto Junior College.

Born in Lathrop and raised in Modesto, California, he continues to live in his hometown. He is married to Robin and has two adult step-sons, Tyler and Eric. He has written novels, screenplays, short stories, stage plays, children's and non-fiction books. Most of his stories are about his hometown and the Central Valley heartland.

https://www.facebook.com/ken.white.7106

OTHER BOOKS BY KEN WHITE

Tyranny of the Downbeat
Sarah's Game
Getaway Day
Nights on the Point
That Happiness Thing: A Hometown Fable
Touchstones: Life and Times of Modesto
Twelve Days of Central Valley Christmas
The Flatland Chronicles
Counting on Christmas

9 781734 022216